ANALYTICAL METHODS IN BIN-LOAD ANALYSIS

Developments in Civil Engineering

ANALYTICAL METHODS IN BIN-LOAD ANALYSIS

ANDREW DRESCHER

Department of Civil and Mineral Engineering,
University of Minnesota, Minneapolis, MN, USA

ELSEVIER
Amsterdam – Oxford – New York – Tokyo
1991

ELSEVIER SCIENCE PUBLISHERS B.V.
Sara Burgerhartstraat 25
P.O. Box 211, 1000 AE Amsterdam, The Netherlands

Distributors for the United States and Canada:

ELSEVIER SCIENCE PUBLISHING COMPANY INC.
655 Avenue of the Americas
New York, NY 10010, U.S.A.

ISBN 0-444-88368-1 (Vol. 36)
ISBN 0-444-41715-X (Series)

Printed in the Netherlands

PREFACE

The storage and handling of bulk materials is a cross-disciplinary field of technology with applications in several branches of engineering, including civil, chemical, mechanical, agricultural and materials processing. Accordingly, the experimental findings and the theoretical backgrounds for the design and operation of storage facilities such as bins and hoppers are dispersed among books and journals of various disciplines. This book is an attempt at a one volume, systematic presentation of some of the analytical methods used in the analysis of loads that bulk materials exert on the walls of bins or hoppers. Methods for shaping their geometry to provide an adequate operational function are also discussed.

This book was conceived during my lectures on the storage and flow of bulk materials in the Graduate School of the University of Minnesota. However, it is neither a standard textbook with worked-out problems nor a compendium of design formulae, charts, practical rules and case histories. Emphasis is placed on the theoretical basis for methods that apply to those handling operations that involve a slow or moderate motion of bulk material and that allow solid mechanics to be applied successfully. Rapid flows in ducts and chutes where a fluid mechanics approach is more appropriate are not considered. Examples of the application of these methods to some boundary-value problems should, nevertheless, appeal to practicing engineers.

Three groups of analytical methods that have found application in the analysis of bin-loads and bin/hopper geometry design are presented in detail: the limit state methods, the methods of differential slices, and the methods of plastic limit analysis. All are approximate methods with various degrees of simplification. The limit state methods involve least approximations, thus being regarded as the most accurate. On the other hand, the simplicity and flexibility of the less accurate methods of differential slices makes them the primary tool in bin-load analysis in engineering practice. The methods of plastic limit analysis are located somewhere in between the other two methods with respect to approximations involved.

Chapter 1 briefly describes the mechanics of storage and flow of bulk materials in bins and hoppers. The mechanical properties of bulk materials and their mathematical description are discussed in Chapter 2, preparatory to the discussion of the methods of analysis. Emphasis is placed on plastic properties and corresponding plastic models for bulk materials. Chapter 3 deals with the theoretical basis of the various methods for the analysis of wall stresses and impediments to flow. Chapters 4, 5 and 6 illustrate the application of these methods to quasi-static, inertial steady, and inertial unsteady processes of handling bulk materials in bins and hoppers, and the resulting loads. Methods for analyzing impediments to free gravitational discharge, such as arching and channeling, are discussed in Chapters 7 and 8.

Encouragement and help in writing this book came from Professor Charles Fairhurst, former Head, and Professor Steven Crouch, present Head of the Civil and Mineral Engineering Department of the University of Minnesota. Dr. Radoslaw Michalowski provided several suggestions as to the presentation of the material. Mr. Chunhua Han, a graduate student in the CME Department, assisted in verification of solutions and numerical examples. Mrs. Karella Michalowski edited the text and Mrs. Andrine Strack typeset the text. I am grateful for their contributions.

A. Drescher

CONTENTS

4. Bin-Loads in Quasi-Static Mass Flow   **85**

5. Bin-Loads in Steady Inertial Mass Flow   **145**

6. Bin-Loads in Unsteady Inertial Mass Flow   **163**

7. Arching   **175**

1 MECHANICS OF STORAGE AND FLOW OF BULK SOLIDS

Before we proceed with a brief description of the mechanics of storage and flow of bulk solids in storage facilities, some explanation of terms that are used throughout this book is necessary. We begin with terms related to storage facilities geometry.

The dimensions of structures for bulk materials storage and handling operations range from several meters in grain, cement or coal silos, to less than a meter in small facilities for some powders. In this book, no distinction is made as to the absolute dimensions of these structures. Instead, two main groups are distinguished, depending on the inclination of the lateral walls with respect to the direction of action of gravity: all structures with vertical walls are called *bins*, and all structures with sloping walls - *hoppers*. Both terms are generic, and do not specify the horizontal cross-section of a structure. Thus, structures with cross-sections that are, for instance, square, rectangular, circular, or polygonal are all called either bins or hoppers. The shape of the cross-section appears as an adjective, e.g., *square bin* or *conical hopper*. For storage facilities consisting of an upper part with vertical walls and a lower part with sloping walls, the term *bin/hopper* is used.

The term "bin" or "hopper" will not apply to a particular type of storage facility whose height/width ratio is small (≤ 1). These facilities are usually called *bunkers* and are not considered in this book.

Further, when the term "bin" is used, no direct reference is made to the shape or location of its outlets. Although all bins are either flat-bottomed with one or more outlets, or are connected to a hopper, they are considered here as fully open (Figure 1.1a), unless the size and location of an outlet is specified. This assumption is made merely for convenience in separately analyzing the wall stresses in the vertical and converging parts of a bin/hopper. Accordingly, when the term "hopper" is used, we imply that there is a fully open cross-section through which bulk material may be drawn out of the hopper (Figure 1.1b). Also, unless it is stated otherwise, a constant and equal slope of all walls is assumed. An exception will be made if, in a hopper with a rectangular cross-section, two walls are vertical and at a great distance apart (wedge type). Since the motion of particles in this type of hopper is approximately parallel to one plane, we will use the term *plane hopper*. A similar term also will apply to a bin with an elongated rectangular cross-section: *plane bin*.

In regard to bulk solids handling in storage facilities, we can distinguish three

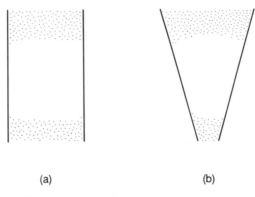

(a)   (b)

Figure 1.1   *(a) Bin and (b) hopper*

basic operational phases: 1) *filling*, 2) *storage*, and 3) *discharge*. In the filling phase, with the outlet closed, bulk material is supplied in small quantities at the top of the bin or hopper and usually falls freely. The shape of the upper surface of the loosely heaping-up material depends on whether the material is supplied at one or more locations (Figure 1.2a). In most cases, some particles roll over a slope, which may cause particle segregation. The kinetic energy of free-falling particles is small, and the dominant cause of building-up of stresses in the mass, and, possibly, compaction, is the weight of overlayed layers.

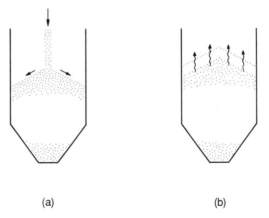

(a)   (b)

Figure 1.2   *(a) The filling and (b) storage phases*

In the storage phase, no material is supplied to or drawn out of the bin or hopper. However, due to ever-present self-weight and the gradual escape of interstitial fluids, a loose mass of particles may become dense (Figure 1.2b). In fine particles, this may lead to an increase of interparticle bonding, thereby causing a significant increase in the overall strength. This is not the case with coarse particles whose overall strength results predominantly from surface friction.

The third, discharge phase begins with the instant of opening of the outlet. The mechanics of discharge strongly depends on the geometry of the bin or hopper, mechanical properties of the bulk solid, and interaction between the bulk solid and the walls of the hopper or bin. In medium or densely packed materials, when the outlet is first opened, a well-defined zone of dilated (rarified) material propagates toward the upper surface. This zone is less visible in loosely packed materials. In hoppers with steep and smooth walls, the dilation zone spreads over the entire width of the hopper and, in some cases, may contain bands of intense loosening (rupture zones, shear bands). Once the dilation zone reaches the top of the material, all particles contained in the hopper are in downward motion and the flow is called *mass-flow* (Figure 1.3a). In hoppers with less steep walls, or with walls that are rough, the dilation zone may be confined to the central part of the material. With progressing discharge from a hopper, the particles located at the upper surface fall into the central region, which may also gradually widen. Thus, stagnant (dead) regions may exist until the central zone disappears due to widening. We will call this mode of flow *plug-flow* (Figure 1.3b). Similar modes of flow occur in bin/hopper storage structures.

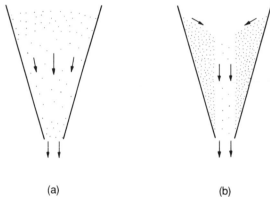

(a)   (b)

Figure 1.3   *(a) Mass-flow and (b) plug-flow in a hopper*

In flat-bottomed bins, however, the mode of flow strongly depends on the size, location, and number of openings. For example, if the bottom houses a single, centrally located outlet, stagnant regions form in the vicinity of the outlet, and the flowing region assumes the shape of a funnel. The flow in the funnel part may be regarded as flow in an internally formed hopper. If the funnel extends up to the walls, all material above will be in motion eventually, and the mode of flow may be called *mass/funnel-flow* (Figure 1.4a). If, however, the funnel reaches up to the upper surface of the bulk material, pure *funnel-flow* occurs, with the width of the funnel usually gradually increasing (Figure 1.4b). In extreme cases, when the funnel is very narrow and nearly vertical, we again may regard it as *plug-flow* (Figure 1.4c). The presence of more than one opening results in the interaction of the above modes of flow. In the literature, often only the two basic modes are distinguished: the mass- and the funnel-flow modes.

Regardless of the mode of flow that occurs in a given bin or hopper, large shearing and, possibly, volumetric deformation develop within the moving mass, and the state of stress drastically differs from that in the filling and storage phases.

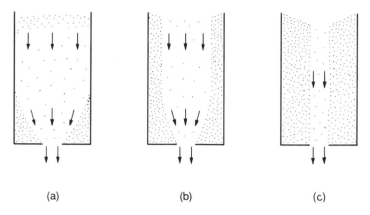

(a) (b) (c)

Figure 1.4 *(a) Mass/funnel-flow, (b) funnel-flow and (c) plug-flow in a bin*

Although it is very difficult to obtain accurate stress measurements within the bulk material, there are indications that in the latter two operational phases the trajectories of the major principal stress σ_1 are approximately vertical, with a slight bending toward the walls (Figure 1.5a). The corresponding state of stress in the bulk material mass is called *active*. On the other hand, during the discharge phase in a hopper that operates in the mass-flow mode, the trajectories of the major principal stress σ_1 become approximately horizontal, again with some curvature at the walls (Figure 1.5b). This state of stress is called *passive*. Partial drawdown of bulk material in a hopper may result in the passive state in the lower section and the active state in the upper one (Figure 1.5c). The terms active/passive are taken from soil mechanics, where a similar pattern of principal stress trajectories is observed behind a rigid retaining wall that is moving away from or into the soil mass, respectively (cf. Terzaghi, 1943).

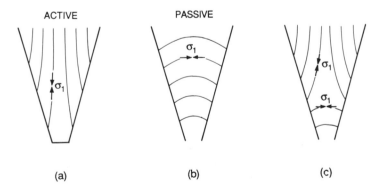

(a) (b) (c)

Figure 1.5 *Trajectories of major principal stress σ_1 during (a) filling/storage, (b) discharge and (c) partial discharge phases*

The redistribution of stresses within the bulk material that takes place upon opening of the outlet affects the magnitude and distribution of wall stresses. Numerous experiments on full scale and model storage structures have revealed bin wall stresses during discharge greater than those during the filling or storage phase (Figure 1.6a). In hoppers, with the outlet closed, wall stresses increase towards the bottom, and decrease to zero when the bulk material is drawn out (Figure 1.6b). Also, during partial discharge from hoppers and bins, a peak of wall stresses is observed at the transition zone from the active to the passive state (Figure 1.7a). A similar phenomenon has been reported in bin/hopper storage structures, with the peak in wall stresses observed close to the transition from the bin to the hopper section (Figure 1.7b). This peak may be associated with the change in slope of the walls, and also with the fully passive state in the hopper and the active state in the bin.

In bins and hoppers that operate in the funnel- or plug-flow mode, due to the presence of dead zones the distribution of stresses in the bulk material is more complex and less understood. For this reason, predicting wall stresses in this type of storage structure is more difficult and often unsatisfactory.

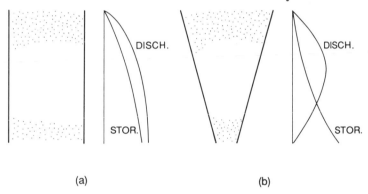

(a)   (b)

Figure 1.6   *Wall stresses during storage and discharge phases, (a) bin and (b) hopper*

The drawdown of bulk materials from bins and hoppers, whether free-gravitational or controlled by a receiving assembly (e.g., a conveyor), may be interrupted by the spontaneous formation of arches or domes (Figure 1.8a). This highly undesirable phenomenon, called *arching* in this book, may occur in fine bulk solids if the size of the outlet is small. Above an arch or dome the material is at rest and additional energy must be supplied, e.g. through vibration, to break the arch or dome and resume discharge. Another phenomenon impeding continuous flow takes place when the flow of the material in an inner core is not followed by the flow of the particles surrounding the core. Then, an empty channel or pipe forms, leaving a nearly vertical slope of stagnant material (Figure 1.8b). This impediment to flow, which we will call *channeling*, is, again, characteristic for finely grained bulk solids and may occur in storage structures that operate in the plug- or funnel-flow modes.

The above discussion of flow modes, wall stress distributions, and possible flow obstructions merely illustrates the fundamental phenomena observed in operating

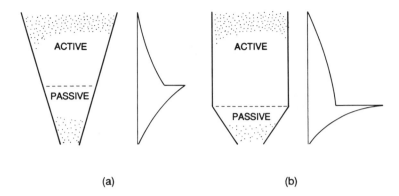

Figure 1.7   *Wall peak stresses in (a) hopper and (b) bin/hopper*

hoppers and bins. For more detailed description the reader is referred to, for instance, Jenike (1961, 1964a), Jenike, Johanson and Carson (1973a, 1973b, 1973c), Arnold, McLean and Roberts (1981), Tüzün, Houlsby, Nedderman and Savage (1982).

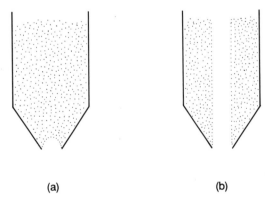

Figure 1.8   *(a) Arching and (b) channeling*

2 MECHANICAL PROPERTIES OF BULK SOLIDS

2.1 INTRODUCTION

In spite of the immense diversity in the size, shape, spatial arrangement, and chemical composition of particles constituting bulk solids of various origins, certain similarities in their mechanical behavior make it possible to discuss them jointly. These similarities stem from the discrete nature, at macro and submacro levels, of all bulk materials, which makes their behavior essentially different from that of metals. Soils display a similar discrete nature, and there is a close resemblance in the mechanical behavior of these two groups of materials. Consequently, bulk materials constitutive modeling closely follows that applicable to soils, as soil mechanics has been developed over a much longer period of time than the mechanics of bulk materials.

However, the resemblance between bulk materials and soils behavior only applies to processes of slow and moderate flow that occurs in handling operations in bins and hoppers. In such processes bulk materials may be modeled as solids. In rapid flow through chutes, fluid-like behavior becomes apparent (cf. Jenkins and Cowin, 1979). In this chapter, only solid mechanics modeling concepts are discussed. The bulk materials are assumed to be isotropic and homogeneous one-phase solids (the latter means that interparticle fluid flow effects are ignored). The specific mass, density, is then a volume average of the densities of particles and fluids filling pores.

2.2 STRESS-STRAIN RESPONSE OF BULK SOLIDS

To fully determine the mechanical behavior of bulk solids, experiments are required where all possible stress or strain states are induced in the material specimen. Such tests are extremely difficult, if not impossible, to perform. Simplified tests are utilized, therefore, where only some stress or strain state components vary, and the results are generalized to more complex cases.

A simple, yet accurate, and conceptually elegant test is the triaxial compression test (cf. Bishop and Henkel, 1962). This test, invented for testing the strength of soils, has become the fundamental test for both research and routine testing of all geomaterials. Although its applicability for testing bulk materials is restricted to coarse or strongly bonded particles, and to moderate or high stress levels, it is instructive to analyze this test and its typical results first. A test that has found a wide application in testing bulk materials composed of fine and weak particles, the direct shear test, will be discussed in Section 2.6.

In the triaxial compression test, a cylindrical specimen surrounded by a sealing membrane is subjected to an overall confining fluid pressure and, additionally, loaded along its axis (Figure 2.1). With the assumption of uniformity of stress throughout the specimen, an axisymmetric state of stress can be induced, with two equal principal stresses either smaller or greater than the remaining third principal stress. The deformation of the specimen is also axisymmetric, with principal strains aligned along the principal stresses. Thus, a well-defined stress and strain state exists in the specimen, and their mutual relation can be tested accurately.

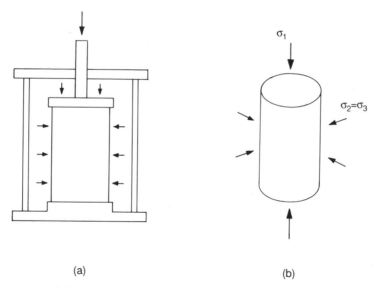

(a) (b)

Figure 2.1 *(a) Schematic diagram of the triaxial compression apparatus and (b) stresses acting on the specimen*

In the standard triaxial compression test, the confining pressure is kept constant, and the vertical load is gradually increased by kinematically controlled lowering of the loading piston. The motion of the piston can be reversed, which leads to axial unloading of the specimen, and this can be followed by reloading. In a more sophisticated test, the confining pressure may be varied to follow any desired sequence of axisymmetric stress states. It is also possible to follow a desired sequence of axisymmetric strain states. By plotting various stress-strain curves, the behavior of a given material can be represented geometrically, and this may serve for the selection of a mathematical constitutive model.

Two types of tests are regarded as fundamental for constitutive model evaluation: a) pure isotropic compression, and b) shearing under constant isotropic stress. In the first test, all principal stresses are equal, $\sigma_1 = \sigma_2 = \sigma_3$, and the state of stress can be represented by a single quantity. It is convenient to introduce quantity p, defined as

$$p = \frac{1}{3}(\sigma_1 + \sigma_2 + \sigma_3) = \frac{1}{3}(\sigma_1 + 2\sigma_2) \tag{2.1}$$

which in a general stress state represents the isotropic stress. The deformation induced in the specimen is purely volumetric, with the volumetric strain defined by

$$\varepsilon_p = -\frac{dV}{V_0} = \varepsilon_1 + \varepsilon_2 + \varepsilon_3 = \varepsilon_1 + 2\varepsilon_2 \tag{2.2}$$

where dV is the increment of initial volume V_o, and ε_1, ε_2, and ε_3 are the principal strains.

Throughout this book, compressive normal stresses, and normal strains corresponding to shortening of a line are taken as *positive*. Accordingly, a positive volumetric strain implies compaction.

The curve relating p to ε_p is known as the *isotropic compression characteristic*, or the *isotropic stress-strain curve*. Figure 2.2 shows two typical isotropic stress-strain curves obtained from tests on loose and dense bulk material specimens subjected to a loading/unloading cycle.

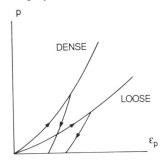

Figure 2.2 *Isotropic stress-strain curves for a loose and a dense bulk material*

In the second type of test, axial stress σ_1 differs from stresses $\sigma_2 = \sigma_3$ that act in the horizontal plane. This difference can be described by quantity q, defined as

$$q = \sqrt{\frac{2}{3}}(\sigma_1 - \sigma_2) \tag{2.3}$$

which is proportional to the maximum shear stress. Similarly, quantity ε_q, defined as

$$\varepsilon_q = \sqrt{\frac{2}{3}}(\varepsilon_1 - \varepsilon_2) \tag{2.4}$$

is proportional to the maximum shear strain. Note that coefficients $\sqrt{\frac{2}{3}}$ result from requiring the specific work $\Delta d = \sigma_1 \varepsilon_1 + 2\sigma_2 \varepsilon_2$ to be expressed as $\Delta d = p\varepsilon_p + q\varepsilon_q$.

The curve relating q and ε_q is the *shear stress-strain curve*. For bulk materials this curve strongly depends on isotropic stress p, and on the initial density of the material ρ_0.

Figures 2.3a and 2.3b demonstrate typical shear stress - strain characteristics of a loose and a dense material, respectively, tested under constant isotropic stress p. Figures 2.3c and 2.3d show the volumetric strain - shear strain response obtained in such tests. The influence of the isotropic stress on the stress-strain curves is illustrated in Figure 2.4.

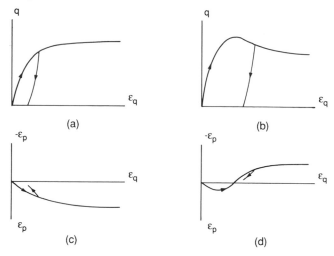

Figure 2.3   *Shear stress-strain and volumetric-shear strain curves for (a), (c) loose and (b), (d) dense bulk material tested under constant isotropic stress*

Referring to the stress-strain curves above, we can make some general remarks directly. First of all, except for a very small range of initial strains, deformations are predominantly irrecoverable. This applies equally to the compression test and to the shear test. Since rate-dependent effects due to material *viscosity* play a secondary role, irrecoverable effects can be identified with *plastic* properties. Secondly, shear resistance is limited, although it significantly increases with an increase in isotropic stress. This effect, by analogy to dry friction surface resistance, can be called the *internal friction effect*. The maximum shear resistance in an initially loose material is attained at large strains, where positive volume changes (*compaction, consolidation*) cease. An increasing monotone shear resistance is called *hardening*. A drastically different response is observed in a dense material: over an initial small strains region the material displays hardening, which is then followed by a drop in the shear stress resistance called *softening*, with an asymptotic state that may be noticeably below the peak shear stress. The initial small volume changes are positive, and around peak shear stress state become negative (*dilation*), which persists over a large strain range until finally the material deforms incompressibly.

The coupling between volume and shear strains is probably the most striking feature of all granular type solids. Consequently, in a shear test with the isotropic stress varying freely, a very complex stress-strain curve can be obtained, with several hardening/softening and compaction/dilation regions of response. The state of deformation at the end of such a test depends on the entire sequence of induced stresses. Similarly, the state of stress depends on the sequence of induced strains if they are prescribed. This type of mechanical behavior is termed *path-dependent*, and can be described by hardening/softening plastic models.

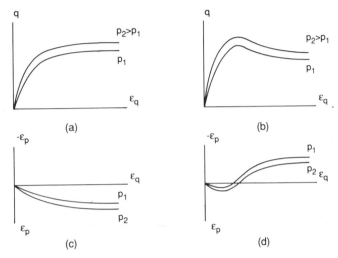

Figure 2.4   *Shear stress-strain and volumetric-shear strain curves for (a), (c) loose and (b), (d) dense bulk material tested under various isotropic stresses*

2.3 THE RIGID-HARDENING/SOFTENING PLASTIC MODEL

Historically, the hardening/softening plastic models were introduced much later than the perfectly plastic model described in Section 2.4. However, the former models contain the latter one as a special case, and, therefore, it seems appropriate to begin our considerations with a more general case.

First attempts in modeling plastic hardening of soils can be found, perhaps, in the work of Drucker, Gibson and Henkel (1957). Extensive research, both theoretical and experimental, that stimulated development of various hardening/softening soil models was undertaken by Roscoe and his co-workers (cf. Roscoe, Schofield and Wroth, 1958, Roscoe and Poorooshasb, 1963, Roscoe, Schofield and Thurairajah, 1963), and by Rowe (1962). A hardening/softening model devised for bulk solids was suggested first by Jenike and Shield (1959).

Presently, there are several models with various degrees of complexity, and they are used in numerical solutions to geotechnical and bulk materials handling operations problems. A monograph by Desai and Siriwardane (1984) presents those models with emphasis on geologic materials. Unfortunately, the mathematical complexity of the models precludes the use of analytical methods of solution. Since this book is concerned with analytical methods, a detailed description of these models will not be given here. Rather, only one particular, simple hardening/softening plastic model will be discussed to illustrate the basic concepts underlying more sophisticated cases (cf. Mróz and Kwaszczyńska, 1971).

The fundamental simplification introduced here is the neglect of the elastic response of bulk materials to loads. This is acceptable if the magnitude of plastic strains significantly surpasses the magnitude of elastic strains. In many handling operations on bulk materials large deformations do occur, and the simplification above is then acceptable. When ignoring the elastic response, the actual stress-strain curves must be modified, and this is shown in Figures 2.5 and 2.6.

The neglect of elastic strains means that, unless the state of stress reaches a certain limiting value, no deformations take place in the material; the material behaves rigidly. The limiting value of stresses causing plastic deformation depends, however, on the magnitude of previously induced strains. This is demonstrated in Figures 2.6a and 2.6b by two points, M and N. In Figure 2.6a, $q_N > q_M$ for $\varepsilon_{qN} > \varepsilon_{qM}$ (hardening), whereas in Figure 2.6b $q_N < q_M$ for $\varepsilon_{qN} > \varepsilon_{qM}$ (softening), and the global response can be termed *rigid-hardening/softening plastic behavior*. There are various possibilities of relating the limiting value of stress to induced strains. The simplest one is to assume that volumetric strains govern the limiting stress. Volumetric strains can be related to other parameters that describe volume changes: porosity, void ratio, specific volume or density of the material. In the following we will select the last quantity, density ρ, as the parameter that governs the hardening and softening response of bulk materials.

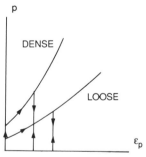

Figure 2.5   *Modified, rigid-plastic, isotropic stress-strain curves*

The concept of volume changes governing the hardening/softening behavior of soils is inherent in the so-called *critical state model* originated by the works of Roscoe and co-workers, and described in great detail in books of Schofield and Wroth (1968), and Atkinson and Bransby (1978). The critical state model differs from the one discussed here in that elastic strains are incorporated, and the specific volume, or void ratio, is used as the hardening parameter. In the following presentation of the rigid-hardening/softening plastic model, emphasis will be placed on its general structure rather than on its particular form suitable for a given soil or bulk material.

The fundamental element of any plastic model is a function that defines limiting states of stress that must be reached for plastic strains to occur. In a hardening/softening model, this function, called the *yield condition*, depends on the hardening parameter (in our case, density ρ). Referring to the triaxial compression test, where the state of stress is uniquely defined by the previously introduced quantities p and q, we can write the yield condition as

$$F(p, q, \rho) = 0 \qquad (2.5)$$

In a general, three-dimensional state of stress, we have

$$F(\sigma_{ij}, \rho) = 0 \qquad (2.6)$$

where σ_{ij} denotes the *stress tensor* which defines the state of stress at a given material point. Explicitly, with $i, j = x, y, z$, and two identical indices reduced to one,

$$\sigma_{ij} = \begin{vmatrix} \sigma_x & \sigma_{xy} & \sigma_{xz} \\ \sigma_{yx} & \sigma_y & \sigma_{yz} \\ \sigma_{zx} & \sigma_{zy} & \sigma_z \end{vmatrix} \qquad (2.7)$$

where σ_x, σ_{xy}, ... etc., are components of stress vectors acting on three mutually perpendicular planes (stress state components). The function $F(\sigma_{ij}, \rho)$ must be such that a change of coordinate system does not affect its value; this will be fulfilled, for instance, if $F(\sigma_{ij}, \rho)$ is a function of principal stresses.

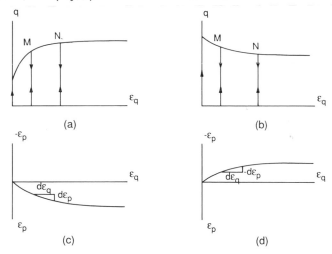

Figure 2.6   *Modified shear stress-strain and volumetric-shear strain curves for (a), (c) loose and (b), (d) dense bulk material*

The actual form of the yield condition for a given bulk material can be determined only from tests. It is possible, however, to discuss its general character by referring to the stress-strain curves depicted in Figures 2.5 and 2.6. It will be useful, also, to utilize a geometrical representation of the stress state and the yield condition. The general state of stress defined by (2.7) can be conceived as a vector in a nine-dimensional stress space. The yield condition (2.6) can then be thought of as a family of surfaces, passing through endpoints of vectors, with a parameter

ρ. Alternatively, in a ten-dimensional space, the yield condition becomes a single surface. This somewhat obscure picture is greatly simplified if the number of variables reduces to three or two. For instance, axisymmetric states of stress are fully defined by two quantities, p and q. This stress state then can be represented as a vector in the p, q-plane, and yield condition (2.5) as a family of *yield curves* with ρ as a parameter. These yield curves can also be regarded as cross-sections of the *yield surface* in the p, q, ρ-space.

Figure 2.7a shows the yield curve representing the initial yield condition, i.e., corresponding to initial density ρ_o. On account of plastic deformation under isotropic compression (Figure 2.5), the yield curve intersects with the positive p-axis (point A). Also, the limited resistance of bulk materials to isotropic tensile stresses suggests that the curve intersects with the negative p-axis (point B). The shear limiting stresses q, corresponding to various isotropic stresses p (Figure 2.6), define the shape of the curve in between two limiting isotropic stress points. Thus, the yield curve is closed, and its interior defines stress states in which the material behaves rigidly.

Suppose now that the endpoint of the vector representing the stress state is located at the initial yield curve, and shear plastic strains develop due to a small increment in stress. Referring to Figure 2.6, we observe that an increase in shear strains is accompanied by either a positive or a negative volumetric strain, compaction or dilation, which is equivalent to an increase or decrease, respectively, of the density ρ of the material. As parameter ρ changes, a new yield curve can be drawn, and it is located either outside or inside the initial yield curve. Since a denser bulk material displays a greater resistance to shear and isotropic compression, yield curves for $\rho > \rho_0$ are located outside the initial one. The opposite holds if $\rho < \rho_0$, and the material dilates.

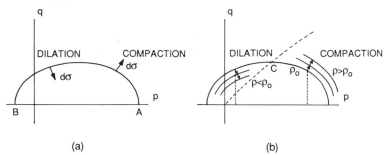

(a)   (b)

Figure 2.7   *(a) Initial and (b) current yield curves*

The sign of volumetric strains depends on the stress state from which a stress increment is applied. Clearly, an increment in isotropic stress must cause compaction, and so will stress-increments from points located in the vicinity of point A in Figure 2.7a. On the other hand, tensile stresses will lead to dilation, as will stress-increments from states close to point B. Thus, the yield curve can be divided into two regimes, those of compaction and dilation. For a stress-increment vector $d\sigma$ originating at the right part of the yield curve compaction occurs, and the stress state may shift onto a new, expanded yield curve. However, if the stress-increment originates at the left part of the yield curve dilation must occur, density drops and the yield curve shrinks. This means that the stress-increment vector $d\sigma$ must point towards the interior of the initial yield curve. This is demonstrated in Figure 2.7b, where sectors of expanding and shrinking yield curves are drawn for two stress paths.

The evolution of the current yield curve depends on the stress path induced, which may include loading in one volume change regime, unloading, and reloading in the other regime. For each current yield curve two different volume change regimes exist, which implies the presence of a separation boundary, indicated in Figure 2.7b as the dashed curve. For a smooth transition from the dilation to the compaction regime, the separation boundary should define states where neither an increase nor a decrease in density occurs. In other words, the deformation at the boundary should be incompressible. The existence of shear deformations without volume change is supported by experimental results shown in Figure 2.3: the states at large shearing strains. These states are referred to as the *critical states*, and gave name to the model.

In the hardening/softening model considered, the critical state is attained at large strains for stress paths that originate and remain in one volumetric strain regime. Theoretically, the model also allows for the critical state to be reached directly if the stress path touches the initial yield curve at its intersection point with the critical state line (point C in Figure 2.7b).

The discussion above was purely qualitative, and did not specify as to how the volumetric strains should be related to shear strains in a given stress path. A rule, called the *flow rule*, is thus required. Since the response of the model is path-dependent, the flow rule cannot relate the stresses and strains explicitly; the stress- and strain-increments are used instead.

The state of plastic strain-increments is defined by the strain-increment tensor $d\varepsilon_{ij}$

$$d\varepsilon_{ij} = \begin{vmatrix} d\varepsilon_x & d\varepsilon_{xy} & d\varepsilon_{xz} \\ d\varepsilon_{yx} & d\varepsilon_y & d\varepsilon_{yz} \\ d\varepsilon_{zx} & d\varepsilon_{zy} & d\varepsilon_z \end{vmatrix} \tag{2.8}$$

the components of which can be calculated by spatial differentiation of the displacement-increments u_i, similar to the way that the strains are calculated from the displacements

$$d\varepsilon_{ij} = -\frac{1}{2}\left[\frac{\partial u_i}{\partial x_j} + \frac{\partial u_j}{\partial x_i}\right] \tag{2.9}$$

where the negative sign in front of (2.9) results from compaction being taken as positive.

In the case of the triaxial compression test, two quantities define the strain-increment state, namely

$$d\varepsilon_p = d\varepsilon_1 + d\varepsilon_2 + d\varepsilon_3 = d\varepsilon_1 + 2d\varepsilon_2$$

$$d\varepsilon_q = \sqrt{\tfrac{2}{3}}(d\varepsilon_1 - d\varepsilon_2) \tag{2.10}$$

By introducing the $d\varepsilon_p, d\varepsilon_q$-plane, with its axes aligned along the axes of the p, q-plane, and with its origin at a considered p, q-point on the yield curve, we can represent the strain-increment state as a vector also (Figure 2.8a). The orientation of vector $d\varepsilon$ defines ratio $d\varepsilon_q/d\varepsilon_p$, which varies along each yield curve; in the compaction regime this ratio is positive, $d\varepsilon_p > 0$, whereas in the dilation regime it becomes negative, $d\varepsilon_p < 0$. Thus, by specifying the orientation of $d\varepsilon$ at all points on all yield curves, we know the ratio of shear to volumetric strain-increments for all possible stress-paths.

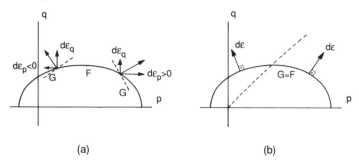

(a)   (b)

Figure 2.8   *Strain-increment vectors in (a) compaction and (b) dilation regimes*

The orientation of $d\varepsilon$ vectors is uniquely defined by a curve to which $d\varepsilon$ vectors are locally normal (Figure 2.8a). Such a curve can then be regarded as *potential*. Denoting the potential by $G(p, q, \rho)$, we can express normality of $d\varepsilon$ vectors as

$$d\varepsilon_{p,q} = d\lambda \frac{\partial G(p, q, \rho)}{\partial p, q} \tag{2.11}$$

or, writing (2.11) separately for both strain-increments,

$$d\varepsilon_p = d\lambda \frac{\partial G(p, q, \rho)}{\partial p}$$
$$d\varepsilon_q = d\lambda \frac{\partial G(p, q, \rho)}{\partial q} \tag{2.12}$$

Generalizing (2.11) on an arbitrary strain-increment state, we have

$$d\varepsilon_{ij} = d\lambda \frac{\partial G(\sigma_{ij}, \rho)}{\partial \sigma_{ij}} \tag{2.13}$$

which again means normality of the $d\varepsilon_{ij}$ vector to potential $G(\sigma_{ij}, \rho)$ in the nine-dimensional stress and strain-increment space.

A particular form of the flow rule, which is called the *associative flow rule*, is obtained if the potential coincides with the yield condition, i.e., when

$$G(\sigma_{ij}, \rho) = F(\sigma_{ij}, \rho) \tag{2.14}$$

On the other hand, if the potential differs from the yield condition,

$$G(\sigma_{ij}, \rho) \neq F(\sigma_{ij}, \rho) \tag{2.15}$$

the flow rule is called *non-associative*.

In equations (2.11)-(2.13) $d\lambda$ is not a material constant, but a dimensional multiplier, whose magnitude results from the requirement that every stress increment $d\sigma_{ij}$ causing plastic deformation is located on an expanded or shrunken yield surface (or curve). Mathematically, the differential of the yield condition $dF(\sigma_{ij}, \rho) = 0$, i.e.,

$$dF(\sigma_{ij}, \rho) = \frac{\partial F(\sigma_{ij}, \rho)}{\partial \sigma_{ij}} d\sigma_{ij} + \frac{\partial F(\sigma_{ij}, \rho)}{\partial \rho} d\rho = 0 \tag{2.16}$$

The increment in density $d\rho$ and the increment in volumetric strain $d\varepsilon_{kk}$ are related by

$$d\varepsilon_{kk} = -\frac{dV}{V} = \frac{d\rho}{\rho} \tag{2.17}$$

On the other hand, from flow rule (2.13),

$$d\varepsilon_{kk} = d\lambda \frac{\partial G(\sigma_{ij}, \rho)}{\partial \sigma_{kk}} \tag{2.18}$$

which, substituted into (2.17), gives

$$d\rho = \rho d\lambda \frac{\partial G(\sigma_{ij}, \rho)}{\partial \sigma_{kk}} \tag{2.19}$$

On substituting (2.19) into (2.16), and rearranging, we arrive at

$$d\lambda = \frac{\dfrac{\partial F(\sigma_{ij}, \rho)}{\partial \sigma_{ij}} d\sigma_{ij}}{-\rho \dfrac{\partial F(\sigma_{ij}, \rho)}{\partial \rho} \dfrac{\partial G(\sigma_{ij}, \rho)}{\partial \sigma_{kk}}} \tag{2.20}$$

Finally, flow rule (2.13) can be written as

$$d\varepsilon_{ij} = \frac{\dfrac{\partial F(\sigma_{ij}, \rho)}{\partial \sigma_{ij}} d\sigma_{ij}}{-\rho \dfrac{\partial F(\sigma_{ij}, \rho)}{\partial \rho} \dfrac{\partial G(\sigma_{ij}, \rho)}{\partial \sigma_{kk}}} \frac{\partial G(\sigma_{ij}, \rho)}{\partial \sigma_{ij}} \tag{2.21}$$

The partial differentials in (2.21) represent gradients of the yield surface and potential with respect to density and stress components (directional cosines of the normals).

In the case of the triaxial compression test, equations (2.12) become

$$d\varepsilon_p = \frac{\dfrac{\partial F(p, q, \rho)}{\partial p} dp + \dfrac{\partial F(p, q, \rho)}{\partial q} dq}{-\rho \dfrac{\partial F(p, q, \rho)}{\partial \rho}}$$

$$d\varepsilon_q = \frac{\dfrac{\partial F(p, q, \rho)}{\partial p} dp + \dfrac{\partial F(p, q, \rho)}{\partial q} dq}{-\rho \dfrac{\partial F(p, q, \rho)}{\partial \rho} \dfrac{\partial G(p, q, \rho)}{\partial p}} \frac{\partial G(p, q, \rho)}{\partial q} \tag{2.22}$$

For the associative flow rule, the vector representing the strain-increment is normal to the yield curve (surface). Then, the critical state line separating compaction from dilation passes through the maxima of the yield curves (Figure 2.8b).

2.4 THE RIGID-PERFECTLY PLASTIC MODEL

The rigid-perfectly plastic model was originally invented for the description of plastic deformations of metals. Its first application to soils is due to Drucker and Prager (1952). In problems concerning flow of bulk materials, it first was applied rigorously by Jenike (1964b). It should be noted, however, that there are several earlier works, beginning with Coulomb (1773), where part of the model, the yield condition, has been successfully employed for determining limiting stresses in soils or bulk materials.

By definition, the *perfectly plastic* model disregards any hardening or softening that a real material may exhibit during straining. If, in addition, the elastic properties are ignored, the term *rigid-perfectly plastic* model is used. In a diagram that represents the relationship between shear stress and shear strain under constant isotropic stress, e.g., the q, ε_q-diagram, the response of the rigid-perfectly plastic model is a straight line parallel to the shear strain-axis (Figure 2.9). Upon first loading, no deformation takes place until the limiting stress is reached, and the strains develop unlimitedly unless the stress is reduced. Unloading and reloading follow a vertical line, until the limiting stress is applied again and plastic deformation resumes. The consequence of the shear stress-strain curve being parallel to the strain-axis is an undetermined magnitude of strains, and also of strain-increments, that occur in a material element when stresses reach the limiting value. In other words, the deformation of an element, or body, cannot be found from limiting stresses, and kinematic boundary conditions (displacement-increments) must be specified.

Generalization of the limiting stress in the q, ε_q-plane to a three-dimensional state of stress implies a yield condition that is independent of the amount of strains induced. This is the first fundamental difference with respect to the rigid-hardening/softening model, where the yield condition is a function of induced strains (density). Mathematically, the yield condition can be expressed as

$$F(\sigma_{ij}) = 0 \qquad (2.23)$$

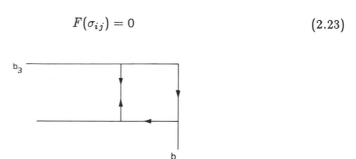

Figure 2.9 *Shear stress-strain curve for the rigid-perfectly plastic model*

Yield condition (2.23) is insufficient to fully define the rigid-perfectly plastic model, and a flow rule must be introduced to describe its deformation. Two groups of flow rules have been suggested in the literature to describe rigid-perfectly plastic behavior of soil-like materials. The first group is based on the assumption that, regardless of the particular form of straining of a material element, the principal stress axes coincide with the principal strain-increment axes, and the flow rules are called *coaxial*. In the second group, deviation between those axes is allowed for, and the flow rules are called *non-coaxial* (cf. Tüzün, Houlsby, Nedderman and Savage, 1982). Since the non-coaxial flow rules are still under theoretical and experimental investigation, we will limit our discussion to coaxial flow rules. These rules have proven applicability in many boundary-value problems, and ample experimental data have been collected in their support.

The general form of coaxial flow rules is usually assumed to be potential, i.e., the strain-increments are related to stresses by a relationship similar to that describing deformation of the rigid-hardening/softening model

$$d\varepsilon_{ij} = d\lambda \frac{\partial G(\sigma_{ij})}{\partial \sigma_{ij}} \tag{2.24}$$

Note that a rule relating only two tensors, $d\varepsilon_{ij}$ and σ_{ij}, implies coaxiality. If function $G(\sigma_{ij})$ is identical to function $F(\sigma_{ij})$ describing the yield condition, the flow rule is again called *associative*; otherwise, the flow rule is *non-associative*. In contrast to flow rule (2.13), however, multiplier $d\lambda$ in (2.24) is undetermined, for the magnitude of strain-increments cannot be specified by the flow rule. This is the second difference between the rigid-perfectly plastic model and the rigid-hardening/softening model. Flow rule (2.24) imposes only a restriction on ratios between components of $d\varepsilon_{ij}$. For example, the ratio of two components of $d\varepsilon_{ij}$, $d\varepsilon_1$ and $d\varepsilon_2$ for instance, is independent of $d\lambda$. As we will show in Chapter 3, in spite of the undeterminancy of multiplier $d\lambda$, the number of equations avaliable is sufficient to determine stresses and strain-increments within a plastically deforming region, provided static and kinematic boundary conditions are given.

In flow rule (2.24) the deformation of a material element is described by strain-increments which are related to displacement-increments by expression (2.9). Over a small time interval dt, the displacement-increment u_i can be directly related to the velocity of material point v_i, which, over this time interval, can be assumed constant

$$u_i = v_i dt \tag{2.25}$$

Thus, the incremental deformation of the rigid-perfectly plastic model can be equally described by the strain-increment tensor $d\varepsilon_{ij}$ and by the strain-rate tensor $\dot{\varepsilon}_{ij}$, whose components are related to velocities by the following expression

$$\dot{\varepsilon}_{ij} = -\frac{1}{2}\left[\frac{\partial v_i}{\partial x_j} + \frac{\partial v_j}{\partial x_i}\right] \tag{2.26}$$

The use of strain-rates is convenient in many engineering problems, for the boundary conditions are often formulated in terms of the velocities, or the velocities of particles are of primary interest. Flow rule (2.24), expressed in terms of strain-rates, becomes

$$\dot{\varepsilon}_{ij} = \dot{\lambda}\frac{\partial G(\sigma_{ij})}{\partial \sigma_{ij}} \tag{2.27}$$

where $\dot{\lambda}$ is introduced for the undetermined multiplier.

Let us consider now the adequacy of the rigid-perfectly plastic model in describing deformability of bulk solids which actually display a hardening/softening behavior. The key to answering this question is the shear stress-strain perfectly plastic response of the model that is represented by a straight line parallel to the strain-axis. Referring to Section 2.2, the perfectly plastic response characterizes asymptotic states that, in terms of the hardening/softening model, correspond to the critical state. The critical state can be reached either directly or asymptotically, depending on the stress path induced in a material element. If the critical state is reached directly, and elastic strains are ignored, the response is precisely that of the rigid-perfectly plastic model (Figure 2.10a). If large shear deformations are induced before the stress-strain curve significantly levels off, approximation of the material behavior by the rigid-perfectly plastic model is less accurate (Figure 2.10b). However, if the material is initially compacted, and the stress-strain curve is hardening/softening, the response in the vicinity of the peak again is close to that of the rigid-perfectly plastic model (Figure 2.10b).

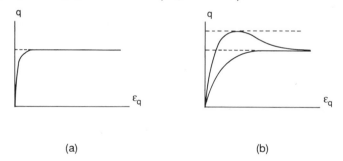

(a)   (b)

Figure 2.10   *Approximations of (a) critical and (b) peak states by the rigid-perfectly plastic model*

2.5 YIELD CONDITIONS AND FLOW RULES

Our discussion in Sections 2.3 and 2.4 concentrated on the general formulation and qualitative behavior description of the rigid-hardening/softening and rigid-perfectly plastic models. The first model describes the actual behavior of bulk materials more adequately than the second one. However, effective analytical methods for analyzing bin-loads and impediments to flow exist only if the behavior is approximated by the rigid-perfectly plastic model. In this section, therefore, we will discuss the specific forms of yield conditions and flow rules for this model as applied to critical and peak states of the hardening/softening response of bulk solids.

Due to the unavailability of experimental methods that would allow for testing material samples in all possible three-dimensional stress and strain states, the mathematical form of yield conditions and flow rules is formulated from the results of simple tests and then generalized. Since in many tests, e.g., the triaxial compression test, principal stresses and strains are measured, the yield condition and flow rule are often formulated first in terms of these quantities.

Several tests on soils and bulk materials indicate that the shear stress-strain curve is only slightly affected by the magnitude of the intermediate principal stress. Thus, the critical combination of stresses that correspond to the critical or peak states can be expressed approximately as a function only of the major and minor principal stress. This means that yield condition $F(\sigma_{ij})$ can be written generally as

$$F(\sigma_1, \sigma_2) = 0 \qquad (\sigma_1 > \sigma_3 > \sigma_2) \qquad (2.28)$$

To represent function (2.28) geometrically, the principal stress space can be used, where the stress state is represented by a vector with the values of principal stresses σ_1, σ_2, σ_3 as components (Figure 2.11a). The function $F(\sigma_1, \sigma_2)$ defines a surface parallel to the σ_3-axis. However, since the numbering of the major and minor principal stresses is arbitrary ($\sigma_1 > \sigma_3 > \sigma_2$, $\sigma_1 > \sigma_2 > \sigma_3$, etc.), there are six expressions (2.28) and six surfaces in the stress space, each parallel to one of the principal axes, and which define a solid (Figure 2.11b). A stress state that is represented by a vector with its endpoint within the solid does not cause yielding, and vectors with endpoints located outside are inadmissible. Another representation of yield condition (2.28) can be given in the σ_1, σ_2 stress-plane, with (2.28) depicted as two lines.

The most important and useful feature of (2.28) is the possibility of representing the yield condition in Mohr's diagram, where the stress state is represented by three Mohr's circles, each spanning two of the three principal stresses (Figure 2.12). Since (2.28) is independent of σ_3, only the largest circle is meaningful. A set of circles representing the set of σ_1, σ_2-values satisfying (2.28) is uniquely defined by their envelopes placed symmetrically with respect to the σ_n-axis. An envelope, termed the *yield locus*, is a geometrical representation of the yield condition. A circle that is within the envelopes represents states that do not induce yielding, and circles crossing the envelopes are inadmissible.

A direct relation holds between the mathematical form of (2.28) and its geometrical representation. For a non-linear function $F(\sigma_1, \sigma_2)$, the surfaces defining the solid in the principal stress space are curvilinear, and so are the lines in the principal stress plane and the yield locus in Mohr's diagram. For a linear form of (2.28), all representations lead to planes or straight lines.

Experiments on soils and bulk solids reveal that, for coarse particles with no interparticle bonding, the yield locus corresponding to the critical state can be approximated by a straight line passing through the origin (Figure 2.13). Denoting the angle of inclination of this line to the σ_n-axis by δ, we can write

$$\sigma_t = \sigma_n \tan \delta \qquad (2.29)$$

Using trigonometric identities that result from Mohr's circle tangent to the yield locus, we can express the shear and normal stresses as functions of principal stresses,

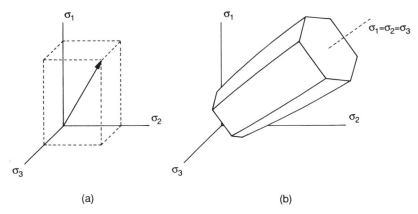

(a) (b)

Figure 2.11 *(a) Principal stress space and (b) yield surface*

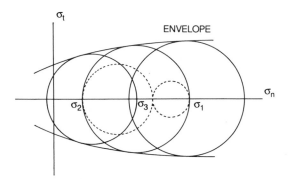

Figure 2.12 *Yield locus*

and write equation (2.29) as

$$\sigma_1 - \sigma_2 = (\sigma_1 + \sigma_2) \sin \delta \qquad (2.30)$$

Equations (2.29) and (2.30) are alternative forms of the yield condition for the critical state. Since equation (2.29) was first postulated by Coulomb (1773), and Mohr's diagram is convenient for its representation, the yield condition described by (2.29) or (2.30) is called the *Mohr-Coulomb yield condition*.

A similar, approximately linear, yield locus is obtained for peak states, with the angle of inclination $\phi > \delta$ (Figure 2.13). The δ angle is often called the *effective angle of internal friction*, and the angle ϕ - the *instantaneous angle of internal friction*. Accordingly, the yield condition for the critical states is called the *effective yield condition*, and that corresponding to peak states - the *instantaneous yield condition*.

In the principal stress space, six equations (2.30) define a threefold symmetry pyramid (Figure 2.14a). The cross-section of the pyramid by a plane perpendicular to the space diagonal, $\sigma_1 = \sigma_2 = \sigma_3$, is an irregular hexagon (Figure 2.14b).

Consider now the yield condition for materials composed of fine particles. For a given material the interparticle bonds depend on the degree of consolidation (time

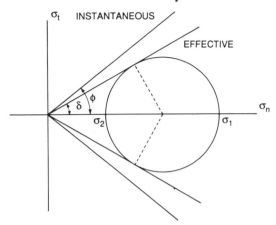

Figure 2.13   *Effective and instantaneous yield loci for a coarse bulk solid*

dependent compaction) that is induced by compressive stresses. Once the material is consolidated, and further stressing does not surpass the previous magnitude of compressive stresses, the bonds can be weakened only in the course of shearing deformation; this is observed as softening of the material. The ultimate state is the critical state where all bonds are fully destroyed.

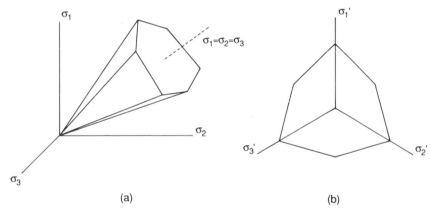

(a)   (b)

Figure 2.14   *(a) Mohr-Coulomb yield surface and (b) cross-section for a coarse bulk material*

The yield locus for the critical state is a slightly curved line. Since tests at very low stress levels are difficult to perform, the exact location of the intersection point of this line with the σ_n-axis cannot be assessed accurately. An approximation that is often made assumes that the yield locus is a straight line that passes through the coordinate origin (Figure 2.15a). Then, the equation for the yield locus is given by (2.29) or (2.30). Some authors (cf. Molerus, 1978, Enstad, 1981) suggested a yield locus that intercepts the σ_t-axis at a small distance c_e, which leads to

$$\sigma_t = \sigma_n \tan \delta + c_e \qquad (2.31)$$

where c_e is the *effective cohesion*.

The location of the yield locus corresponding to peak states depends on the degree of initial consolidation. If, in the course of stressing, no further consolidation is induced, the yield locus is a line that passes above the coordinate origin (Figure 2.15a). The equation for this line is usually taken as linear

$$\sigma_t = \sigma_n \tan \phi + c \tag{2.32}$$

where c is called the *instantaneous cohesion* or, simply, *cohesion*. The cohesion is a function of initial consolidation, or initial density ρ_0, whereas angle ϕ is approximately constant. Thus, a set of instantaneous yield loci is obtained, each corresponding to a given ρ_0 (Figure 2.15b). The range over which each yield locus is valid terminates at Mohr's circle tangent to the effective yield locus, for stress states to the right induce additional consolidation and an increase in c.

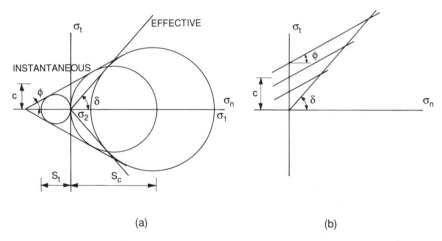

(a)   (b)

Figure 2.15 *(a) Effective and instantaneous yield loci and (b) set of yield loci for a fine bulk material*

In terms of principal stresses, equation (2.32) is

$$\sigma_1 - \sigma_2 = (\sigma_1 + \sigma_2) \sin \phi + 2c \cos \phi \tag{2.33}$$

and its geometrical represention in the principal stress space is an irregular pyramid with its apex shifted into the quadrant of tensile principal stresses. Equation (2.33) also holds for yield condition (2.31), with c_e replacing c.

A particular form of (2.32) is obtained if $\phi = 0$, i.e., when no frictional resistance is present in the material (Figure 2.16a). Some soil-like materials do exhibit insignificant internal friction, and the assumption $\phi = 0$ is warranted. The yield condition (2.32) then becomes

$$\sigma_t = c \tag{2.34}$$

or, from (2.33)

$$\sigma_1 - \sigma_2 = 2c \tag{2.35}$$

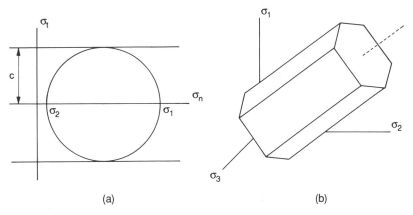

(a)   (b)

Figure 2.16   *(a) Tresca yield locus and (b) yield surface*

Yield condition (2.34) or (2.35) is called the *Tresca yield condition*. In the principal stress space, its representation is a prism with a regular hexagon cross-section (Figure 2.16b).

As seen from Figure 2.15a, cohesion c can be related directly to uniaxial compressive strength S_c and angle of internal friction ϕ. For $\sigma_2 = 0$ and $S_c = \sigma_1$, equation (2.33) gives

$$S_c = \frac{2c \cos \phi}{1 - \sin \phi} \tag{2.36}$$

which again is a function of consolidation. The range over which condition (2.33) holds can be expressed as a function of the stress state that is represented by Mohr's circle tangent to both the instantaneous yield condition and the effective yield condition. Using (2.30), (2.33), and (2.36), the maximum allowable compressive principal stress σ_1 is

$$\sigma_1 = S_c \frac{(1 - \sin \phi)(1 + \sin \delta)}{2(\sin \delta - \sin \phi)} \tag{2.37}$$

Equation (2.32), and its equivalent form (2.33), are generally accepted as sufficiently accurate approximations of the instantaneous yield condition in the allowable range of compressive stresses. Non-linear conditions were also suggested in the literature (cf. Jenike, Elsey and Woolley, 1960, Stainforth, Ashley and Morley, 1970/71), although their use in bin-load analysis has not found a wide application. In some handling operations, tensile stresses may develop in the bulk material mass, and the form of the yield condition in this range is of interest. A formal extension of equation (2.32) onto the negative σ_n-range implies a linear relationship, with uniaxial tensile strength S_t (Figure 2.15a), defined as a positive quantity, given by

$$S_t = \frac{2c \cos \phi}{1 + \sin \phi} \tag{2.38}$$

and with ratio S_c/S_t

$$\frac{S_c}{S_t} = \frac{1 + \sin \phi}{1 - \sin \phi} \tag{2.39}$$

Although testing of bulk solids in the range of tensile stresses is very inaccurate, experiments show a much lower uniaxial tensile strength S_t than that predicted by (2.38). Also, the mechanism of deformation under tensile stresses is different from the shearing mode that holds in the range of compressive stresses; under tension materials tend to separate (see Section 3.5.4). A modification of yield condition (2.33) that accounts for measured values of S_t and the separation mechanism is a circular sector of the yield locus (Figure 2.17). This circular sector, termed the *tension cut-off*, is tangent to Mohr's circle representing uniaxial tensile strength at point A located on the σ_n-axis. All yielding stress states $\sigma_1 < \sigma_1^*$ are represented by Mohr's circles passing through point A, $\sigma_2 = -S_t$, which implies that the circular yield locus is not an envelope. Consequently, the yield condition cannot be expressed as a function of two principal stresses. In the tension cut-off region, the yield condition is

$$\sigma_2 = -S_t \tag{2.40}$$

and in the principal stress space it is represented by three planes perpendicular to the principal axes.

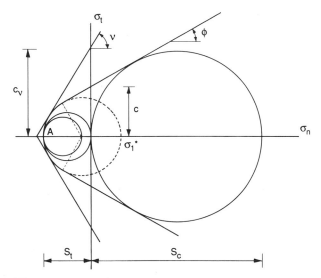

Figure 2.17   *Yield locus with a tension cut-off*

The circular sector of the yield locus also can be described by angle ν of local inclination of a tangent line intersecting the σ_t-axis at distance c_ν (Figure 2.17). The angle ν and distance c_ν can be regarded as a *pseudo angle of internal friction* and *pseudo cohesion*, respectively; $\phi \leq \nu \leq \pi/2$, $c \leq c_\nu \leq \infty$. Using (2.33), (2.36) and an equation similar to (2.33) with ν replacing ϕ and c_ν replacing c, the pseudo cohesion can be expressed as

$$c_\nu = \frac{1}{\cos \nu} \left[S_t \frac{\sin \nu - \sin \phi}{1 - \sin \phi} + S_c \frac{1 - \sin \nu}{2} \right] \tag{2.41}$$

Alternatively, a parameter q may be introduced, defined as

$$q = 2 \frac{S_t(1 + \sin \phi)}{S_c(1 - \sin \phi)} \tag{2.42}$$

such that $q = 2$ for S_c/S_t given by (2.39), and $q = 1$ when the tangency point of the circular sector and the straight line is located at the σ_t-axis. Then

$$c_\nu = \frac{c}{\cos \nu} \left[q \frac{\sin \nu - \sin \phi}{\cos \phi} + \frac{\cos \phi(1 - \sin \nu)}{1 - \sin \phi} \right] \tag{2.43}$$

As mentioned above, the effect of the intermediate stress on material response is small, and usually disregarded. Sophisticated tests on soils (with all three principal stresses varying), however, reveal that the actual shape of the yield surface, when cross-sectioned by a plane normal to the space diagonal, is curvilinear rather than straight-sided; the experimental points are located outside the sides of the hexagon shown in Figure 2.14b. Thus, an alternative to a pyramidal yield condition is a condition that is represented by a cone (Figure 2.18a). This yield condition, known as the *von Mises-Schleicher yield condition*, is given by

$$(\sigma_1 - \sigma_2)^2 + (\sigma_1 - \sigma_3)^2 + (\sigma_2 - \sigma_3)^2 = [a(\sigma_1 + \sigma_2 + \sigma_3) - b]^2 \tag{2.44}$$

where a and b are constants that can be related to the angle of internal friction and cohesion. In the particular case of a material without internal friction, $a = 0$, and (2.44) reduces to

$$(\sigma_1 - \sigma_2)^2 + (\sigma_1 - \sigma_3)^2 + (\sigma_2 - \sigma_3)^2 = b^2 \tag{2.45}$$

which is called the *von Mises yield condition*. In the principal stress space, (2.45) is represented by a circular cylinder (Figure 2.18b).

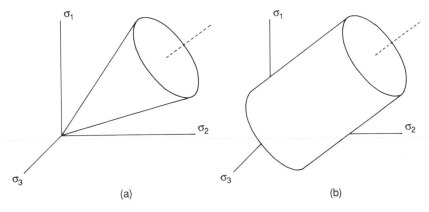

(a)   (b)

Figure 2.18   *(a) Von Mises-Schleicher and (b) von Mises yield surfaces*

Yield conditions (2.44) and (2.45) depend on all three principal stresses, and in Mohr's diagram no single envelope defines yielding states of stress; Mohr's diagram is inappropriate for geometrically representing these conditions.

Note that all yield conditions considered are represented in the stress space by convex yield surfaces. A fuller description of the various possible yield conditions for the rigid-perfectly plastic model is given, for example, by Paul (1968).

Let us proceed now to specifying flow rules. For flow rule (2.27), it suffices to define function $G(\sigma_{ij})$, or, in terms of principal stresses, function $G(\sigma_1, \sigma_2, \sigma_3)$. Geometrically, this function can be represented in a way similar to that used for $F(\sigma_1, \sigma_2, \sigma_3)$. The principal strain-rate space is introduced, with axes parallel to the axes of the principal stress space, and with its origin at the endpoint of the stress vector. By plotting the strain-rate vector with components $\dot{\varepsilon}_1$, $\dot{\varepsilon}_2$, $\dot{\varepsilon}_3$, an elemental plane that is normal to the vector can be drawn (Figure 2.19a). A surface, which is locally parallel to all elemental planes, represents potential $G(\sigma_1, \sigma_2, \sigma_3)$.

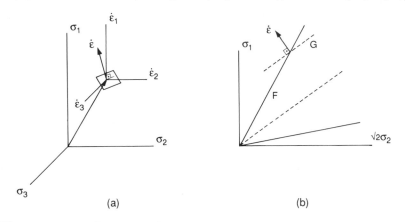

Figure 2.19 *Geometrical representations of the stress and strain-rate states, (a) stress space and (b) cross-section*

Consider first potentials describing plastic deformation at critical states, where shear deformation takes place without any change in volume: material deforms incompressibly. Thus, the strain-rate vectors plotted at the various points of the effective Mohr-Coulomb pyramid must be normal to the space diagonal; the component of the strain-rate vector parallel to the space diagonal represents the volumetric strain-rate. A surface that is normal to these strain-rate vectors must be parallel to the diagonal, and, hence, cannot coincide with the Mohr-Coulomb pyramid. In other words, potential $G(\sigma_1, \sigma_2, \sigma_3)$ differs from the yield condition, and the flow rule for critical states is non-associative. This is demonstrated in Figure 2.19b, which shows a cross-section of the pyramid by a plane $\sigma_2 = \sigma_3$. Various particular forms can be assumed for potential $G(\sigma_1, \sigma_2, \sigma_3)$. For example, expressions identical to (2.35) or (2.45), with an arbitrary magnitude of parameters c and b, respectively, describe surfaces that are parallel to the space diagonal.

Figure 2.20a shows the effective Mohr-Coulomb pyramid and potential (2.35), while in Figure 2.20b their cross-section by a plane normal to the space diagonal is drawn with superimposed strain-rate vectors. Along the sides of the pyramid, the orientation of the strain-rate vectors is unique, and the components of the strain-rate vector can be derived from (2.27) by appropriate differentiation of (2.35). For side OAB ($\sigma_1 > \sigma_3 > \sigma_2$), we have

$$
\begin{aligned}
\dot{\varepsilon}_1 &= \dot{\lambda}_1 \\
\dot{\varepsilon}_2 &= -\dot{\lambda}_1 \\
\dot{\varepsilon}_3 &= 0
\end{aligned}
\tag{2.46}
$$

which implies a state of plane-strain. A similar result pertains to all remaining sides of the pyramid. Along the edges of the pyramid, however, there is some freedom in the orientation of the strain-rate vector; any orientation within a fan bounded by normals to the adjacent sides of the potential is admissible. The components of the strain-rate vector along the edge can be calculated as a linear combination of vectors corresponding to each side. For instance, for edge OB, we obtain

$$
\begin{aligned}
\dot{\varepsilon}_1 &= \dot{\lambda}_1 \\
\dot{\varepsilon}_2 &= -(\dot{\lambda}_1 + \dot{\lambda}_2) \\
\dot{\varepsilon}_3 &= \dot{\lambda}_2
\end{aligned}
\tag{2.47}
$$

and the deformation is three-dimensional; $\dot{\lambda}_1$ and $\dot{\lambda}_2$ are multipliers $\dot{\lambda}$ at adjacent sides.

In all cases

$$
\dot{\varepsilon}_1 + \dot{\varepsilon}_2 + \dot{\varepsilon}_3 = \dot{\varepsilon}_x + \dot{\varepsilon}_y + \dot{\varepsilon}_z = 0
\tag{2.48}
$$

which means the deformation is incompressible as required.

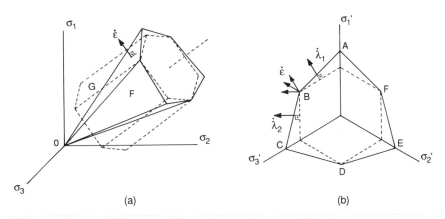

(a)   (b)

Figure 2.20 *Effective yield surface and potential leading to incompressibility, (a) stress space and (b) cross-section*

The non-associative, incompressible flow rule describes results of tests where the stress path lies either in the dilation or the compaction regime, with the critical state approached once: see path OAB in Figure 2.21a, which shows a cross-section of the effective yield surface by the plane $\sigma_2 = \sigma_3$. During uninterrupted flow of bulk materials in bins and hoppers, a material element may undergo subsequent straining at various stress levels corresponding to the critical state: see path $OACB$ in Figure 2.21a, with sector CB lying on the effective yield surface. For such a stress path, a potential flow rule enforcing incompressible deformation is inadequate, for the density of the material at point B is greater than at point C. To account for consolidation along CB, the surface representing the potential must be oriented in the space so that the volumetric component of the strain-rate vector is positive. Figure 2.21b shows an example of the potential taken as a pyramid oriented opposite to the effective Mohr-Coulomb pyramid. The equation describing the potential is identical to (2.33), where $\phi' < 0$ is substituted for angle ϕ and c is an arbitrary constant. Obviously, the flow rule is again non-associative, although the potential is essentially different from that corresponding to incompressible behavior.

Non-associativeness of flow rules may cause difficulties in analytically solving some engineering boundary-value problems and certain methods do fail. These difficulties disappear if the flow rule is associative. For this reason, the actual volumetric deformations of bulk materials are often ignored and the associative flow rule is assumed. In spite of this approximation, often satisfactory solutions are obtained, and use of the associative flow rule is warranted (see Chapters 4, 7, and 8).

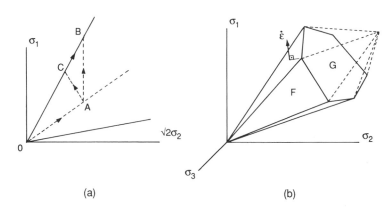

(a)   (b)

Figure 2.21 *(a) Stress path and (b) effective yield surface and potential leading to compaction*

Figure 2.22 shows the effective yield surface and its cross-section with strain-rate vectors resulting from the associative flow rule. The components of the strain-rate vector, located at side OAB, are

$$
\begin{aligned}
\dot{\varepsilon}_1 &= \dot{\lambda}_1(1 - \sin\delta) \\
\dot{\varepsilon}_2 &= -\dot{\lambda}_1(1 + \sin\delta) \\
\dot{\varepsilon}_3 &= 0
\end{aligned}
\tag{2.49}
$$

and along edge OB

$$\dot{\varepsilon}_1 = \quad \dot{\lambda}_1(1 - \sin\delta)$$
$$\dot{\varepsilon}_2 = -(\dot{\lambda}_1 + \dot{\lambda}_2)(1 + \sin\delta) \tag{2.50}$$
$$\dot{\varepsilon}_3 = \quad \dot{\lambda}_2(1 - \sin\delta)$$

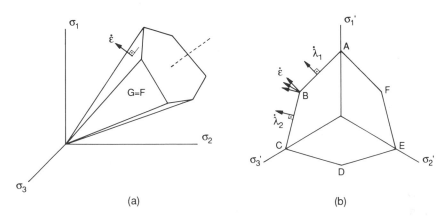

Figure 2.22 *Effective yield surface and associative potential, (a) stress space and (b) cross-section*

The volumetric strain-rate for side OAB is

$$\dot{\varepsilon}_1 + \dot{\varepsilon}_2 + \dot{\varepsilon}_3 = -2\dot{\lambda}_1 \sin\delta \tag{2.51}$$

for edge OB is

$$\dot{\varepsilon}_1 + \dot{\varepsilon}_2 + \dot{\varepsilon}_3 = -2(\dot{\lambda}_1 + \dot{\lambda}_2)\sin\delta \tag{2.52}$$

and in both cases the material dilates. Table 2.1 lists the relations between the principal stresses and the signs of the principal strain-rates for all the sides and edges of the pyramid.

The three types of flow rules for critical states can be obtained directly if the potential is assumed to be a surface with an edge. This is demonstrated in Figure 2.23, which shows the cross-section of the principal stress space by plane $\sigma_2 = \sigma_3$ (see also Figure 2.21b). At the corner of this cross-section, the strain-rate vector lies in a fan bounded by normals to the adjacent sides. Thus, incompressibility, compaction or dilation can be regarded as special cases (Jenike and Shield, 1959).

Now consider peak states for a consolidated material. The volumetric strain-shear strain curve shown in Figure 2.3d indicates that around peak states material dilates when sheared. Thus, the strain-rate vector must be inclined to the space diagonal so that its volumetric component is negative (dilation). Again, various functions can be selected for the potential, with (2.33) or (2.44) as examples, and with the parameters that govern the opening of the pyramid or cone adjusted to account for the experimentally observed dilation. Denoting parameter ϕ in (2.33) by ϕ', we can express the strain-rate vector components for side OAB and edge OB of the Mohr-Coulomb pyramid by (2.49) and (2.50), respectively, with δ substituted

Table 2.1				
OA	$\sigma_1 > \sigma_2 = \sigma_3$	$\dot{\varepsilon}_1 > 0$	$\dot{\varepsilon}_2 < 0$	$\dot{\varepsilon}_3 < 0$
OAB	$\sigma_1 > \sigma_3 > \sigma_2$	$\dot{\varepsilon}_1 > 0$	$\dot{\varepsilon}_2 < 0$	$\dot{\varepsilon}_3 = 0$
OB	$\sigma_1 = \sigma_3 > \sigma_2$	$\dot{\varepsilon}_1 > 0$	$\dot{\varepsilon}_2 < 0$	$\dot{\varepsilon}_3 > 0$
OBC	$\sigma_3 > \sigma_1 > \sigma_2$	$\dot{\varepsilon}_1 = 0$	$\dot{\varepsilon}_2 < 0$	$\dot{\varepsilon}_3 > 0$
OC	$\sigma_1 = \sigma_2 < \sigma_3$	$\dot{\varepsilon}_1 < 0$	$\dot{\varepsilon}_2 < 0$	$\dot{\varepsilon}_3 > 0$
OCD	$\sigma_3 > \sigma_2 > \sigma_1$	$\dot{\varepsilon}_1 < 0$	$\dot{\varepsilon}_2 = 0$	$\dot{\varepsilon}_3 > 0$
OD	$\sigma_2 = \sigma_3 > \sigma_1$	$\dot{\varepsilon}_1 < 0$	$\dot{\varepsilon}_2 > 0$	$\dot{\varepsilon}_3 > 0$
ODE	$\sigma_2 > \sigma_3 > \sigma_1$	$\dot{\varepsilon}_1 < 0$	$\dot{\varepsilon}_2 > 0$	$\dot{\varepsilon}_3 = 0$
OE	$\sigma_2 > \sigma_1 = \sigma_3$	$\dot{\varepsilon}_1 < 0$	$\dot{\varepsilon}_2 > 0$	$\dot{\varepsilon}_3 < 0$
OEF	$\sigma_2 > \sigma_1 > \sigma_3$	$\dot{\varepsilon}_1 = 0$	$\dot{\varepsilon}_2 > 0$	$\dot{\varepsilon}_3 < 0$
OF	$\sigma_1 = \sigma_2 > \sigma_3$	$\dot{\varepsilon}_1 > 0$	$\dot{\varepsilon}_2 > 0$	$\dot{\varepsilon}_3 < 0$
OFA	$\sigma_1 > \sigma_2 > \sigma_3$	$\dot{\varepsilon}_1 > 0$	$\dot{\varepsilon}_2 = 0$	$\dot{\varepsilon}_3 < 0$

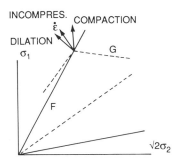

Figure 2.23   *Potential with a corner*

by ϕ'. In the particular case of $\phi' = \phi$, the potential coincides with the yield condition and the flow rule is associative.

2.6 DETERMINATION OF FLOW PARAMETERS OF BULK SOLIDS

In this section, we will briefly discuss experimental methods for determining parameters and functions that characterize the behavior of bulk solids and their interaction with bin or hopper walls. These parameters, often called *flow parameters*, are essential in the calculation of bin-loads and in the analysis of arching and channeling that are based on the rigid-perfectly plastic model.

    Two types of laboratory tests have found a wide application in routine testing of soil-like and bulk materials: the triaxial compression test and the direct shear test. The triaxial compression test, described in Section 2.2, is suitable only for testing coarse bulk materials, and for a relatively high level of compressive stresses.

For materials consisting of fine and structurally weak particles, difficulties arise in preparation of cylindrical specimens, and testing under low stresses. The direct shear test is indispensable here, and our further consideration will be devoted to this test.

The direct shear test, first introduced for testing soils, was adapted to bulk solids by Jenike (1961). The idea of the direct shear test stems from the yield condition that is independent of the intermediate principal stress, expression (2.28). Mohr's diagram can be utilized then to geometrically represent the yield condition as an envelope of limiting Mohr's circles. This envelope, the yield locus, also can be obtained directly if the set of σ_n, σ_t-values at tangency points of the yield locus and Mohr's circles is known. In the direct shear test it is assumed beforehand that these normal and shear stresses can be measured; this is often questioned as unverifiable, and the test is regarded as less accurate than the triaxial compression test. Nevertheless, the simplicity of the test and ease in applying low stress levels makes it an important engineering test for yield condition evaluation. Although some information about the potential in the flow rule also can be deduced from this test, the potential is usually assumed beforehand rather than experimentally determined.

Figure 2.24a shows a schematic diagram of the direct shear apparatus. A horizontally split cylindrical cell filled with a bulk material is loaded vertically by a constant deadload. Kinematically controlled horizontal loading induces displacement of one part of the cell, thereby causing shearing of the material in a thin layer adjacent to the separation plane. Assuming a uniform distribution of normal stresses σ_n and shear stresses σ_t over the shear zone (Figure 2.24b), one can directly evaluate their magnitude from applied loads and the known cross-section of the cell. By measuring the horizontal displacement of the moving part of the cell and the vertical displacement of the plate carrying the vertical load, one can then draw stress-displacement curves. Figure 2.25a shows an example of a shear stress-horizontal displacement curve, and a vertical displacement - horizontal displacement curve, for a bulk material compacted under consolidating stress σ_{nc} and tested under normal stress $\sigma_n < \sigma_{nc}$. Note that strains cannot be determined accurately, for the thickness of the sheared layer is unknown. Nonetheless, these curves resemble those obtained from the triaxial compression test, and allow for locating critical and peak states.

Each pair of peak σ_n, σ_t-values is usually obtained from a separate test on a newly prepared specimen identically consolidated under stress σ_{nc} and tested under $\sigma_n \leq \sigma_{nc}$. It is possible, however, to use one specimen, as long as the shearing is interrupted at a peak state, the normal stress reduced, and the specimen sheared again to a new peak state (Figure 2.25b). Depending on the chemical properties of the material, the magnitude of the limiting shear stress may or may not depend on time lapse t during which the specimen is subjected to consolidating stress σ_{nc}; in some materials an increase in interparticle bonding with time takes place. The set of σ_n, σ_t-values, for $t = 0$ or $t > 0$, that correspond to a consolidating stress σ_{nc} is plotted in Mohr's diagram and joined by a curve (Figure 2.26a). This curve is identified with the instantaneous yield locus. A set of instantaneous yield loci is obtained by testing specimens consolidated at various normal stresses σ_{nc} (Figure

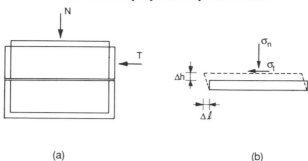

(a)   (b)

Figure 2.24 *(a) Schematic diagram of the direct shear apparatus and (b) shear zone*

2.26b). The effective yield locus is obtained by drawing a curve tangent to Mohr's circles passing through points on the instantaneous yield loci that correspond to the consolidating normal stress σ_{nc} (Figure 2.26b).

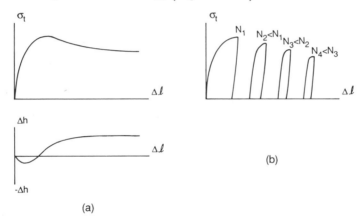

(a)

Figure 2.25 *Typical results of a direct shear test, (a) monotone shearing and (b) multiple shearing*

Linear approximations (2.29) or (2.32) are often used, and the governing parameters determined. The parameters δ and ϕ are found from the inclination of the instantaneous and effective yield loci. The second parameter in (2.32), c, is usually replaced by uniaxial compressive strength S_c. The relation between S_c and the major principal stress σ_1 induced during consolidation (with the latter found from Mohr's circles shown in Figure 2.26b) defines the sensitivity of the bulk material to consolidation (Figure 2.27).

A detailed description of the specimen preparation, testing procedures and data interpretation is given, for example, in the work of Jenike (1964a). Computer codes and approximation formulae also have been devised to aid in results elaboration (cf. Stainforth, Ashley and Morley, 1970/71, Rooda, 1975).

Another parameter that enters any bin-load calculation is the unit weight of a bulk material, denoted by γ. Usually, a constant unit weight is assumed, regardless

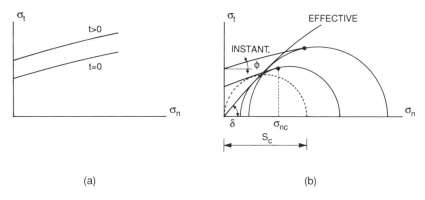

(a)   (b)

Figure 2.26   *(a) Yield locus dependence on time and (b) instantaneous and effective yield loci*

of the level of stress that exists in a deformed material element. This is an engineering approximation, as with increasing normal stresses the material becomes compacted, and unit weight increases. This effect can be tested in the direct shear apparatus, by weighing the cell containing variously consolidated bulk material.

The direct shear apparatus shown in Figure 2.24 is designed for testing shear resistance under compressive normal stresses and relatively small horizontal displacements. An annular shear apparatus allows for large displacements (cf. Carr and Walker, 1967/68). Testing material response under tensile stresses is much more difficult, and other methods have been suggested in the literature (cf. Schubert, 1975).

Further, the direct shear apparatus may serve for determining the resistance to shear between the bulk material and the material of the bin or hopper wall. The bulk material/wall interface resistance plays a significant role in bin-loads analysis, and, to a lesser extent, in the analysis of obstructions to flow.

Figure 2.27   *Uniaxial compressive strength S_c as a function of consolidating stress σ_1*

Two types of interface resistance may be distinguished: purely frictional (dry friction), and frictional/adhesive (sticking friction). Both can be determined in the direct shear apparatus by placing a sample of the wall material in one part of the cell. By inducing slip of the bulk material over the wall material, the shear stress-horizontal displacement response can be measured (Figure 2.28a). Selecting the maximum resistance or the asymptotic resistance at various normal loads, curves

$\sigma_t = f(\sigma_n)$ can be drawn in Mohr's diagram. If function $\sigma_t = f(\sigma_n)$ is linear, and the line passes through the origin (Figure 2.28b), the resistance is purely frictional, and can be described by

$$\sigma_t = \sigma_n \tan \varphi_w \tag{2.53}$$

where φ_w is called the *wall friction angle*. The angle φ_w corresponding to maximum shear resistance is the *static angle of wall friction*, and that corresponding to asymptotic resistance is the *kinematic angle of internal friction*. The first angle pertains to a small displacement, whereas the second one pertains to fully developed slip.

In some materials particles may adhere to the walls, and the curve representing maximum resistance is located above the origin. For a straight-line response (Figure 2.28b), equation (2.53) becomes

$$\sigma_t = \sigma_n \tan \varphi_w + c_w \tag{2.54}$$

and represents two contributions to shear resistance: frictional and cohesive. The measure of the interface resistance to tension (adhesion) is tensile strength S_{tw}, and determines the location of the tension cut-off.

An analysis of factors affecting wall friction can be found, for example, in the works of Roberts, Ooms and Scott (1984) and Moriyama and Jimbo (1986).

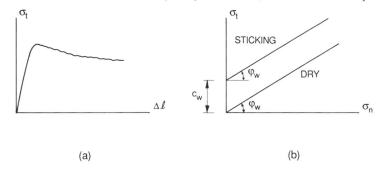

(a)   (b)

Figure 2.28   *(a) Typical results of bulk material/wall shear resistance and (b) dry and sticking friction*

Summing up our discussion, the following flow parameters are essential for bin-load and obstruction to flow analyses that are based on the rigid-perfectly plastic model: effective angle of friction δ, instantaneous angle of friction ϕ, uniaxial compressive strength S_c, or cohesion c, uniaxial tensile strength S_t, unit weight γ, wall dry friction or sticking friction angle φ_w, and wall cohesion c_w or adhesion S_{tw}.

3 ANALYTICAL METHODS OF SOLUTION FOR THE RIGID-PERFECTLY PLASTIC MODEL

3.1 INTRODUCTION

The rigid-perfectly plastic model for bulk solids is a crude approximation of their complex mechanical behavior. Nonetheless, it describes their limited capacity of sustaining stresses when they are subjected to shear strains. Since shear strains are induced on bulk materials in bins and hoppers during handling operations, use of the rigid-perfectly plastic model in such cases seems justified. Further, the equations that govern the rigid-perfectly plastic model are simpler than those pertaining to hardening/softening models; the yield condition is independent of induced strains. This is particularly important if analytical solutions to boundary-value problems are sought. In spite of the seemingly simple structure of this model, however, effective solutions can be obtained only for a limited class of problems. Approximate methods, therefore, will be discussed to overcome the mathematical difficulties encountered.

The mathematical structure of the rigid-perfectly plastic model is given by the yield condition and the flow rule. The yield condition is an algebraic function of the stress state components, and can be symbolically written as

$$F(\sigma_{ij}) = 0 \tag{3.1}$$

whereas the flow rule is potential, in general non-associative

$$\dot{\varepsilon}_{ij} = \dot{\lambda} \frac{\partial G(\sigma_{ij})}{\partial \sigma_{ij}} \tag{3.2}$$

An exact solution for stresses in a body must satisfy the local equilibrium equations

$$\frac{\partial \sigma_{ij}}{\partial x_j} - \gamma_i = 0 \tag{3.3}$$

if the problem considered is quasi-static, or the equations of motion

$$\frac{\partial \sigma_{ij}}{\partial x_j} - \gamma_i = -\rho a_i \tag{3.4}$$

if the problem is dynamic (inertial). Along the boundary, the components of the stress state are related to the boundary stresses (tractions) T_i by

$$T_i = -\sigma_{ij} n_j \tag{3.5}$$

where n_j is the outward unit normal, and the negative sign in equation (3.5) results from the assumed convention for stresses (see Section 2.2). The right-hand side term in equation (3.4) represents the inertial forces, being the product of the density ρ and the acceleration of particles a_i, the latter given by the material time derivative of the velocity v_i

$$a_i = \frac{\partial v_i}{\partial t} + v_j \frac{\partial v_i}{\partial x_j} \tag{3.6}$$

The density ρ, and the unit weight γ_i, are related by

$$\gamma_i = \rho g_i \tag{3.7}$$

where g_i is the acceleration of gravity. From the principle of mass conservation, which for a unit volume V of a material is

$$\rho V = \text{const.} \tag{3.8}$$

the continuity equation expressing the rate of change in mass is

$$\frac{d\rho}{dt} + \rho \frac{\partial v_i}{\partial x_i} = 0 \tag{3.9}$$

Since the strain-rates $\dot{\varepsilon}_{ij}$ in flow rule (3.2) are related to the velocity v_i by

$$\dot{\varepsilon}_{ij} = -\frac{1}{2} \left[\frac{\partial v_i}{\partial x_j} + \frac{\partial v_j}{\partial x_i} \right] \tag{3.10}$$

the solution to a given problem is formulated in terms of velocities. Velocities v_i must satisfy the kinematic boundary conditions along that portion of the boundary where they are specified.

The last requirement for the solution for stresses and velocities results from fully dissipative deformation of a rigid-perfectly plastic material. Accordingly, the specific rate of work of stresses on corresponding strain-rates (specific rate of energy dissipation) must be non-negative

$$\Delta \dot{d} = \sigma_{ij} \dot{\varepsilon}_{ij} \geq 0 \tag{3.11}$$

for no energy can be recovered from a plastic material. Equations (3.2)-(3.7), and (3.9)-(3.11) are written in suffix notation for a general three-dimensional case, and their explicit form will be given later when needed.

Consider now the number of unknowns to be found in an exact solution to a general, three-dimensional boundary-value problem, and the number of equations available. There are six unknown components of the stress state σ_{ij}, three components of the velocity v_i, and the unknown multiplier $\dot{\lambda}$. The strain-rate components can be found from the velocities by means of equations (3.10). The equations available are the three equilibrium or motion equations (3.3) or (3.4), six equations resulting from the flow rule (3.2), and the equation describing the yield condition (3.1). Thus, there are, in total, ten unknowns in ten equations. Although the number of unknowns equals the number of equations, there are no analytical methods available for solving a general, dynamic, three-dimensional problem. Even restricting the analysis to quasi-static problems, effective analytical methods for a three-dimensional case are unknown. Solutions become possible if particular quasi-static problems of plane-strain and axisymmetry are considered, although in many cases a numerical solution to the governing equations has to be used.

In the following sections of this chapter we will present three groups of analytical methods that can be used for solving certain problems related to storage and flow of bulk materials in bins and hoppers, assuming the rigid-perfectly plastic model for the material. These groups of methods are: limit state methods, methods of differential slices, and limit analysis methods. Examples of the application of these methods for determining loads on bins and hoppers and shaping their geometry to prevent obstructions to flow will be given in the remaining chapters of this book.

3.2 PROBLEM FORMULATION

Before we proceed to describe the aforementioned three groups of methods, let us consider again the two types of problems that are discussed in this book.

The first type pertains to determination of bin-loads, or, more precisely, stresses, that act on bin or hopper walls during either a storage or discharge phase. In general, the wall stresses result from the mass forces associated with gravity, inertial forces associated with accelerations of particles, and surcharge that may be applied to the upper surface of the bulk material. In quasi-static problems, where inertial forces are disregarded, and in the absence of surcharge, the wall stresses result from the self-weight of the material. Since any type of real storage structure has finite dimensions, quasi-static equilibrium requires that the vectorial sum of all wall and bottom stresses equals the total weight of the material in the bin or hopper; the vertical resultant of all wall and bottom stresses equals the weight, and global equilibrium in the horizontal direction is identically satisfied. Thus, the problem reduces to finding the partition of stresses between the walls and bottom, and their distribution. In contrast to quasi-static problems, the vectorial sum of wall and bottom stresses no longer equals the total weight of the material if the process is considered inertial. Also, if the storage structure is assumed to be of infinite height, global equilibrium does not provide any useful information.

The second type of problem deals with impediments to flow. In analyzing arching, the stresses along the walls are of no interest. It is the stress state within a hanging mass, with a lower surface free-of-stresses, that is the objective of the analysis. If such a stress state can be found, arching occurs, otherwise an arch or dome collapses, and the material discharges from the bin or hopper. Likewise, in analyzing channeling, the stress state within the mass adjacent to an empty channel is of interest.

Consider now the boundary conditions that characterize both types of problems. In the first type, the boundary conditions at the upper surface of the bulk material are given in terms of stresses. Along the walls, some information on stresses may be obtained from frictional resistance of the interface. At the bottom level, however, the boundary conditions strongly depend on the operational phase. If the outlet of a bin or hopper is closed, it provides support for the material and reactions are to be found. On the other hand, if the outlet is open, either static or kinematic boundary conditions are prescribed there, depending on whether the outflow is free or controlled by a receiving assembly. Thus, the boundary conditions may be specified at one or two surfaces. In the second type of problem, well-defined zero boundary stresses exist at all exposed surfaces of the bulk material.

The existence of well-defined boundary conditions at more than one surface of the bulk material causes significant difficulties in constructing solutions that satisfy all boundary conditions. In fact, several solutions for stresses presented in the literature satisfy the boundary conditions at one surface only. Although these solutions cannot be regarded as exact, they often yield results acceptable from an engineering point of view. We will discuss this issue in more detail when presenting solutions to both types of problems considered in this book.

3.3 LIMIT STATE METHODS

The notion of a *limit state* refers to a limiting state of stress that can develop in a material subjected to external loads. For a material modeled by a rigid-perfectly plastic solid, the limiting state of stress is defined by the yield condition (3.1), which imposes constraints on the allowable state of stress. The stress state components can assume values neither larger nor smaller than the yield condition requires. Accordingly, the *limit state methods* aim at determination of external loads that equilibrate the limiting state of stress. In other words, the existence of a limiting state of stress within a portion or throughout the whole volume of the material is assumed beforehand.

Limit state methods have been developed primarily for analyzing geotechnical problems (cf. Sokolovskii, 1960, 1965). Their application to problems of storage and flow of bulk materials was demonstrated by Jenike (1964b), Johanson (1964), Savage (1967), Savage and Yong (1970), Horne and Nedderman (1976, 1978b), Wilms and Schwedes (1985), and others.

Limit state methods are not concerned with deformations that may develop in a material at the limiting state of stress. From the equations that describe the rigid-perfectly plastic solid only the yield condition is utilized. In this regard, solutions obtained by these methods are incomplete. A complete solution for a rigid-perfectly plastic solid requires not only determination of stresses, but also of velocities (strain-rates). Nonetheless, the knowledge of stresses that develop within a bulk material stored or discharged from a bin or hopper permits direct evaluation of wall stresses and, thus, bin-load.

A solution for stresses that is unrelated to deformations can be sought only if the problem considered is quasi-static. In quasi-static problems, the variation of stresses within a material is governed by local equilibrium equations (3.3) rather than by equations of motion (3.4) that contain terms involving the velocities. However, the local equilibrium equations and the yield condition do not provide a sufficient number of equations for solving a three-dimensional problem. These relations provide only four equations in all, whereas there are six unknown stress state components. Consequently, the problem is statically indeterminate. It becomes statically determinate in the particular cases of plane-strain and axisymmetry, provided the boundary conditions are formulated in terms of stresses. In the following, we will discuss these cases separately.

3.3.1 Limit State in Plane-Strain

The state of plane-strain occurs whenever the velocities of material points are parallel to one plane, say the x, y-plane, and are independent of the z-coordinate that is normal to this plane. An example is the flow in a plane bin or plane hopper with the z-axis oriented along its length. It follows then, that along the z-coordinate the principal strain-rate $\dot{\varepsilon}_z = \dot{\varepsilon}_3 = 0$, whereas the two remaining non-zero principal strain-rates $\dot{\varepsilon}_1$ and $\dot{\varepsilon}_2$ are oriented in the x, y-plane (Figure 3.1a). Since for a material whose deformation is described by potential flow rule (3.2) the principal stresses are coaxial with the principal strain-rates, there are no shear stresses $\sigma_{xz} = \sigma_{zx}$ and $\sigma_{yz} = \sigma_{zy}$, and the number of stress components that characterize the state of stress in plane-strain reduces to four, i.e., σ_x, σ_y, $\sigma_{xy} = \sigma_{yx}$, and $\sigma_z = \sigma_3$.

For the Mohr-Coulomb type yield condition represented in the principal stress space by a pyramid (Figure 2.14), and for the potential flow rules considered in Section 2.5, a plane-strain state with $\dot{\varepsilon}_3 = 0$ corresponds to side OAB where

$$\sigma_1 \geq \sigma_3 \geq \sigma_2 \qquad (3.12)$$

Thus, the limiting principal stresses σ_1 and σ_2, and henceforth the stresses σ_x, σ_y, and σ_{xy}, are unaffected by the magnitude of the stress σ_3, and the number of stress components to be determined in plane-strain reduces to three: σ_x, σ_y, and σ_{xy}.

To analyze the equations that are available for determining the stresses in plane-strain the form of the Mohr-Coulomb type yield condition must be selected first. In the following, we will select yield condition (2.33), which becomes identical to condition (2.30) if $\phi = \delta$ and $c = 0$. Thus, a general case of a frictional/cohesive material will be discussed here rather than its particular cases separately. However, the analysis will not pertain to the case of a purely cohesive material described by yield condition (2.35). Although all bulk materials exhibit some internal friction, this case will be considered separately merely for completeness.

The set of equations that are available for solving a general state of stress in

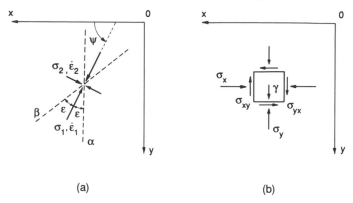

(a)   (b)

Figure 3.1 *(a) Orientation of principal stresses and (b) stress components in plane-strain*

plane-strain consists of two equilibrium equations (Figure 3.1b)

$$\frac{\partial \sigma_x}{\partial x} + \frac{\partial \sigma_{xy}}{\partial y} = 0$$
$$\frac{\partial \sigma_{yx}}{\partial x} + \frac{\partial \sigma_y}{\partial y} = \gamma \tag{3.13}$$

and of yield condition (2.33), which, expressed in terms of σ_x, σ_y, and σ_{xy}, becomes (Figure 3.2)

$$(\sigma_x - \sigma_y)^2 + 4\sigma_{xy}^2 - (\sigma_x + \sigma_y + 2c\cot\phi)^2 \sin^2\phi = 0 \tag{3.14}$$

Thus, there are three unknowns in three equations, and the problem is statically determinate. In other words, the equations that govern the stresses are uncoupled from the equations that result from the flow rule and govern the velocities.

The method of solution of the two partial differential equations in (3.13), and algebraic equation (3.14), was given by Sokolovskii (1939) (cf. Sokolovskii, 1960, 1965), and is essentially identical to Lévy's method (Lévy, 1871) widely used in solving plane-strain plasticity problems in metals (cf. Hill, 1950). This method is known as the *method of characteristics*, and its principles will be outlined below.

By introducing two new variables, $\sigma = \sigma(x, y)$ and $\psi = \psi(x, y)$, the three equations (3.13) and (3.14) can be replaced by two equations. The variable σ is defined as

$$\sigma = \frac{1}{2}(\sigma_1 + \sigma_2) + c\cot\phi \tag{3.15}$$

and in Figure 3.2 represents the distance from point A to the center of Mohr's circle. The variable ψ is the angle of inclination of the principal stress σ_1 with respect to the x-axis (Figure 3.1a), and is related to the stress components by

$$\tan 2\psi = \frac{2\sigma_{xy}}{\sigma_x - \sigma_y} \tag{3.16}$$

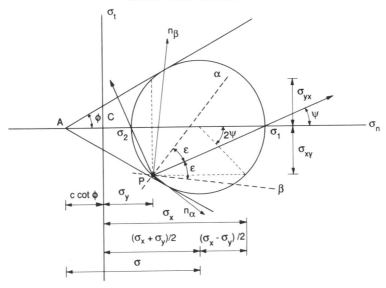

Figure 3.2   *Mohr's circle tangent to the Mohr-Coulomb yield locus*

With the help of Figure 3.2, the components of the stress state can be expressed as

$$\sigma_x = \sigma(1 + \sin\phi\cos 2\psi) - c\cot\phi$$
$$\sigma_y = \sigma(1 - \sin\phi\cos 2\psi) - c\cot\phi \qquad (3.17)$$
$$\sigma_{xy} = \sigma\sin\phi\sin 2\psi$$

Note that the yield condition is identically satisfied if expressions (3.17) are substituted into equation (3.14). By differentiating (3.17) with respect to the x- and y-coordinate, respectively, and substituting the result into equilibrium equations (3.13), the following set of two equations is obtained

$$(1 + \sin\phi\cos 2\psi)\frac{\partial\sigma}{\partial x} + \sin\phi\sin 2\psi\frac{\partial\sigma}{\partial y} - 2\sigma\sin\phi\sin 2\psi\frac{\partial\psi}{\partial x} + 2\sigma\sin\phi\cos 2\psi\frac{\partial\psi}{\partial y} = 0$$

$$(3.18)$$

$$\sin\phi\sin 2\psi\frac{\partial\sigma}{\partial x} + (1 - \sin\phi\cos 2\psi)\frac{\partial\sigma}{\partial y} + 2\sigma\sin\phi\cos 2\psi\frac{\partial\psi}{\partial x} + 2\sigma\sin\phi\sin 2\psi\frac{\partial\psi}{\partial y} = \gamma$$

Since the coefficients in (3.18) depend on variables σ and ψ, equations (3.18) are quasi-linear rather than linear. The type of these equations is hyperbolic, which can be established by equating to zero the characteristic determinant of equations (3.18) supplemented by expressions for differentials of σ and ψ (cf. Hill, 1950, and also Appendix A). The solution to a set of hyperbolic differential equations can be found by the method of characteristics. The *characteristics* are lines along which the partial differential equations (3.18) become ordinary differential equations. These lines, denoted as the α- and β-lines, are given by the following differential equations

$$\frac{dy}{dx} = \tan(\psi + \varepsilon) \qquad \alpha\text{-line}$$
$$(3.19)$$
$$\frac{dy}{dx} = \tan(\psi - \varepsilon) \qquad \beta\text{-line}$$

where

$$\varepsilon = \frac{\pi}{4} - \frac{\phi}{2} \qquad (3.20)$$

Thus, for $\phi > 0$, the α- and β-lines are non-orthogonal, and are symmetrically located with respect to the directions of the principal stresses σ_1 and σ_2 (Figure 3.1a). Also, as seen from Figure 3.2, the characteristics coincide with planes where Mohr's circle is tangent to the yield locus, i.e., with planes where the shear and normal stresses satisfy equation (2.32). Note that point P in Figure 3.2 represents the *pole of normals*; the intersection with the circle of a line, drawn from P, that is parallel to the normal of a plane gives shear and normal stresses acting on that plane. The relations for variables σ and ψ along the characteristics are

$$\begin{aligned} d\sigma + 2\sigma \tan \phi \, d\psi = \gamma(dy + \tan \phi \, dx) & \qquad \alpha\text{-line} \\ d\sigma - 2\sigma \tan \phi \, d\psi = \gamma(dy - \tan \phi \, dx) & \qquad \beta\text{-line} \end{aligned} \qquad (3.21)$$

Since equations (3.19) contain the unknown variable ψ, the orientation of the characteristics can be found only by utilizing equations (3.21). In other words, the full set of equations (3.19) and (3.21) must be considered to obtain the solution for σ and ψ. Analytic integration of equations (3.21) is possible only if the right-hand side terms disappear, i.e., when $\gamma = 0$, or $dx = dy = 0$. A numerical scheme is thus required, where the differentials are approximated by the finite differences. Once the values of σ and ψ are found within a considered region, the components of the stress state can be calculated by means of (3.17). Note that equations (3.19) and (3.21) are also valid for yield condition (2.30) if ϕ is replaced by δ. Obviously, expression (3.15), which defines the variable σ, does not contain the second right-hand side term.

The solution to equations (3.19) and (3.21) can be obtained if the stress boundary conditions formulate one of the following three boundary-value problems: the *Cauchy problem*, the *characteristic problem*, or the *mixed problem*. The Cauchy problem is formulated if along a line that is neither an α- nor a β-characteristic the values of σ and ψ are given. The solution can then be constructed within a triangle, curvilinear in general, bounded by the characteristics emerging from the endpoints of the line where σ and ψ are specified (Figure 3.3a). The characteristic problem exists if σ and ψ are given along the α- and β-lines that intersect at a point. The region of solution is limited to within a quadrangle, curvilinear in general, bounded by the conjugate characteristics (Figure 3.3b). A particular characteristic problem occurs when one of the characteristics degenerates to a singular point, with various values of σ and ψ, but with $dx = dy = 0$ (Figure 3.3c). The characteristics that emerge from the singular point form a fan. The last, mixed problem exists if the values of σ and ψ are given along one of the characteristics, whereas along an intersecting non-characteristic line a relation between σ and ψ, or only one of them, is specified (Figure 3.3d).

For each of the boundary-value problems described above, the solution cannot be extended beyond characteristics that emerge from the end boundary points where the values of σ and ψ are given. On the other hand, the solution for one of the problems may provide boundary-values of σ and ψ for another problem. In other words, solutions can be nested.

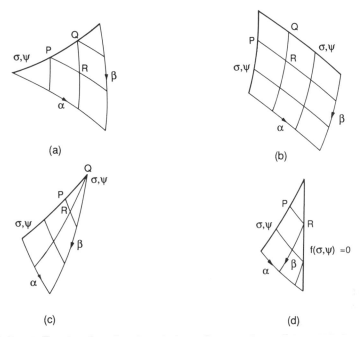

(a)

(b)

(c)

(d)

Figure 3.3 *Boundary-value problems in the method of characteristics,*
(a) Cauchy, (b) characteristics, (c) degenerated character-
istic and (d) mixed

Figure 3.4 shows an example of a net of characteristics that is the result of subsequent solutions of the boundary-value problems described above. It is assumed here that along the line AA' the material is subjected to a uniformly distributed vertical stress σ_{y0}, and the lines AC, CC' and $A'C'$ are rigid walls with an angle of wall friction φ_w. The geometry of this problem, and the boundary conditions selected, resemble those which occur in a shallow plane bin with a closed outlet, in which the bulk material is subjected to an external pressure. In the following, we will present details of this solution, with the assumption that the limiting state of stress is defined by effective yield condition (2.30).

The construction of the solution begins from line AA', where the boundary conditions formulate the Cauchy problem. In fact, for the boundary stresses given by pressure σ_{y0}, the directions of the principal stresses at line $A'A$ must coincide with the vertical and horizontal directions. Referring to our discussion about the orientation of principal stresses during storage phase that was given in Chapter 1, we select the active case, where principal stress σ_1 coincides with the y-direction. Thus, along AA', we have

$$\psi = \frac{\pi}{2} \tag{3.22}$$

Next, using yield condition (2.30) and (3.15), the magnitude of σ along AA' is

$$\sigma = \frac{\sigma_{y0}}{1 + \sin \delta} \tag{3.23}$$

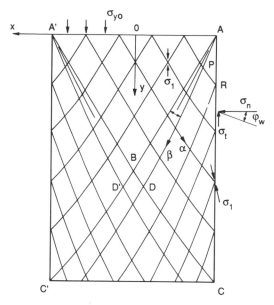

Figure 3.4   *Characteristics in a plane bin*

Boundary conditions (3.22) and (3.23) uniquely define the Cauchy problem bounded by the α- and β-lines emerging from points A' and A, respectively (Figure 3.4).

For the particular case of horizontal line AA', and for constant distribution of pressure σ_{y0}, the solution for stresses below line $A'A$ actually can be obtained without using equations (3.19) and (3.21). Since in the vicinity of line $A'A$ the stress state is independent of the x-coordinate, it suffices to consider equilibrium equations (3.13), which reduce to

$$\frac{\partial \sigma_x}{\partial x} = 0$$
$$\frac{\partial \sigma_y}{\partial y} = \gamma \tag{3.24}$$

Using the boundary condition

$$y = 0 \qquad \sigma_y = \sigma_{y0} \tag{3.25}$$

we obtain from the second equation (3.24)

$$\sigma_y = \sigma_1 = \gamma y + \sigma_{y0} \tag{3.26}$$

The horizontal normal stress σ_x is directly obtained from yield condition (2.30)

$$\sigma_x = \sigma_2 = (\gamma y + \sigma_{y0}) \frac{1 - \sin \delta}{1 + \sin \delta} \tag{3.27}$$

The stress state described by (3.26) and (3.27) is known as the *Rankine active state*, whereas a similar state with principal stress σ_1 oriented horizontally is known as the *Rankine passive state* (Rankine, 1857, Terzaghi, 1943). In both cases the net of characteristics consists of straight lines (Figure 3.4). The solutions also hold if $\sigma_{y0} = 0$, i.e., when the boundary is stress-free.

However, if either the boundary is curvilinear or the boundary stresses are non-homogeneously distributed, numerical integration of (3.19) and (3.21) must be used to solve the Cauchy problem. For this, the boundary is subdivided into sectors, with the values of σ and ψ assigned to the nodal points. The location of an intersection point R of the α- and β-lines that emerge from two neighboring nodal points P and Q (Figure 3.3a) is found from equations (3.19), which, written in terms of finite differences, become

$$\begin{aligned} y_R - y_P &= (x_R - x_P)\tan(\psi_P + \varepsilon) \\ y_R - y_Q &= (x_R - x_Q)\tan(\psi_Q - \varepsilon) \end{aligned} \qquad (3.28)$$

Next, the values of σ_R and ψ_R at point R are calculated from equations (3.21), which take the form

$$\begin{aligned} \sigma_R - \sigma_P + 2\sigma_P(\psi_R - \psi_P)\tan\delta &= \gamma[y_R - y_P + (x_R - x_P)\tan\delta] \\ \sigma_R - \sigma_Q - 2\sigma_Q(\psi_R - \psi_Q)\tan\delta &= \gamma[y_R - y_Q - (x_R - x_Q)\tan\delta] \end{aligned} \qquad (3.29)$$

The procedure is repeated for all nodal points along the boundary, and also for the points located within the region (Figure 3.3a). Note that equations (3.28) and (3.29) are the simplest possible first order forward difference approximations of equations (3.19) and (3.21), and they give accurate results only for a dense spacing of nodal points. Other, higher order approximations are possible, where iterative procedures lead to high accuracy for fewer nodal points.

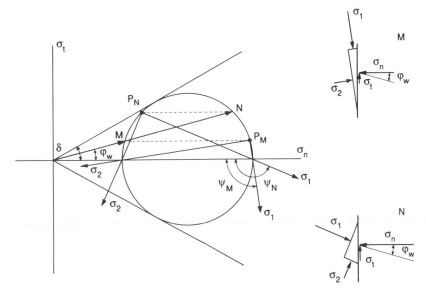

Figure 3.5   *State of stress at a wall*

Consider now the region that is enclosed between bounding characteristic AB and wall AC. The limiting state of stress that exists within this region must be in equilibrium with wall stresses whose inclination is limited by the angle of wall friction φ_w (Figure 3.4). If the wall friction is not fully mobilized, the actual orientation of the stress vectors along the wall is unknown, and the solution cannot be uniquely constructed. If we assume, however, that fully mobilized friction does exist, the normal and tangential components of the wall stresses, $\sigma_n = \sigma_x$ and $\sigma_t = -\sigma_{yx} = -\sigma_{xy}$ (see sign convention for stresses, Figure 3.1b), are related by

$$-\sigma_{xy} = \sigma_x \tan \varphi_w \qquad (3.30)$$

which imposes a condition on the inclination of the principal stress σ_1 at the wall. Figure 3.5 shows the limiting state of stress at the wall and the stress vector inclined at the angle φ_w. Two cases are possible depending on whether this vector ends at point M or N, which affects the orientation of principal stress σ_1. Referring again to Chapter 1, we observe that the orientation that corresponds to point M pertains to the active state, whereas that corresponding to point N pertains to the passive state. Using (3.17), we can write relation (3.30) as

$$\sin \delta \sin 2\psi = -(1 + \sin \delta \cos 2\psi) \tan \varphi_w \qquad (3.31)$$

which, solved for ψ, gives

$$\psi = (3 - \alpha)\frac{\pi}{4} + \frac{\alpha}{2}(\omega - \alpha\varphi_w) \qquad (3.32)$$

with

$$\omega = \arcsin \frac{\sin \varphi_w}{\sin \delta} \qquad (3.33)$$

where $\alpha = 1$ for the active state, and $\alpha = -1$ for the passive case. Note that equation (3.32) is independent of the magnitude of σ, and thus ψ is constant along the wall. For a material with cohesion, substitution of expressions (3.17) into (3.30) leads to a relation for ψ that is implicit and depends on σ, and therefore ψ varies along the wall.

For $\varphi_w > 0$ equation (3.32) gives $\psi > \pi/2$, which means that at the corner point A there are two different values of ψ; $\psi = \pi/2$ which corresponds to the Rankine active state within ABA', and $\psi > \pi/2$ resulting from wall friction. It is possible, however, to assume point A as a singular point, where the α-line reduces to zero-length, and the β-lines emanate within a fan bounded by AB and AD. Within this fan, the degenerated characteristic problem exists, with σ and ψ known along AB, and at point A. The value of σ at this point can be derived from equation $(3.21)_1$, which, on integration, gives

$$\sigma = \sigma_{AB} e^{-2 \tan \delta (\psi - \psi_{AB})} \qquad (3.34)$$

and σ_{AB}, ψ_{AB}, correspond to line AB at point A. In a numerical scheme, the fan angle is subdivided into small intervals $\Delta\psi$ and the corresponding σ found from equation (3.34). Next, equations (3.28) and (3.29) are used to construct the net of characteristics in region ABD. It should be noted here that for stress-free boundary AA' we have $\sigma_{AB} = 0$, and the value of σ that corresponds to a different ψ cannot be found by integration of equation $(3.21)_1$. This can be circumvented if we assume an arbitrarily small value of σ_{y0} or if we postulate a particular radial solution that will be discussed later.

To extend the solution up to wall AC, the mixed problem must be solved within region ACD. From a nodal point P along AD that is closest to point A (Figure 3.4), the location of the intersection point R of the α-line with wall AC is found from equation

$$y_R - y_P = \frac{1}{2}[\tan(\psi_R + \varepsilon) + \tan(\psi_P + \varepsilon)](x_R - x_P) \qquad (3.35)$$

where angle ψ_R is given by (3.32). The magnitude of σ at point R is then calculated from $(3.29)_1$. The solution may now be continued down to a point along BC, by solving the characteristic problem defined by σ and ψ along line AD, and at point R. The procedure above is repeated for all points along wall AC, until the solution is obtained for all of ACD.

Having completed the solution within ABC, and, for reason of symmetry, also in $A'BC'$, the remaining region BCC' can be solved as a regular characteristic problem by means of (3.28) and (3.29), with the initial values of σ and ψ known along BC and BC'. The frictional boundary conditions along CC' do not directly enter the solution. The resulting stresses along CC', σ_y and σ_{xy}, must not, however, violate the admissible inclination resulting from angle φ_w.

In the example shown in Figure 3.4, the stress field within the material is continuous everywhere with two singular points A and A'. Accordingly, the distribution of wall and bottom stresses is also continuous, with examples given in Section 4.2. In some cases, however, the boundary conditions may prevent construction of a continuous stress field, and stress discontinuities must be introduced. The stress discontinuity is a surface, with its intersection of the x, y-plane being a line, across which two limiting states of stress exist. These two states of stress, however, cannot be arbitrary, for the stress vector that acts at the surface must be continuous to fulfill the equilibrium requirement. Considering two elements located on both sides of the stress discontinuity (Figure 3.6a), we conclude that the only permissible discontinuity applies to the normal stress components that are parallel to the discontinuity surface. In Mohr's diagram (Figure 3.6c), the limiting stress states on both sides of the discontinuity are represented by two intersecting circles, with the intersection point representing the end of the stress vector that is continuous across the discontinuity surface. The occurrence of a stress discontinuity affects the net of characteristics which no longer consists of a smooth pattern of α- and β-lines; across a discontinuity the characteristics undergo a kink (Figure 3.6b), for the principal stresses σ_1 for both Mohr's circles are oriented differently. Further, the orientation of the stress discontinuity, shown in Figure 3.6c by the dashed line that is orthogonal to the line joining poles P^- and P^+, cannot coincide with the α- and β-lines. Obviously, for a stress discontinuity meeting a rigid wall, the distribution of wall stresses will show a jump in the normal and tangential stress.

Construction of discontinuous stress fields is by far more complicated than that of continuous fields, as the location of the stress discontinuity is unknown in advance (cf. Savage, Yong and McInnes, 1969, Horne and Nedderman, 1976).

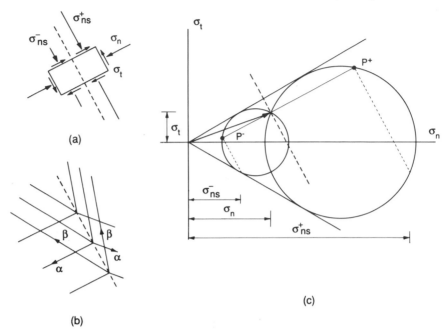

(a)

(b)

(c)

Figure 3.6   *(a) Discontinuous state of stress, (b) characteristics across discontinuity and (c) Mohr's circles*

The method of characteristics presented above, operating with two variables σ and ψ defined by (3.15) and (3.16), must be modified if the yielding of a material is described by Tresca yield condition (2.35). In fact, the second right-hand side term in (3.15), and, thus, the variable σ assume infinity if $\phi = 0$. This singularity can be removed by defining the variable σ differently, namely

$$\sigma = \frac{1}{2}(\sigma_1 + \sigma_2) - \gamma y \tag{3.36}$$

The components of the stress state are now (Figure 3.7)

$$\begin{aligned}
\sigma_x &= \sigma + c \cos 2\psi + \gamma y \\
\sigma_y &= \sigma - c \cos 2\psi + \gamma y \\
\sigma_{xy} &= c \sin 2\psi
\end{aligned} \tag{3.37}$$

and the equilibrium equations (3.13) expressed in terms of σ and ψ

$$\begin{aligned}
\frac{\partial \sigma}{\partial x} - 2c \sin 2\psi \frac{\partial \psi}{\partial x} + 2c \cos 2\psi \frac{\partial \psi}{\partial y} &= 0 \\
\frac{\partial \sigma}{\partial y} - 2c \cos 2\psi \frac{\partial \psi}{\partial x} + 2c \sin 2\psi \frac{\partial \psi}{\partial y} &= 0
\end{aligned} \tag{3.38}$$

do not contain the unit weight γ. Alternatively, in the definition of σ the second right-hand side term can be omitted, which leads to a set similar to (3.38) with γ present at the right-hand side (cf. Sokolovskii, 1965).

Set (3.38) is hyperbolic, with orthogonal characteristics given by

$$\frac{dy}{dx} = \tan(\psi + \varepsilon) \qquad \alpha\text{-line}$$
$$\frac{dy}{dx} = \tan(\psi - \varepsilon) \qquad \beta\text{-line}$$

(3.39)

where

$$\varepsilon = \frac{\pi}{4}$$

(3.40)

The relations for σ and ψ along the characteristics are

$$d\sigma + 2cd\psi = 0 \qquad \alpha\text{-line}$$
$$d\sigma - 2cd\psi = 0 \qquad \beta\text{-line}$$

(3.41)

and they can be directly integrated, giving

$$\sigma + 2c\psi = \text{const} \qquad \alpha\text{-line}$$
$$\sigma - 2c\psi = \text{const} \qquad \beta\text{-line}$$

(3.42)

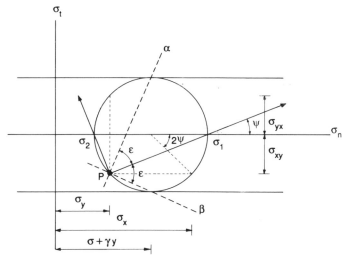

Figure 3.7 *Mohr's circle tangent to the Tresca yield locus*

Solutions to set (3.39) and (3.41) can be obtained for the same three boundary-value problems as for the case of a frictional material. In general, numerical integration of (3.39) is required.

Let us consider now a particular class of limit state solutions, termed *radial stress fields* (cf. Sokolovskii, 1965), that are useful in solving problems with stress-free boundaries (cf. Horne and Nedderman, 1976), and in the analysis of stresses in tall hoppers (cf. Jenike, 1964b, Johanson, 1964). These solutions can only be constructed for a cohesionless material and for problems where the bounding surfaces or walls are straight.

In a radial stress field the components of the stress state at a generic point are assumed to be linear functions of its distance to a common origin. Thus, in the polar coordinate system r, θ of Figure 3.8a (which is convenient for solving problems with a stress-free upper boundary), the components σ_r, σ_θ, and $\sigma_{r\theta}$, and also σ_1 and σ_2, are linear functions of the radius r. Equilibrium equations (3.3), and yield condition (2.30), are now expressed as

$$\frac{\partial \sigma_r}{\partial r} + \frac{\partial \sigma_{r\theta}}{r\partial \theta} + \frac{\sigma_r - \sigma_\theta}{r} = \gamma \sin \theta$$

$$\frac{\partial \sigma_{r\theta}}{\partial r} + \frac{\partial \sigma_\theta}{r\partial \theta} + \frac{2\sigma_{r\theta}}{r} = \gamma \cos \theta \tag{3.43}$$

$$(\sigma_r - \sigma_\theta)^2 + 4\sigma_{r\theta}^2 - (\sigma_r + \sigma_\theta)^2 \sin^2 \delta = 0 \tag{3.44}$$

The set (3.43), (3.44) can be reduced to two differential equations if two new variables, $\sigma = \sigma(r, \theta)$ and $\eta = \eta(r, \theta)$, are introduced. The variable σ is defined as

$$\sigma = \frac{1}{2}(\sigma_1 + \sigma_2) \tag{3.45}$$

and the variable η represents the angle of inclination of principal stress σ_1 with respect to radius r (Figure 3.8b). Note that angle η is related to angle ψ by

$$\eta = \psi - \theta \tag{3.46}$$

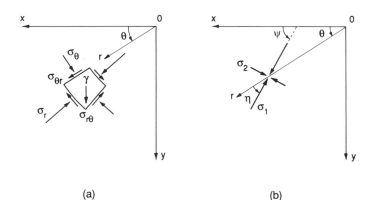

(a)   (b)

Figure 3.8   *(a) Stress components and (b) orientation of principal stresses in a radial stress field*

From Mohr's diagram (Figure 3.9), the stress components are

$$\sigma_r = \sigma(1 + \sin \delta \cos 2\eta)$$

$$\sigma_\theta = \sigma(1 - \sin \delta \cos 2\eta) \tag{3.47}$$

$$\sigma_{r\theta} = \sigma \sin \delta \sin 2\eta$$

and they identically satisfy yield condition (3.44). For a radial stress field, variable σ must also depend linearly on radius r, and can be expressed as

$$\sigma = \gamma r \kappa(\theta) \qquad (3.48)$$

where $\kappa(\theta)$ is an unknown dimensionless function; γ is introduced in (3.48) as a dimensional constant. Using (3.48), differentiating (3.47) with respect to r and θ, and substituting the result into equilibrium equations (3.43), we obtain the following set of ordinary differential equations

$$\sin\delta \sin 2\eta \frac{d\kappa}{d\theta} + 2\kappa \sin\delta \cos 2\eta \left[\frac{d\eta}{d\theta} + 1\right] + \kappa(1 + \sin\delta \cos 2\eta) = \sin\theta$$

$$(1 - \sin\delta \cos 2\eta)\frac{d\kappa}{d\theta} + 2\kappa \sin\delta \sin 2\eta \left[\frac{d\eta}{d\theta} + 1\right] + \kappa \sin\delta \sin 2\eta = \cos\theta \qquad (3.49)$$

which are independent of γ due to the particular form of expression (3.48). Equations (3.49) are linear with respect to the derivatives, which can thus be expressed as

$$\frac{d\kappa}{d\theta} = \frac{\cos(2\eta + \theta) + \kappa \sin 2\eta}{\cos 2\eta - \sin\delta}$$

$$\frac{d\eta}{d\theta} = \frac{\sin\theta - \sin\delta \sin(2\eta + \theta) - \kappa \cos^2\delta}{2\kappa \sin\delta (\cos 2\eta - \sin\delta)} - 1 \qquad (3.50)$$

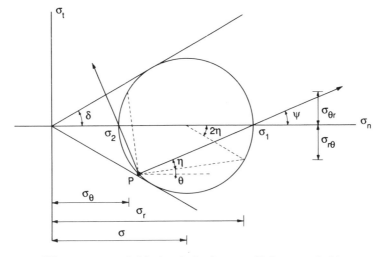

Figure 3.9   *Mohr's circle for a radial stress field*

    Consequently, the solution for a radial stress field reduces to solving two ordinary differential equations for κ and η. The components of the stress state can then be found from (3.47) and (3.48). Integration of equations (3.50) requires a numerical scheme in which the values of κ and η are incrementally found for a given increment of θ beginning from boundary conditions η_0 and κ_0. In most practical problems, however, only angle η is known at two boundaries.

This can be illustrated in an example of the radial stress field in a hopper (Figure 3.10), in which the origin of the r, θ-system is located at the vertex (Jenike, 1964b); we will call this field the *vertex radial stress field*. Angle η at the right wall can be found from the condition of fully mobilized friction

$$\sigma_{r\theta} = \sigma_\theta \tan \varphi_w \tag{3.51}$$

which upon substitution of (3.47) and rearrangement gives

$$\eta = (3 + \alpha)\frac{\pi}{4} - \frac{\alpha}{2}(\omega - \alpha\varphi_w) \tag{3.52}$$

where ω is given by (3.33). On the other hand, for reasons of symmetry, angle η is also known along the vertical y-axis (Figure 3.10)

$$\eta = (3 + \alpha)\frac{\pi}{4} \tag{3.53}$$

From these two boundary conditions for η, the value of κ_0 at one boundary, either at the wall or at the vertical axis, can now be found from the condition that, when used in the equations for κ and η, the resulting angle η at the other boundary satisfies the corresponding boundary condition. Usually several values for κ_0 are assumed at one boundary and the resulting η at the other boundary is calculated from (3.54) until the boundary condition for η is met. Note that for the system of coordinates of Figure 3.10 with γ pointing downward, equations for κ and η are

$$\begin{aligned}
\frac{d\kappa}{d\theta} &= \frac{\sin(2\eta + \theta) + \kappa \sin 2\eta}{\cos 2\eta - \sin \delta} \\
\frac{d\eta}{d\theta} &= \frac{\sin \delta \cos(2\eta + \theta) - \cos \theta - \kappa \cos^2 \delta}{2\kappa \sin \delta (\cos 2\eta - \sin \delta)} - 1
\end{aligned} \tag{3.54}$$

Although in the solution for the radial stress field the method of characteristics is not utilized, it is possible to construct a pattern of characteristics which are inclined with respect to the direction of σ_1 at the angle $\pm\varepsilon$. In the polar coordinate system of Figure 3.10, their orientation is given by

$$\frac{dr}{d\theta} = r \cot(\eta \pm \varepsilon) \tag{3.55}$$

Since η is a function of θ only, the characteristics form a family of geometrically similar curves; this is shown in Figure 3.10 where the passive state was assumed.

3.3.2 Limit State in Axisymmetry

Traditionally, the term *axisymmetry* refers to a particular state of stress that may develop in a material whose deformations are independent of the circumferential

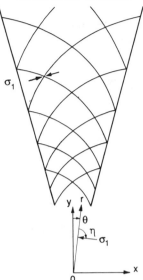

Figure 3.10   *Vertex radial stress field*

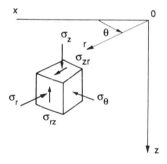

Figure 3.11   *Stress components in an axisymmetric state of stress*

θ-coordinate of the cylindrical system r, θ, z (Figure 3.11); the corresponding deformation is also called axisymmetric. Excluding a twisting type of motion, axisymmetric deformation takes place when motion is confined to the axial r, z-plane, i.e., when the circumferential component of the velocity is zero (see Section 8.2.2). The corresponding state of deformation is, in general, three-dimensional, with one of the principal strain-rates aligned along the θ-coordinate, $\dot{\varepsilon}_3 = \dot{\varepsilon}_\theta$, and the two remaining ones, $\dot{\varepsilon}_1$ and $\dot{\varepsilon}_2$, oriented in the axial plane. This also applies to principal stresses σ_1, σ_2, and σ_3, which are coaxial with the principal strain-rates if the flow rule of the material is potential.

The particular stress state that is usually considered in limit state solutions assumes principal stress σ_3 to be equal to one of the remaining two: either $\sigma_3 = \sigma_2$ or $\sigma_3 = \sigma_1$. This assumption is known as the *Haar-von Kármán hypothesis* (Haar and von Kármán, 1909), and, for the Mohr-Coulomb yield condition (2.30) or (2.33) represented in the principal stress space by a pyramid, corresponds to edges OA or

OB (Figure 2.22). Which of the two possibilities, OA or OB, should be used in a given problem can be established only if the sign of the principal strain-rate $\dot{\varepsilon}_3$ is known. Since $\dot{\varepsilon}_3$ is given by

$$\dot{\varepsilon}_3 = \dot{\varepsilon}_\theta = -\frac{v_r}{r} \tag{3.56}$$

its sign depends on the sign of the radial component of velocity v_r: for motion towards the z-axis, $\dot{\varepsilon}_3 > 0$, whereas for outward motion, $\dot{\varepsilon}_3 < 0$. Referring to Table 2.1, $\dot{\varepsilon}_3 > 0$ along OB, and $\dot{\varepsilon}_3 < 0$ along OA. Further analysis will be limited to the inward flow, i.e., to edge OB where

$$\sigma_1 = \sigma_3 > \sigma_2 \tag{3.57}$$

Consider now the equations that are available for stresses in the axisymmetric state above. Equilibrium equations (3.3) written in the r, θ, z-system are

$$\frac{\partial \sigma_r}{\partial r} + \frac{\partial \sigma_{rz}}{\partial z} + \frac{\sigma_r - \sigma_\theta}{r} = 0$$
$$\frac{\partial \sigma_{rz}}{\partial r} + \frac{\partial \sigma_z}{\partial z} + \frac{\sigma_{rz}}{r} = \gamma \tag{3.58}$$

yield condition (2.33) is

$$(\sigma_r - \sigma_z)^2 + 4\sigma_{rz}^2 - (\sigma_r + \sigma_z + 2c \cot \phi)^2 \sin^2 \phi = 0 \tag{3.59}$$

and the assumption $\sigma_\theta = \sigma_3 = \sigma_1$ gives

$$\sigma_\theta = \frac{1}{2}(\sigma_r + \sigma_z) + \frac{1}{2}[(\sigma_r - \sigma_z)^2 + 4\sigma_{rz}^2]^{\frac{1}{2}} \tag{3.60}$$

Thus, as in the case of plane-strain, the stresses are statically determinate.

The method of solving equations (3.58), (3.59), and (3.60) is identical to that for plane-strain (Berezantzev, 1948). With the help of two new variables, σ and ψ, defined by (3.15) and (3.16) with r, z replacing x, y, the stress components are

$$\sigma_r = \sigma(1 + \sin \phi \cos 2\psi) - c \cot \phi$$
$$\sigma_z = \sigma(1 - \sin \phi \cos 2\psi) - c \cot \phi$$
$$\sigma_{rz} = \sigma \sin \phi \sin 2\psi \tag{3.61}$$
$$\sigma_\theta = \sigma(1 + \sin \phi) - c \cot \phi$$

and equilibrium equations (3.58) become

$$(1 + \sin \phi \cos 2\psi)\frac{\partial \sigma}{\partial r} + \sin \phi \sin 2\psi \frac{\partial \sigma}{\partial z} - 2\sigma \sin \phi \sin 2\psi \frac{\partial \psi}{\partial r} + 2\sigma \sin \phi \cos 2\psi \frac{\partial \psi}{\partial z}$$
$$= -\frac{\sigma}{r} \sin \phi (\cos 2\psi - 1)$$
$$\sin \phi \sin 2\psi \frac{\partial \sigma}{\partial r} + (1 - \sin \phi \cos 2\psi)\frac{\partial \sigma}{\partial z} + 2\sigma \sin \phi \cos 2\psi \frac{\partial \psi}{\partial r} + 2\sigma \sin \phi \sin 2\psi \frac{\partial \psi}{\partial z}$$
$$= \gamma - \frac{\sigma}{r} \sin \phi \sin 2\psi$$

$$\tag{3.62}$$

Equations (3.62) are hyperbolic with the characteristics given by

$$\frac{dz}{dr} = \tan(\psi + \varepsilon) \qquad \alpha\text{-line}$$
$$\frac{dz}{dr} = \tan(\psi - \varepsilon) \qquad \beta\text{-line}$$

(3.63)

and the relations holding along the α- and β-lines, respectively, are

$$d\sigma + 2\sigma \tan \phi \, d\psi = \gamma(dz + \tan \phi \, dr) - \frac{\sigma}{r} \tan \phi [\cos \phi \, dr + (1 + \sin \phi) dz]$$
$$d\sigma - 2\sigma \tan \phi \, d\psi = \gamma(dz - \tan \phi \, dr) - \frac{\sigma}{r} \tan \phi [\cos \phi \, dr + (1 + \sin \phi) dz]$$

(3.64)

where ε is given by (3.20). Thus, the characteristics in axisymmetry are identically inclined with respect to the direction of σ_1, as for plane-strain. Clearly, for $r = \infty$, relations (3.64) become identical to (3.21).

Solutions to (3.63) and (3.64) can be obtained for the three types of boundary-value problems discussed in Section 3.3.1, and they can be either continuous or discontinuous. Unfortunately, accurate solutions have been found only for geotechnical problems where the stress field is continuous (cf. Cox, Eason and Hopkins, 1961). In bins and hoppers stress discontinuities always occur, and attempted numerical schemes turned out to be inadequate for providing reliable results (cf. Nedderman, 1981).

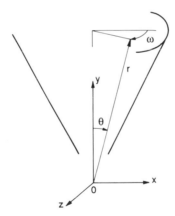

Figure 3.12 *Coordinate system for an axisymmetric vertex radial stress field*

It is possible, however, to obtain exact solutions if a vertex radial axisymmetric stress field is postulated (Jenike, 1964b). For the system of spherical coordinates r, θ, ω shown in Figure 3.12, the four available equations for stresses, i.e., the equilibrium equations

$$\frac{\partial \sigma_r}{\partial r} + \frac{\partial \sigma_{r\theta}}{r \partial \theta} + \frac{1}{r}(2\sigma_r - \sigma_\theta - \sigma_\omega + \cot \theta \sigma_{r\theta}) = -\gamma \cos \theta$$
$$\frac{\sigma_{r\theta}}{\partial r} + \frac{\partial \sigma_\theta}{r \partial \theta} + \frac{1}{r}[\cot \theta(\sigma_\theta - \sigma_\omega) + 3\sigma_{r\theta}] = \gamma \sin \theta$$

(3.65)

yield condition (3.44), and assumption (3.57) (which leads to (3.60) with ω replacing z), can be reduced with the help of (3.47) and (3.48) to two equations for the derivatives of the two functions κ and η defined for the radial stress field in Section 3.3.1

$$\frac{d\kappa}{d\theta} = \frac{\sin(2\eta + \theta) + \kappa \sin 2\eta + \kappa \sin \delta [\cot \theta (1 + \cos 2\eta) - \sin 2\eta]}{\cos 2\eta - \sin \delta}$$

$$\frac{d\eta}{d\theta} = \frac{\sin \delta \cos(2\eta + \theta) - \cos \theta - \kappa \cos^2 \delta}{2\kappa \sin \delta (\cos 2\eta - \sin \delta)}$$
$$- \frac{\kappa \sin \delta (1 + \sin \delta)(\cot \theta \sin 2\eta + \cos 2\eta - 1)}{2\kappa \sin \delta (\cos 2\eta - \sin \delta)} - 1$$

(3.66)

Again, the boundary conditions for η at the wall and at the center line, (3.52) and (3.53), must be used to determine the initial value of κ_0 for numerical integration of equations (3.66).

Finally, we must mention that stress states other than the Haar-von Kármán stress state are admissible in axisymmetric deformation problems (Cox, Eason and Hopkins, 1961), although their application to bin-load analysis has not been investigated in the literature.

3.4 DIFFERENTIAL SLICE METHODS

The term *differential slice methods* is used in this book for two approximate analytical methods for evaluation of stresses that a bulk material exerts on the rigid walls of bins and hoppers. These methods are the *method of slices* and the *method of integral relations*. Although the underlying concepts in both methods are essentially different, certain similarities in their application to bin-load analysis suggest a joint presentation. For these similarities the first method will be referred to as the *direct method of slices*, and the second one as the *indirect method of slices*.

The origin of the direct method of slices goes back to 1895, when H.A. Janssen published his paper on loads in bins. Following this fundamental work, numerous applications of this method have been presented in the literature (cf. Walker, 1966, Walters, 1973a, 1973b, Enstad, 1975, 1977). Besides its primary use in bin-load analysis, the method has found application in problems such as limit loads on geotechnical and mining structures (cf. Terzaghi, 1943, Vardoulakis, Graf and Gudehus, 1981, Drescher and Zhang, 1986), in the analysis of stresses developing in concrete or soil specimens tested under compression (cf. Kwaszczyńska, Mróz and Drescher, 1969, Drescher and Vardoulakis, 1982), and in the analysis of metal-forming processes (cf. Shroeder and Webster, 1949, Lippman, 1960).

The indirect method of slices (the method of integral relations) was introduced by Dorodnitsyn (1959, 1962) for solving some non-linear problems in fluid mechanics. Its application to bin-load analysis is due to Savage and Yong (1970), and Savage and Sayed (1979, 1981).

In the following sections, we will outline the fundamentals of both methods, beginning with the direct method of slices.

3.4.1 The Direct Method of Slices

The direct method of slices is based on the concept of a material element that is finite in one or two dimensions. The remaining dimensions of the element are infinitesimal, and the element is called the *differential slice*, or *slice*, in short. The element spans the material between supporting walls with its infinitesimal sides aligned along them. Although the geometry of a slice is virtually arbitrary, it must be selected so that no gap or overlap occurs between adjacent slices.

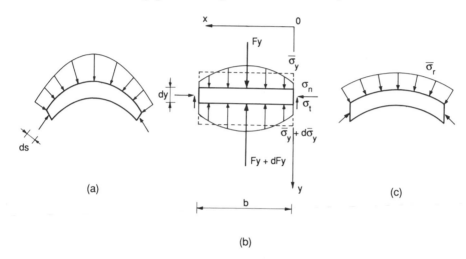

Figure 3.13 *Differential slices, (a) curvilinear, (b) plane and (c) cylindrical*

Operating with an element of finite dimensions reduces the number of coordinates along which the variation of stresses is to be found. For example, if two dimensions of a slice are finite, the problem becomes spatially one-dimensional. Accordingly, the equilibrium or motion equations for the slice will become ordinary differential equations in contrast to the partial differential equations that apply to an infinitesimal element. This is the main and useful feature of the direct method of slices, as integration of the former equations is simpler than that of the partial differential equations.

The equilibrium or motion equations for a slice are expressed in terms of forces that are resultants of stresses that act over the finite dimensions of the slice, mass forces that act within the slice, and local stresses that act at its infinitesimal sides. In general, force equilibrium and moment equilibrium are required. For slices that are geometrically symmetric and subjected to a symmetric stress distribution (Figure 3.13a), the moment equilibrium, and the force equilibrium in two of the directions are identically satisfied, and the number of governing equations reduces to one.

Consider, for example, a prismatic weightless slice spanning walls distance b apart in a plane bin, subjected to a symmetric stress distribution in the x, y-plane (Figure 3.13b). The only non-trivial equilibrium equation applies to the vertical

y-direction, and becomes

$$F_y - (F_y + dF_y) - 2\sigma_t \, dy = 0 \qquad (3.67)$$

or

$$\frac{dF_y}{dy} + 2\sigma_t = 0 \qquad (3.68)$$

where F_y is the resultant force of stresses acting over the distance b, and σ_t is the tangential component of the stress vector acting at the wall.

In spite of the simplicity of the equilibrium equations for a slice, equation (3.68) cannot be directly integrated because it contains two uknowns, F_y and σ_t, and the problem is statically indeterminate. Furthermore, both unknowns are of a different character: one is the force F_y, and the other the local stress component σ_t. However, the resultant force F_y can be resolved into an average vertical stress $\overline{\sigma}_y$

$$\overline{\sigma}_y = \frac{1}{b} \int_0^b \sigma_y dx = \frac{F_y}{b} \qquad (3.69)$$

and equation (3.68) can be written as

$$\frac{d\overline{\sigma}_y}{dy} + \frac{2\sigma_t}{b} = 0 \qquad (3.70)$$

Although equilibrium equation (3.68) holds for any symmetric shape of a slice spanning parallel walls, the resolution of the resultant force into an average stress may require additional assumptions. For example, if a circular slice is selected (Figure 3.13c), we may assume that the average stress is vertical or normal to the slice, which in turn will affect the form of the equilibrium equation expressed in terms of the average stress; this also applies to slices that span inclined walls. In general, any distribution of stresses over the finite dimension of a slice can be postulated, and the corresponding average stress found. In this manner, various assumptions about the stress distribution motivated by experimental observations can be tested.

The use of the average stress is not yet sufficient to remove the statical indeterminancy in the equilibrium equation for a slice. A relationship between the average stress and the wall stresses that enter into the equilibrium equation is necessary. Such a relationship can be either directly postulated or derived from a mechanical model for the bulk material. In particular, in Section 4.3 we will analyze relationships that result from postulating the rigid-perfectly plastic model, and the location of plastic states within a slice. Since from the equations governing the model only the yield condition will be utilized, and the choice of the location of the plastic states is somewhat arbitrary, the direct method of slices can be regarded as an approximate limit state method.

Finally, in applications of the direct method of slices to bin-loads analysis in Chapters 4, 5, and 6, and also in Chapter 7 where arching is considered, the average stress acting on a slice will be denoted by the greek letter σ without a bar, e.g., σ_y rather than $\overline{\sigma}_y$.

3.4.2 The Indirect Method of Slices

The indirect method of slices, or the method of integral relations, is an approximation method for converting partial differential equations into ordinary differential equations. The resulting system of ordinary differential equations can then be solved, either analytically or numerically, much more easily than the original set. Here, we will concentrate on this method's application to bin-load analysis.

The exact solution for stresses that exist in a region occupied by a material subjected to external loads must satisfy partial differential equations of local equilibrium (3.3) or equations of motion (3.4). For quasi-static problems, and a stress state independent of one coordinate, z, for instance, the equilibrium equations are

$$\frac{\partial \sigma_x}{\partial x} + \frac{\partial \sigma_{xy}}{\partial y} = 0$$

$$\frac{\partial \sigma_{yx}}{\partial x} + \frac{\partial \sigma_y}{\partial y} = 0$$

(3.71)

where body forces are neglected. Let the region of solution in the x, y-plane be bounded by two walls, parallel to the y-axis, at a distance b apart (Figure 3.14). To convert equations (3.71) we integrate the former set over distance b

$$\int_0^b \frac{\partial \sigma_{xy}}{\partial y} dx + \sigma_{xb} - \sigma_{x0} = 0$$

$$\int_0^b \frac{\partial \sigma_y}{\partial y} dx + \sigma_{xyb} - \sigma_{xy0} = 0$$

(3.72)

where $\sigma_{x0}(y) \neq \sigma_{xb}(y)$, $\sigma_{xy0}(y) \neq \sigma_{xyb}(y)$ are the normal and shear stresses at the boundaries. If the character of the distribution of stresses σ_y and σ_{xy} is known over distance b, e.g., it is polynomial, after differentiation of these polynomials, substitution into (3.72) and integration over the width b, a set of ordinary differential equations of equilibrium is obtained. Solution to the latter set can be found analytically or numerically, providing the number of unknowns equals the number of equations available. If the method discussed is applied in solving a problem for a rigid-perfectly plastic material, besides the two equations in (3.72), additional equations relating the stresses at the boundaries can be derived from the yield condition. It is also possible, however, to subdivide distance b into N strips of width b/N, and perform integration of equilibrium equations (3.71) over each strip. N sets of ordinary differential equations are thus obtained, which permits the increasing of the number of unknown functions in the polynomials. The subdivision of distance b into N strips yields an N-th approximation of the original system. With no subdivision a first approximation, or one-strip approximation, is obtained. We will now illustrate the method in a simple example.

Let the variation of stresses σ_y and σ_{xy} over distance b be given by (Figure 3.14)

$$\sigma_y = \sigma_{yb}(y) \left[\frac{x}{b}\right]^2$$

$$\sigma_{xy} = \sigma_{xyb}(y) \left[\frac{x}{b}\right]$$

(3.73)

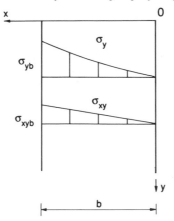

Figure 3.14   *One-strip approximation*

Differentiation of (3.73) with respect to y gives

$$\frac{\partial \sigma_y}{\partial y} = \frac{\partial \sigma_{yb}}{\partial y} \left[\frac{x}{b} \right]^2$$

$$\frac{\partial \sigma_{xy}}{\partial y} = \frac{\partial \sigma_{xyb}}{\partial y} \left[\frac{x}{b} \right] \tag{3.74}$$

Substituting (3.74) into (3.72) and integrating, we obtain

$$\frac{b}{2} \frac{d\sigma_{xyb}}{dy} + \sigma_{xb} - \sigma_{xo} = 0$$

$$\frac{b}{3} \frac{d\sigma_{yb}}{dy} + \sigma_{xyb} = 0 \tag{3.75}$$

Set (3.75) is a one-strip approximation of equilibrium equations (3.71) for the assumed variation of stresses (3.73). It allows the determining of boundary stresses σ_{yb} and σ_{xyb} if the relations between stresses σ_{x0}, σ_{xb} and stresses σ_{xyb}, σ_{yb} are known. These relations can be obtained from the yield condition of the material and from the static boundary conditions holding along the walls (see Section 4.4).

Although the method of integral relations does not directly introduce the concept of a slice, the ordinary differential form of the equilibrium equations resulting from integration of the stress distribution over a selected coordinate renders both methods somewhat similar. In particular, if at the bounding walls the boundary conditions were set as $\sigma_{xb} = \sigma_{x0}$, and $\sigma_{xyb} = -\sigma_{xy0}$, the first of equations (3.72) would be satisfied identically, and the second one, in view of equation (3.69), would be identical to (3.70). To take full advantage of the method of integral relations, a subdivision into N-strips and different boundary conditions along bounding integration walls should be considered. Also, both methods operate on stresses, and from the equations governing the rigid-perfectly plastic model only the yield condition is used. In this regard, the method of integral relations, or the indirect method of slices, can be considered another approximate limit state method.

3.5 LIMIT ANALYSIS METHODS

Plastic limit analysis, or *limit analysis* in short, is a group of methods which aim at determination of quasi-static loads that cause yielding of a mass of material modeled by the rigid-perfectly plastic model obeying a flow rule associative with a yield condition whose geometrical representation is a convex yield surface. The loads are limiting, i.e., no further increase is possible, and the corresponding yielding is identified with unrestricted plastic deformation that is manifested in a collapse, or failure mechanism. Since limit analysis is concerned only with limiting loads, neither the actual stress field nor the actual velocity field associated with the mechanism of plastic deformation are objectives of the analysis. On the other hand, however, effective solutions for the limit load require knowledge of either the stress field or the velocity field, though neither need be a true one.

Limit analysis methods have found wide application in solving numerous engineering problems where exact solutions for stresses and velocities are unknown. Examples can be found in plastic forming of metals (cf. Johnson and Mellor, 1983), structural engineering (cf. Neal, 1956), and geotechnical engineering (cf. Chen, 1975). Use of these methods for analyzing handling operations in bins and hoppers is less known.

Limit analysis in application to frictional/cohesive materials originates from fundamental works of Drucker and Prager (1952), Drucker (1953), Shield (1953), Collins (1969), and others. An extensive treatment of the fundamentals and examples is given by Chen (1975). The bases of the analysis form the *theorems of limit analysis*, upon which the method can be effectively applied to engineering problems; these theorems give lower and upper bounds to the true limit load. Before these theorems are stated, we will identify the limit load in problems of storage and flow of bulk materials.

3.5.1 Limit Load in Bins and Hoppers

The notion of a limit load is associated with a mechanism of collapse. The limit load must either induce collapse or the collapse results from a known source, e.g., self-weight, and a supporting load is sought at a moving boundary. An example is a wall moving horizontally with a given velocity into a material or away from it (Figure 3.15). In the first case, Figure 3.15a, the limit load is the force P necessary to induce failure in the material behind the wall. In the second, Figure 3.15b, the limit load is the reaction R that develops when the material collapses due to its own weight, and the wall is pushed away. This example, taken from geotechnics, belongs to the class of *incipient flow* problems. In these problems only the initial failure mechanism is considered, and the change in the limit load due to the change in the geometry of the problem, or the mechanism itself, is disregarded. Another class of problems is called *steady flow*, where neither the collapse mechanism nor the geometry of the boundary change, and the limit load remains constant at any instant of time.

In both types of problems, the surface limit load can be determined only in three cases: 1) the boundary velocities are constant, 2) the boundary velocities are linearly distributed, 3) the distribution of the boundary stresses is known, e.g. uniform (see Appendix B). In the first case, illustrated in the example of Figure 3.15, the limit load is the active force or reaction. In the second, the limit load is the overturning or supporting moment. In the third case, the magnitude of the distributed stress is the limit load. It is also possible to identify the limit load with body forces acting within the material. In the last two cases, the boundary velocities can be arbitrary.

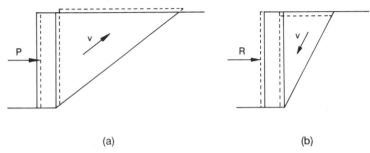

(a)   (b)

Figure 3.15   *Limit load in a retaining wall problem, (a) passive state and (b) active state*

The above requirements impose restrictions on the class of problems where limit analysis methods can be successfully applied. In particular, no information on the actual stress distribution, whether at the surface or within the body, can be inferred from these methods. Accordingly, they are not suitable for direct evaluation of stress distributions on walls of bins and hoppers. In some cases, however, it is possible to obtain information on forces that act over a section of a wall.

Contrary to wall stresses evaluation, limit analysis methods may be useful for analyzing impediments to flow. When analyzing arching, the limit load can be identified with the resultant of stresses that act at the arch or dome and oppose flow (Figure 3.16). If this reaction is greater than zero, flow takes place, as arching occurs with zero-stresses acting at the exposed surfaces of the arch or dome. If, however, the reaction assumes a zero-value, flow may be interrupted, and a stable arch may form. Similarly, considering channeling, the resultant of stresses that oppose failure of the material surrounding a channel may be regarded as the limit load. Alternatively, we may assume a stress-free surface of an arch or channel beforehand, and identify the limit load with either the unit weight of the material that causes collapse, or with the geometry of the arch or channel, e.g., span or height, for which an impediment to flow does not occur.

3.5.2 Theorems of Limit Analysis

The two basic theorems of limit analysis are known as the *lower bound theorem* and the *upper bound theorem*. These theorems are stated below without proof, for which the reader is referred to Appendix B (see also Chen, 1975). These theorems

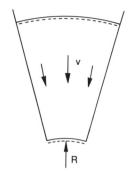

Figure 3.16   *Limit load in a hopper*

can be expressed as:

Lower Bound Theorem
A lower bound on the limit load inducing collapse may be found from any statically admissible solution.

Upper Bound Theorem
An upper bound on the limit load inducing collapse may be found from any kinematically admissible solution.

A statically admissible solution is a solution for stresses within a body which satisfies the following requirements:
1. local equilibrium equations (3.3) and continuity of stress vectors across a stress discontinuity surface,
2. static boundary conditions (3.5),
3. nowhere violates the yield condition (3.1).

In the above definition of an admissible solution no requirement is imposed on the relation between a statically admissible solution and the true one. Thus, any solution that satisfies the above requirements is called admissible, regardless of how "far" or "close" the solution is from the true one. It is obvious, however, that the true solution is also statically admissible. The magnitude of the surface limit load is directly obtained from stresses that result from a statically admissible solution.

A kinematically admissible solution is a solution for velocities within a body which satisfies the following requirements:
1. the strain-rates calculated from the velocity field using equation (3.10) obey flow rule (3.2) with $G(\sigma_{ij}) = F(\sigma_{ij})$,
2. kinematic boundary conditions.

Again, a kinematic solution need not be the true one, although the true solution is kinematically admissible. The second requirement can actually be weakened by allowing for an additional normal component of the velocity at the boundary. This modification plays an important role in problems where frictional sliding occurs along the boundary. The limit load resulting from a kinematically admissible solution is calculated from the balance of energy that is supplied for failure and the energy that is dissipated in the collapse mechanism.

Two other theorems hold for a limit load resisting collapse:

Upper Bound Theorem
An upper bound on the limit load resisting collapse may be found from any statically admissible solution.

Lower Bound Theorem
A lower bound on the limit load resisting collapse may be found from any kinematically admissible solution.

It should be stressed here that the last two theorems apply only to loads on moving boundaries, for loads on stationary supports cannot be regarded as limit loads.

Figure 3.17a graphically illustrates the theorems holding for a limit load inducing collapse, where the symbols P^s and P^k correspond to the limit load obtained from a static and a kinematic solution, respectively, and P^t is the true limit load. A similar diagram for limit loads resisting collapse is shown in Figure 3.17b. By constructing several static and kinematic solutions the difference between the lower and upper bounds can be minimized. At the limit, if both solutions give the same limit load, the true limit load is obtained.

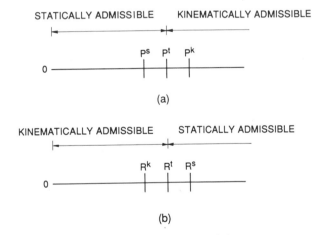

(a)

(b)

Figure 3.17   *Upper and lower bounds for (a) active limit load and (b) resisting limit load*

The limit analysis theorems for a rigid-perfectly plastic material stated above hold only if the flow rule is associative. It may appear, therefore, that limit analysis cannot be utilized if the behavior of a bulk material is described by a non-associative flow rule. It can be shown, however, that the true limit load inducing collapse in a material obeying a non-associative flow rule cannot be greater than that for a material with the associative rule. In other words, a non-associative material cannot be stronger than an associative one. In fact, static solutions for both materials are independent of the flow rule. The true solution for an associative material is also statically admissible, and, in view of the lower bound theorem, the corresponding limit load is the greatest one that results from all statically admissible solutions (Figure 3.17a). Thus, the true limit load for a non-associative material can be only equal to or less than that for an associative material. Since the kinematic solution bounds the true limit load for an associative material from above, it also gives an upper bound to the true solution for a non-associative material. Applying the same reasoning to a limit load resisting collapse, a kinematic solution gives a lower bound now for both the associative and non-associative flow rules. Unfortunately, no bounds to the true limit load for a non-associative material can be established that are based solely on a statically admissible solution; a limit load so determined may be below or above the true limit load as the material may be weaker than an associative one.

Evaluation of a limit load that is based on a statically admissible solution is often termed as the *statical method of limit analysis*. Similarly, the term *kinematical method of limit analysis* is used when a kinematical solution is utilized.

3.5.3 The Statical Method

According to the definition, any solution for stresses that satisfies local equilibrium equations and stress boundary conditions, and does not violate the yield condition, can be regarded as statically admissible. In spite of the seemingly weak requirements imposed, construction of statically admissible fields is, in many cases, difficult. The equilibrium equations are partial differential equations, and only for very simple problems a solution that nowhere violates the yield condition, and satisfies the boundary conditions, can be obtained by direct integration of these equations or guessed. The task is simplified somewhat if the yield condition is directly used in the solution rather than verified afterwards. The equilibrium equations supplemented by the yield condition can then be solved by the limit state methods for plane-strain and axisymmetry problems. These methods were discussed in Section 3.3, and will not be repeated here.

Use of the limit state methods does not imply that the stress field so obtained always can be regarded as a statically admissible solution. The requirements listed in Section 3.5.2 must hold for the whole body, i.e., not only in the portion that actually undergoes collapse. This condition is difficult to meet in problems where the body extends semi-infinitely and the limit load acts on a small portion of its surface. Examples can be found in geotechnical problems, where solutions for stresses are often limited to the region of collapse (cf. Sokolovskii, 1960, 1965). These *partial* solutions cannot be regarded as statically admissible.

Although in bins and hoppers the volume of the material is usually finite, difficulties arise in constructing admissible solutions if static boundary conditions are prescribed at more than one surface. As mentioned in Section 3.2, several existing solutions for stresses violate the boundary conditions at one surface. On the other hand, in problems with stresses specified at one surface only, it may not be possible to identify the collapse mechanism, and, thus, the limit load. An example is the limiting state of stress in a plane bin considered in Section 3.3 (Figure 3.4), which was constructed with the assumption that all walls are rigid and stationary.

This solution could be used only for evaluation of the limit load identified with the resultant of wall stresses if the walls were moving away, i.e., for determining the load on a retaining wall at collapse (Figure 3.15b).

For the reasons above, limit analysis solutions that make use of statically admissible fields have not found application in the analysis of bin-loads. Also, with one exception given by Jenike and Yen (1962), there are no static solutions that could be used for the analysis of obstructions to flow.

In contrast to statically admissible solutions, kinematic solutions are much easier to construct, and they may serve as an approximate tool for analyzing wall stresses and impediments to flow.

3.5.4 The Kinematical Method

A kinematically admissible solution is equivalent to a collapse, or failure, mechanism for which the velocities satisfy the requirements listed in Section 3.5.2. The velocities in the collapse mechanism can be either continuous functions of the location of material points, or they may undergo jumps across isolated velocity discontinuity surfaces. The admissibility of velocity discontinuities, besides stress discontinuities, is yet another feature of the rigid-perfectly plastic model. The following discussion of continuous and discontinuous velocity fields, preparatory to limit load evaluation, will concentrate on a state of plane-strain. Some considerations pertaining to axisymmetric velocity fields will be given in Section 8.2.2. The analysis of the velocity fields complements the analysis of stress fields presented in Section 3.3.

We will begin by considering a continuous kinematically admissible field, with the requirement that the resulting strain-rates must obey the associative flow rule. For plane-strain and motion in the x, y-plane, $\dot{\varepsilon}_z = \dot{\varepsilon}_3 = 0$, the principal strain-rates $\dot{\varepsilon}_1$ and $\dot{\varepsilon}_2$ that result from flow rule (3.2) associative with the Mohr-Coulomb yield condition for a frictional/cohesive material (2.33) are

$$\begin{aligned} \dot{\varepsilon}_1 &= \dot{\lambda}_1 (1 - \sin\phi) \\ \dot{\varepsilon}_2 &= -\dot{\lambda}_1 (1 + \sin\phi) \end{aligned} \tag{3.76}$$

Eliminating the multiplier $\dot{\lambda}_1$ from (3.76), we obtain an equation that interrelates the strain-rates in a kinematically admissible field

$$\dot{\varepsilon}_1 + \dot{\varepsilon}_2 + (\dot{\varepsilon}_1 - \dot{\varepsilon}_2) \sin\phi = 0 \tag{3.77}$$

Since flow rule (3.2) implies coaxiality of the principal stress and strain-rate directions, the angle ξ that principal strain-rate $\dot{\varepsilon}_1$ makes with the x-axis equals angle ψ, defining the orientation of the principal stress σ_1 (see [3.16]). Thus

$$\tan 2\psi = \tan 2\xi = \frac{2\dot{\varepsilon}_{xy}}{\dot{\varepsilon}_x - \dot{\varepsilon}_y} \tag{3.78}$$

and the principal strain-rates can be expressed as (Figure 3.18)

$$\dot{\varepsilon}_{1,2} = \frac{\dot{\varepsilon}_x + \dot{\varepsilon}_y}{2} \pm \frac{\dot{\varepsilon}_x - \dot{\varepsilon}_y}{2\cos 2\psi} \tag{3.79}$$

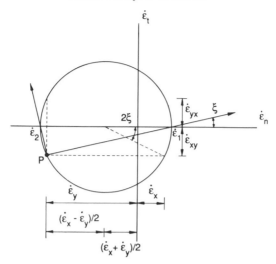

Figure 3.18   *Mohr's circle for strain-rates in an associative material*

On substituting (3.79) into (3.77), and making use of (3.10), we obtain

$$(\cos 2\psi + \sin \phi)\frac{\partial v_x}{\partial x} + (\cos 2\psi - \sin \phi)\frac{\partial v_y}{\partial y} = 0 \qquad (3.80)$$

Equation (3.80) is the first of two equations for the velocities of a continuous failure mechanism. Note that when $\phi = 0$, equation (3.80) becomes

$$\frac{\partial v_x}{\partial x} + \frac{\partial v_y}{\partial y} = 0 \qquad (3.81)$$

which is the incompressibility condition discussed in Section 2.5.

The second is the coaxiality equation (3.78), which, written in terms of velocities, is

$$\tan 2\psi \frac{\partial v_x}{\partial x} - \frac{\partial v_y}{\partial x} - \frac{\partial v_x}{\partial y} - \tan 2\psi \frac{\partial v_y}{\partial y} = 0 \qquad (3.82)$$

Equations (3.80) and (3.82) complete the set that governs the velocities in a kinematically admissible collapse mechanism. This set can be solved only if the distribution of the angle $\psi = \psi(x, y)$, or, in view of (3.78), of angle $\xi = \xi(x, y)$, is known throughout the deforming portion of the material, and the boundary conditions for the velocities are specified. For instance, if the static solution is constructed first, the distribution of angle ψ is known. Otherwise, the distribution of ψ, or ξ, must be postulated. This implies that the kinematic boundary conditions do not uniquely define the velocity field. This is because equations (3.80) and (3.82), with $\psi = \psi(x, y)$ given, are linear rather than quasi-linear partial differential equations, as was the case with equations for stresses. Since the type of set (3.80) and (3.82) is hyperbolic (Shield, 1953), solutions to this set can be obtained by the method of characteristics. The orientation of the velocity characteristics is given by

$$\frac{dy}{dx} = \tan(\psi + \varepsilon) \qquad \alpha\text{-line}$$

$$\frac{dy}{dx} = \tan(\psi - \varepsilon) \qquad \beta\text{-line} \tag{3.83}$$

where

$$\varepsilon = \frac{\pi}{4} - \frac{\phi}{2} \tag{3.84}$$

which means that the velocity characteristics coincide with the stress characteristics. The relations for the velocities along the characteristics are

$$dv_x + \tan(\psi + \varepsilon)dv_y = 0 \qquad \alpha\text{-line}$$

$$dv_x + \tan(\psi - \varepsilon)dv_y = 0 \qquad \beta\text{-line} \tag{3.85}$$

An alternative form of relations (3.85) that is more convenient in solving boundary-value problems is

$$dv_\alpha - (v_\alpha \tan\phi - v_\beta \sec\phi)d\psi = 0 \qquad \alpha\text{-line}$$

$$dv_\beta + (v_\beta \tan\phi - v_\alpha \sec\phi)d\psi = 0 \qquad \beta\text{-line} \tag{3.86}$$

where v_α and v_β are the projections of the velocity vector onto the α- and β-lines (Figure 3.19)

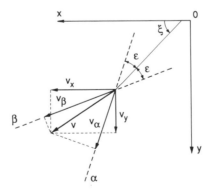

Figure 3.19   *Decomposition of the velocity vector*

Similarly as in the case with equations for stresses discussed in Section 3.3, effective solutions to velocity equations (3.80) and (3.82) can be obtained only if the boundary conditions formulate either a Cauchy, a characteristic, or a mixed boundary-value problem.

Consider now a velocity discontinuity surface whose intersection with the x, y-plane is a line. The velocity discontinuity is regarded as a thin layer across which both the tangential v_t and the normal v_n components of velocity v are distributed linearly and experience rapid change. Thus, the jump in the velocity, denoted by

$[v]$, also is distributed linearly (Figure 3.20a), and the state of deformation within an elemental length of the layer is given by

$$\dot{\varepsilon}_x = 0$$
$$\dot{\varepsilon}_y = -\frac{[v_n]}{\Delta n}$$
$$\dot{\varepsilon}_{xy} = -\frac{[v_t]}{2\Delta n}$$

(3.87)

where Δn is the thickness of the layer. Expressions (3.87) indicate that the deformation within a layer is a combination of shear and dilation. Calculating the principal strain-rates for strain-rate components (3.87), and using (3.76), the ratio between the normal and the tangential component of the velocity jump is

$$\frac{[v_n]}{[v_t]} = \tan\phi$$

(3.88)

which means that jump $[v]$ is inclined to the layer at angle ϕ. In a particular case, when $\phi = 0$, the jump is tangential, and the material in the layer undergoes a pure shear. Thus, regardless of the magnitude of ϕ, shear deformations always occur. For this reason, we will call this type of velocity discontinuity a *shear discontinuity*.

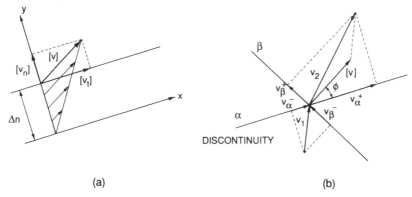

(a)   (b)

Figure 3.20 *(a) Shear velocity discontinuity and (b) decomposition of velocity vectors*

Using (3.78), (3.87), and (3.88), the orientation of σ_1 with respect to the velocity discontinuity is

$$\psi = \frac{3}{4}\pi + \frac{\phi}{2}$$

(3.89)

and the discontinuity is aligned along the velocity characteristic. Since both the velocity and stress characteristics coincide, the shear and normal stresses that act at the velocity discontinuity satisfy equation (2.32).

An expression for the magnitude of the velocity jump along the discontinuity line, e.g., an α-line, can be derived by subtracting $(3.86)_1$ written for both sides of the discontinuity (Figure 3.20b). Observing that v_β is continuous across the line, we have

$$d[v_\alpha] - [v_\alpha] \tan \phi \, d\psi = 0 \tag{3.90}$$

and upon integration

$$[v_\alpha] = [v_{\alpha 0}] e^{(\psi - \psi_0) \tan \phi} \tag{3.91}$$

where $[v_{\alpha 0}]$ and ψ_0 are initial values. This means that the jump increases exponentially unless the discontinuity is a straight line.

All the equations derived above, with δ replacing ϕ, remain unchanged if effective yield condition (2.30) describes yielding of the bulk material. In other words, cohesion c does not affect the velocity field. This is also true if the instantaneous yield condition is modified by the tension cut-off, equation (2.40). This time, angle ϕ is replaced by angle ν, which defines the local tangent to the tension cut-off portion of the yield condition.

A physically important result is obtained if $\nu = \pi/2$ and the velocity discontinuity is considered. In view of (3.88), the inclination of the velocity jump is now normal to the discontinuity, and no shear takes place (Figure 3.21a). Since the corresponding stresses are tensile, large deformations are physically inadmissible, and the material may separate along the discontinuity. This type of velocity discontinuity will be called a *separation discontinuity*. For the angle ν from the range $\phi < \nu < \pi/2$, the velocity jump $[v]$ can be decomposed into jump $[v_1]$ due to separation and jump $[v_2]$ due to shear/dilation (Figure 3.21b), and the discontinuity called a *shear/separation discontinuity*.

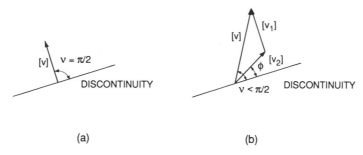

(a)   (b)

Figure 3.21   *(a) Separation and (b) shear/separation velocity discontinuities*

The physical interpretation of a velocity discontinuity, whether of the shear, separation, or shear/separation type, depends on the class of problems considered. In incipient flow problems, the discontinuity is identified with a thin *material layer* that opens due to dilation and pushes the surrounding material apart (Figure 3.22a). However, the change of the density of the material in the layer is disregarded, since only the initial stage of deformation is considered in these problems. In steady flow problems, on the other hand, the velocity discontinuity cannot be a material layer since with elapsing time the particles travel across the discontinuity. It is unnecessary, therefore, to assign any thickness to the layer, and the velocity discontinuity can be regarded as a *shock*. For a stationary shock in a dilating material, the principle of mass conservation (3.8) gives

$$\rho_1 v_{n1} = \rho_2 v_{n2} \tag{3.92}$$

where ρ_1, ρ_2, and v_{n1}, v_{n2} are the densities and normal components of the velocity on both sides of the velocity discontinuity, respectively (Figure 3.22b). Thus, the density and the unit weight of the material are no longer the same on both sides of the discontinuity.

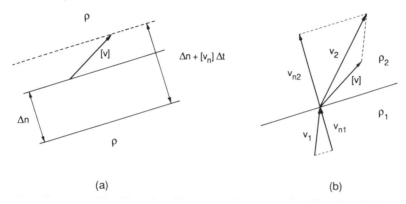

(a)   (b)

Figure 3.22   *(a) Velocity discontinuity in incipient and (b) steady flow problems*

Let us consider now a particular class of kinematically admissible velocity fields that consist of triangular regions with a constant velocity, and that are separated by straight velocity discontinuity lines; these regions will be called the *translational-motion* regions. Since material does not deform in these regions, the only requirement imposed on the field is that the velocity jumps satisfy expression (3.88). Obviously, such a velocity field is unrelated to the stress field, and the orientation of the velocity discontinuity lines can be arbitrary. This type of velocity field does not require use of a numerical scheme for evaluation of velocities within the regions, which is often necessary for integration of equations (3.83) or (3.85) along the characteristics in a continuous velocity field. The velocities can be directly obtained from vectorial summation of velocity and velocity jump vectors across discontinuity lines.

Discontinuous translational-motion type velocity fields are particularly suitable for evaluation of surface limit loads. As was pointed out in Section 3.5.1, one of the cases when the surface limit load can be determined is when the velocity is uniformly distributed along the boundary. Thus, by postulating a translational-motion region adjacent to the boundary, we see that this requirement is fulfilled directly. This observation has been utilized for solving numerous limit load problems in geotechnical engineering (cf. Chen, 1975), where various translational-motion velocity fields, intuitively postulated or derived from experimental observation, provided satisfactory solutions. This type of velocity field can be also applied to analyzing loads during discharge of bulk materials from bins and hoppers, and obstructions to flow in particular.

Figure 3.23a shows an example of a simple discontinuous failure mechanism in a relatively short plane hopper. On account of discharge, when the bulk material is in the critical state, effective yield condition (2.30) is assumed. The mechanism consists of two triangles, ABA' and BCC', where the velocities are vertical, and two triangles, ABC and $A'BC'$, where the velocities are parallel to the walls. Four shear-type velocity discontinuity lines, AB, BC, $A'B$, and BC', separate the triangles, and the velocity jumps across these lines are inclined at the effective angle of internal friction δ. To determine the velocities in each of the four regions, a plan of velocities plotted from an origin, known as a *hodograph*, can be used. The construction of the hodograph begins by assuming a value for the velocity of region ABA', e.g., v_o (Figure 3.23b). Knowing the direction of motion in region ABC, and the direction of the jump across AB, we find the magnitude of the velocity in region ABC, v_{ABC}, as the distance to the point of intersection of these directions. Similarly, from the known direction of motion in region BCC' and the direction of the jump across BC, we find the magnitude of velocity $v_{BCC'}$. Analytic expressions for the velocities in each triangular region can be derived easily by means of trigonometry. Although the orientation of the velocity discontinuity lines in Figure 3.23a has been selected arbitrarily, there are some limitations that result from the hodograph. Velocity v_{ABC} will have a finite value only if the direction of the velocity jump $[v_{AB}]$ intersects the direction of v_{ABC}. Similarly, velocity $v_{BCC'}$ is finite if the direction of $[v_{BC}]$ intersects the vertical direction. Denoting the hopper half-included angle by θ_w, and the angles between lines AB and BC and the horizontal direction by α_1 and α_2, respectively, we observe that the above requirements lead to the following inequalities

$$0 < \alpha_1 < \frac{\pi}{2} - \delta - \theta_w$$

$$0 < \alpha_2 < \frac{\pi}{2} - \delta \tag{3.93}$$

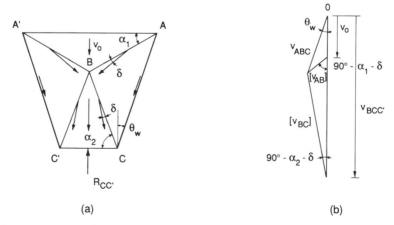

(a)   (b)

Figure 3.23   *(a) Translational failure mechanism and (b) hodograph*

3.5.5 Energy Balance

The preceding analysis was concerned with the construction of kinematically admissible velocity fields. Once a kinematically admissible velocity field associated with a given load is determined, the latter can be calculated from the energy balance, i.e., by equating the rate of work done by external forces to the rate of work dissipated in the velocity field.

The rate of work done by external forces is given by the dot product of all tractions, body forces, and the corresponding velocities. The general form of the expression for the rate of work of external forces $\dot{w}$ is given in Appendix B. For example, referring to the mechanism of failure of Figure 3.23a, the rate of work of external forces is

$$\dot{w} = -R_{CC'}v_{BCC'} + \gamma_{ABA'}V_{ABA'}v_o + 2\gamma_{ABC}V_{ABC}v_{ABC}\cos\theta_w \\ + \gamma_{BCC'}V_{BCC'}v_{BCC'} \tag{3.94}$$

where $V_{ABA'}$, V_{ABC}, $V_{BCC'}$, and $\gamma_{ABA'}$, γ_{ABC}, $\gamma_{BCC'}$ are the volumes and unit weights of the regions ABA', ABC, and BCC', respectively, and $R_{CC'}$ is the resultant of surface stresses along CC' supporting the material above (reaction).

Consider now the rate of energy that is dissipated in a given collapse mechanism. In the case of a plane-strain continuous velocity field the rate of energy dissipation per unit volume of the material $\Delta\dot{d}$, which is given by equation (3.11), can be written as

$$\Delta\dot{d} = \sigma_1\dot{\varepsilon}_1 + \sigma_2\dot{\varepsilon}_2 \tag{3.95}$$

It is possible now to eliminate principal stresses σ_1 and σ_2 from this equation using the yield condition and the flow rule. With the help of yield condition (2.33), principal stress σ_1 can be expressed as a function of stress σ_2, which upon substitution into (3.95) gives

$$\Delta\dot{d} = \frac{\sigma_2(\dot{\varepsilon}_1 + \dot{\varepsilon}_2) + \sigma_2(\dot{\varepsilon}_1 - \dot{\varepsilon}_2)\sin\phi + 2c\cos\phi\,\dot{\varepsilon}_1}{1 - \sin\phi} \tag{3.96}$$

Using (3.76), we find the terms containing the sum and the difference in the principal strain-rates to be opposite in sign, and equation (3.96) reduces to

$$\Delta\dot{d} = \frac{2c\cos\phi}{1 - \sin\phi}\dot{\varepsilon}_1 \tag{3.97}$$

Alternatively, using (3.76) again, we may write

$$\Delta\dot{d} = c\cos\phi\,(\dot{\varepsilon}_1 - \dot{\varepsilon}_2) \tag{3.98}$$

As anticipated, expressions (3.97) and (3.98) are functions only of the strain-rates, which can be found for every element of the material from the velocity field by performing the differentiation given by (3.10). A similar derivation for the three-dimensional deformation field leads to

$$\Delta\dot{d} = c\cos\phi\,(\dot{\varepsilon}_1 - \dot{\varepsilon}_2 - \dot{\varepsilon}_3) \tag{3.99}$$

The total rate of energy dissipated in a collapse mechanism, $\dot{d}$, is an integral of the specific rate taken over the volume.

It is seen from (3.98) or (3.99) that a non-zero rate of energy dissipation is obtained only if the cohesion is greater than zero. Thus, if yielding of a bulk material is described by effective yield condition (2.30), no energy is dissipated in the collapse mechanism. This somewhat surprising result does not contradict condition (3.11), which only requires that no energy can be stored in a plastically deforming material. Note that a non-zero energy dissipation for a purely frictional material would be obtained if its deformation were described by a non-associative flow rule. This time, however, the rate of energy dissipation is a function of the stress state, and cannot be evaluated solely from the velocity field (see Section 3.5.6).

To derive an expression for the rate of energy dissipation at a shear velocity discontinuity line, we observe that equation (3.98) also applies to an elementary volume taken from a layer. Thus, for an element of unit length and thickness Δn

$$\Delta \dot{d}_n = c \cos \phi \, (\dot{\varepsilon}_1 - \dot{\varepsilon}_2) \Delta n \tag{3.100}$$

For the strain-rate field in the layer given by (3.87), the difference in the principal strain-rates is

$$\dot{\varepsilon}_1 - \dot{\varepsilon}_2 = \frac{[v]}{\Delta n} \tag{3.101}$$

and the rate of energy dissipation per unit length of a layer is

$$\Delta \dot{d}_n = c \cos \phi \, [v] \tag{3.102}$$

and attains a zero-value if $c = 0$.

Expression (3.102) also applies to a shear/separation velocity discontinuity. However, the angle of friction and cohesion are no longer constant; c_ν is given by (2.41) or (2.43). Equation (3.102) thus takes the form

$$\Delta \dot{d}_n = \left[S_t \frac{\sin \nu - \sin \phi}{1 - \sin \phi} + S_c \frac{1 - \sin \nu}{2} \right] [v] \tag{3.103}$$

or

$$\Delta \dot{d}_n = c \left[q \frac{\sin \nu - \sin \phi}{\cos \phi} + \frac{\cos \phi (1 - \sin \nu)}{1 - \sin \phi} \right] [v] \tag{3.104}$$

In all cases, the rate of energy dissipation along a discontinuity line, $\dot{d}_n$, is the product of the specific dissipation $\Delta \dot{d}_n$ and the length of the line. For n-lines in a given collapse mechanism the total dissipation is the sum of dissipations along n-lines.

For the example of the collapse mechanism of Figure 3.23a, which models the flow of a bulk material described by the effective yield condition, there is no energy that is dissipated either in the rigid-motion regions or along the velocity discontinuity lines. Thus, from the energy balance, i.e., by setting $\dot{w} = \dot{d}$, we can express the resultant $R_{CC'}$ as

$$R_{CC'} = \gamma_{ABA'} V_{ABA'} \frac{v_0}{v_{BCC'}} + 2\gamma_{ABC} V_{ABC} \frac{v_{ABC}}{v_{BCC'}} \cos \theta_w + \gamma_{BCC'} V_{BCC'} \tag{3.105}$$

It is seen from (3.105) that the resultant $R_{CC'}$ is independent of the magnitude of the velocities, and depends only on their ratio. This result holds for any velocity field, and any yield condition. It is because of the rate-independency of the rigid-perfectly plastic model that a solution to a boundary-value problem is given in terms of the velocity ratios rather than the velocities themselves.

When considering the total rate of energy dissipation in the collapse mechanism of Figure 3.23a, we tacitly assumed that no dissipation takes place along the walls of the hopper. This is true only if the walls are perfectly smooth. In the presence of friction, there is an additional dissipation which is the dot product of the sliding velocity and the stresses acting at the wall (Figure 3.24a). Since in the kinematic solution the stresses are unknown, it might seem that dissipation in friction cannot be determined. It is possible, however, to modify the velocity field so that the dissipation along a wall is zero or attains a known value independent of the magnitude of stress. For dry friction along the wall, the dot product of the velocity and stress will assume a zero-value if the former is inclined at the angle of wall friction φ_w (Figure 3.24b). If the material adheres to the wall, and its resistance to shear is given by (2.54), by postulating again that the velocity vector is inclined at the angle φ_w (Figure 3.24c), we derive the rate of energy dissipation per unit length of wall $\Delta \dot{d}_w$ as

$$\Delta \dot{d}_w = c_w \cos \varphi_w \, v \qquad (3.106)$$

which is independent of the magnitude of stress. It is apparent that equation (3.106) is identical to (3.102), for the velocity in (3.106) represents the velocity jump across the wall. This means that the above modifications in the velocity field are equivalent to introducing a fictitious thin layer of a rigid-perfectly plastic material aligned along the wall, for which the flow rule is associative, with (2.53) or (2.54) regarded as the yield conditions. Note that the weakened second requirement of a kinematically admissible solution is thus utilized. Another possibility of evaluating wall dissipation is discussed in Section 4.5.

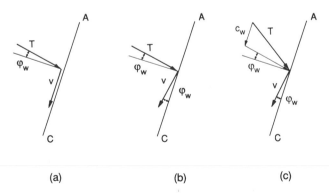

(a)   (b)   (c)

Figure 3.24   *Velocity jump across a rigid wall, (a) unmodified, (b) modified for friction and (c) modified for friction and cohesion*

Figure 3.25a shows the modified velocity field in a hopper, and Figure 3.25b the corresponding hodograph. The resultant across the line CC' is now given by

$$R_{CC'} = \gamma_{ABA'}V_{ABA'}\frac{v_0}{v_{BCC'}} + 2\gamma_{ABC}V_{ABC}\frac{v_{ABC}}{v_{BCC'}}\cos\theta_w$$
$$+\gamma_{BCC'}V_{BCC'} - 2c_w\cos\varphi_w\, l_{AC}\frac{[v_{ABC}]}{v_{BCC'}} \tag{3.107}$$

where it is assumed that the material adheres to the wall.

Let us proceed now to the evaluation of forces that act at the container walls. Although in the kinematic solution the corresponding stress field is unknown, resultants of stresses that act at the boundaries of translational-motion regions can be found. In fact, the energy balance for a translational-motion collapse mechanism is equivalent to the equilibrium of the resultants and weight of a triangular region. Therefore, if the directions of these resultants are known, a polygon of forces can be constructed, and the magnitude of the resultants found. Since the translational-motion regions are separated by velocity discontinuity lines where the shear and normal stresses satisfy (2.29), the local orientation of the stress vectors is known, as is the orientation of their resultants. Construction of the polygon of forces begins from a region where two resultants are unknown, and is carried out subsequently over the whole collapse mechanism. For example, for the mechanism of Figure 3.23a, we begin with region ABA', with the resultants along $A'B$ and AB inclined to the normals by the angle δ (Figure 3.26a). Next, regions $A'BC'$ and ABC are considered, and construction of the polygon ends with region BCC'. If dry friction exists along the hopper walls, the resultants at AC and $A'C'$ are inclined at the angle φ_w. If the material adheres to the wall, the component $c_w l_{AC}$ is calculated first. Figure 3.26b shows the polygon of forces for a symmetrical half of the mechanism of failure of Figure 3.26a, where dry wall friction and constant unit weight (incipient flow) was assumed.

By constructing the polygon of forces, we can directly evaluate the magnitude of the resultant along the wall. Alternatively, the resultant $R_{CC'}$ can be found first from the energy balance, equation (3.105) or (3.107), and the resultant at AC calculated from the global equilibrium of region $ACC'A'$.

It should be mentioned here that the method of forces is identical to the so-called Coulomb method widely used in analyzing stability of soil retaining walls (Coulomb, 1773, Terzaghi, 1943). Thus, the Coulomb method is equivalent to the kinematical method of limit analysis, and furnishes bounds to the true limit load.

The example of the failure mechanism in a plane hopper considered above illustrates the applicability of the kinematic method of limit analysis to certain problems related to storage and flow of bulk materials. Referring to our discussion in Section 3.5.1, the limit load in this example can be identified with the resultant of stresses that oppose flow over sector CC'. According to the limit theorem for loads supporting collapse, a kinematic solution provides a lower estimate of the true supporting load. Alternatively, assuming that this resultant is known, e.g., of zero-value, we can regard the unit weight of the material as the limit load. This time, however, the kinematic solution gives an upper bound to the true load.

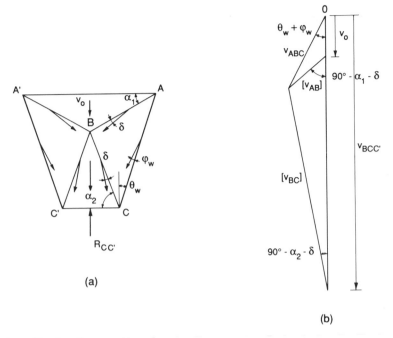

(a)

(b)

Figure 3.25 *(a) Modified velocity field and (b) hodograph*

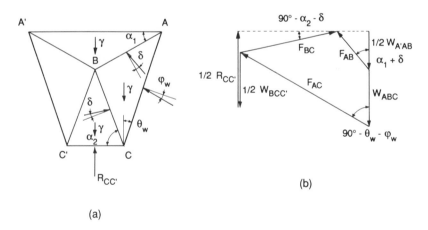

(a)

(b)

Figure 3.26 *(a) Forces in a translational failure mechanism and (b) polygon of forces*

3.5.6 Velocity Field for a Non-Associative Material

Although the kinematical method of limit analysis requires construction of velocity fields that satisfy the associative flow rule, it is interesting to discuss the differences in the fields if a non-associative flow rule is assumed.

The derivation of the velocity equations for a non-associative, incompressible flow rule closely follows the derivation presented in Section 3.5.4. In fact, all the equations derived there still hold if $\phi = 0$. Thus, the set of governing equations becomes

$$\frac{\partial v_x}{\partial x} + \frac{\partial v_y}{\partial y} = 0$$

$$\tan 2\psi \frac{\partial v_x}{\partial x} - \frac{\partial v_y}{\partial x} - \frac{\partial v_x}{\partial y} - \tan 2\psi \frac{\partial v_y}{\partial y} = 0$$

(3.108)

with the characteristics given by

$$\frac{dy}{dx} = \tan(\psi + \varepsilon) \qquad \alpha\text{-line}$$

$$\frac{dy}{dx} = \tan(\psi - \varepsilon) \qquad \beta\text{-line}$$

(3.109)

where

$$\varepsilon = \frac{\pi}{4}$$

(3.110)

and with the relations along the characteristics

$$dv_x + \tan(\psi + \varepsilon)dv_y = 0 \qquad \alpha\text{-line}$$
$$dv_x + \tan(\psi - \varepsilon)dv_y = 0 \qquad \beta\text{-line}$$

(3.111)

or

$$dv_\alpha + v_\beta d\psi = 0 \qquad \alpha\text{-line}$$
$$dv_\beta - v_\alpha d\psi = 0 \qquad \beta\text{-line}$$

(3.112)

if the projections of the velocity onto the α- and β-lines are introduced. Thus, the characteristics are orthogonal and do not coincide with the stress characteristics (Figure 3.27). Velocity discontinuities are admissible, and they coincide with the velocity characteristics. The jump in velocity $[v]$ is tangential to the discontinuity line, and its magnitude is constant along the discontinuity, regardless of whether the latter is a straight or curved line. The shear and normal stresses at the discontinuity no longer satisfy (2.29); the shear stress attains the maximum value $(\sigma_1 - \sigma_2)/2$.

As with the vertex radial stress field, incompressible vertex radial velocity fields have been considered in the literature (Jenike, 1964b). For a plane-strain state, the radial velocity field is defined by

$$v_r = v_r(r, \theta) \qquad v_\theta = 0$$

(3.113)

where the system of coordinates is shown in Figure 3.28. From the incompressibility condition

$$\frac{\partial v_r}{\partial r} + \frac{v_r}{r} = 0$$

(3.114)

we obtain

$$v_r = \frac{f(\theta)}{r}$$

(3.115)

where, for motion towards the origin, $f(\theta)$ is an arbitrary negative function. Clearly, the velocities increase towards the vertex, and there attain an infinite value.

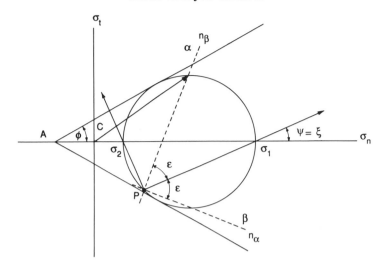

Figure 3.27 *Orientation of velocity characteristics in a non-associative material*

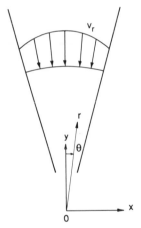

Figure 3.28 *Vertex radial velocity field*

To relate the velocity field (3.115) to the stress field, we make use of the angle η that represents the inclination of principal strain-rate $\dot{\varepsilon}_1$, and therefore also of principal stress σ_1, with respect to the r-axis. For the radial velocity field (3.113), equation (3.78) becomes

$$\left[\frac{\partial v_r}{\partial r} - \frac{v_r}{r} \right] \tan 2\eta = \frac{\partial v_r}{r \partial \theta} \tag{3.116}$$

Eliminating v_r from (3.115) and (3.116) we have

$$\frac{df(\theta)}{d\theta} + 3 f(\theta) \tan 2\eta = 0 \tag{3.117}$$

which, upon integration and substitution into (3.115), gives

$$v_r = A \frac{e^{-2 \int \tan 2\eta(\theta) d\theta}}{r} \tag{3.118}$$

where A is a constant. For an axisymmetric vertex radial velocity field, equations (3.115) and (3.118) become

$$v_r = \frac{f(\theta)}{r^2} \tag{3.119}$$

$$v_r = A \frac{e^{-3 \int \tan 2\eta(\theta) d\theta}}{r^2} \tag{3.120}$$

Finally, we will present expressions for the specific rate of energy dissipation for a frictional/cohesive non-associative material. From (3.95), which holds for any material with principal stresses coaxial with the principal strain-rates, and from the incompressibility condition and yield condition (2.33) we arrive at

$$\Delta \dot{d} = \dot{\varepsilon}_1 [(\sigma_1 + \sigma_2) \sin \phi + 2c \cos \phi] \tag{3.121}$$

or, using (3.76),

$$\Delta \dot{d} = (\dot{\varepsilon}_1 - \dot{\varepsilon}_2) \left[\frac{1}{2} (\sigma_1 + \sigma_2) \sin \phi + c \cos \phi \right] \tag{3.122}$$

which means that the rate of energy dissipation depends on the stresses, and cannot be expressed as a function of the strain-rates only. Analogously, from (3.101) and (3.122), the rate of energy dissipation per unit length of the discontinuity line is

$$\Delta \dot{d}_n = [v](\sigma_n \sin \phi + c \cos \phi) \tag{3.123}$$

and depends on the normal stress σ_n.

3.6 CLOSING REMARKS

In the preceding sections, emphasis was placed on three groups of methods that are suitable for analyzing certain problems related to storage and flow of bulk materials modeled by the rigid-perfectly plastic solid. A fuller analysis of the fundamentals of the rigid-perfectly plastic solid, and problems related to uniqueness and exactness of solutions, can be found in monographs by Hill (1950), Prager and Hodge (1968), Salençon (1977), to name a few.

The methods discussed have been successfully applied in the literature for wall stress evaluation and in the analysis of obstructions to flow; this will be demonstrated in the remaining chapters of this book. These methods are not universal, however, and their application is limited, indeed. The main limitation stems from the fact that the rigid-perfectly plastic model provides no information on the state of stress and deformation before the yield condition is reached. An example where the methods discussed fail is discharge from storage structures which operate in the funnel- or plug-flow mode. Although in the central zone of the flowing material plastic yielding can be assumed, it is highly questionable to extend yielding onto the surrounding material that is at rest. Accordingly, the solutions for wall stresses given in the following chapters will be limited to mass-flow bins and hoppers only. A similar reservation could apply to the filling operational phase, if no plastic deformations develop in the material. It should also be noted that the criteria separating the mass-flow from the funnel- or plug-flow are one of the least theoretically investigated problems and are based, usually, on empirical observations (cf. Jenike, 1964b, and Section 4.2.2).

Further, since the rigid-perfectly plastic model operates on strain-rates rather than on strains, wall deflections, due to their elasticity, cannot be incorporated into the analysis, and all walls must be regarded as rigid.

To account for small deformations before yielding, and wall deflections, elasto-plastic hardening models would have to be used. For those models, however, the mathematical complexity of the governing equations requires use of numerical methods in solving boundary-value problems.

4 BIN-LOADS IN QUASI-STATIC MASS FLOW

4.1 INTRODUCTION

Most efforts aimed at prediction of wall and bottom stresses in bins and hoppers have been devoted to *quasi-static* conditions. Quasi-static analysis assumes that stresses within a mass of bulk material are due exclusively to its own weight, and, in some cases, also due to pressure that is applied to the upper surface of the stored or discharged material. In other words, quasi-static analysis ignores the inertial forces that develop in a moving mass of particles whenever their velocities vary with time and position, thus causing the particles to accelerate or decelerate.

The main reason why quasi-static analysis has attracted considerable attention is the lack of coupling between the stresses and velocities in the equations that govern the state of stress. Neither local nor global equilibrium equations contain terms involving the velocities. This greatly simplifies the analysis which, in most cases, does not require a simultaneous solution for stresses and velocities. As demonstrated in Chapter 3, limit state methods and differential slice methods are examples of effective analytical methods where only the solution for stresses is sought. In the kinematic method of limit analysis, operating on the velocities of particles, the static counterpart of the solution is of no importance.

Quasi-static analysis of wall and bottom stresses in bins and hoppers has been successfully applied to the filling, storage, and discharge operational phases. Although, in the case of discharge, its validity might seem controversial, the results obtained closely approximate the stresses measured on real objects. In most storage facilities significant deviation from the quasi-static condition occurs only in the vicinity of outlets. Furthermore, quasi-static analysis overestimates wall stresses, thus giving a safe load value for the structural design of the storage structures (see Chapters 5 and 6).

Three groups of analytical solutions will be presented, following the order of methods described in Chapter 3, i.e., the limit state methods solutions, the differential slice methods solutions, and the kinematical method of limit analysis solutions. As mentioned in Section 3.6, wall stresses in bins and hoppers that operate in the funnel- or plug-flow mode will be excluded from the analysis, for all methods fail if yielding is restricted to an inner core that is separated from the bin or hopper walls by a stagnant material.

4.2 LIMIT STATE METHODS SOLUTIONS

The solutions for stresses based on the limit state methods are seldom analytical. In most cases a numerical scheme is required to integrate the equations governing the orientation of the stress characteristics and the equations that hold along them. This also applies to particular radial stress field solutions. The non-analytical form of the solutions makes it difficult to present and discuss in detail numerical algorithms employed in solving the various boundary-value problems that occur in analyzing bin-loads in various types of storage structures. Therefore, attention will be focused on the essential features of solutions depending on whether the active or passive state of stress is considered. Accordingly, only examples of stress characteristics fields will be given below to illustrate the solutions.

4.2.1 Stresses in Bins

Referring to our discussion of the limit state method in Section 3.3, the wall and bottom stresses in a storage structure are determined once the limiting stress field is found within the whole mass of the bulk material. In general, the stress field is found by means of the method of characteristics. In some cases, however, a radial stress field can be postulated, either within a portion or throughout the whole mass of the bulk material. The latter case applies only to converging hoppers (the vertex radial stress field, see Section 4.2.2). Further, though both the plane-strain and axisymmetric states can be analyzed, accurate solutions by means of the method of characteristics have been found only for plane-strain. Thus, in this section, only plane bins will be considered.

Consider first a vertical bin with the horizontal upper surface of the bulk material subjected to a uniformly distributed pressure σ_{y0}. Below the surface, two limiting states of stress may exist: active or passive. In the active case, major principal stress σ_1 is directed vertically, whereas in the passive case σ_1 acts in the horizontal direction. The solution for the active state of stress in a shallow bin was discussed in Section 3.3.1. Here, it will be outlined again for a bin of much greater height.

Figure 4.1a shows the mesh of the stress characteristics obtained by numerical integration of equations (3.19) and (3.21). In region ABA', the Cauchy boundary-value problem is solved (Rankine state), regions ABD and $A'BD'$ consist of fans of characteristics emerging from points A and A' (degenerate characteristic problems), and regions ADC and $A'DC'$ are solved as mixed problems. Next, the characteristic problem in the curvilinear quadrangle $BCEC'$ is considered, which allows the solving of the mixed problems within triangles CEF and $C'EF'$. Further solution follows the last two steps, i.e., the characteristic and mixed problems are subsequently solved until the outlet of the bin is reached where the actual boundary conditions may not be satisfied.

The solution presented in Figure 4.1a was obtained by Horne and Nedderman (1976), for bulk material obeying the effective yield condition (2.30), with $\delta = 30°$, $\varphi_w = 25°$, and $\sigma_{y0} = 4\gamma b$, where b is the half-width of the bin. Figure 4.1b shows the distributions of dimensionless wall stresses $\sigma_n/\gamma b$, and $\sigma_t/\gamma b$. The solution for stresses is continuous everywhere, with two singular points A and A'. Thus, the wall stresses are distributed continuously also, although the distribution is not smooth.

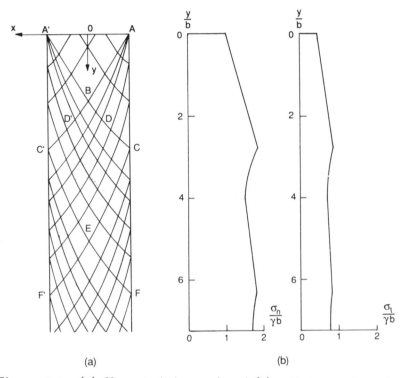

(a)   (b)

Figure 4.1   *(a) Characteristics mesh and (b) wall stresses in a plane bin; active state, $\delta = 30°$, $\varphi_w = 25°$, $\sigma_{y0} = 4\gamma b$ (Horne and Nedderman, 1976)*

If the wall friction angle $\varphi_w = \delta$, the last β-line emanating from singular point A and the last α-line emanating from point A' become tangent to the walls, and all lines along the walls are so inclined. This means that walls are envelopes of stress characteristics. On the other hand, if $\varphi_w = 0$, all α-lines and β-lines throughout the bin are parallel to $A'B$ and AB, respectively, and the wall stresses vary linearly with depth (active Rankine state).

The oscillations in wall stresses, diminishing with increasing depth for $\varphi_w > 0$ (Figure 4.1b), suggest that an asymptotic state of stress exists if the bin is infinitely tall. This asymptotic state of stress is independent of the y-coordinate, and can be directly obtained from equilibrium equations (3.13), yield condition (3.14) with

$\phi = \delta$, $c = 0$, and fully mobilized dry friction along the walls. Integration of equations (3.13) gives

$$\sigma_x = C_1$$
$$\sigma_{xy} = \gamma x + C_2 \tag{4.1}$$

where C_1 and C_2 are constants which can be determined from the boundary conditions

$$x = 0 \qquad \sigma_{xy} = 0$$
$$x = b \qquad \sigma_{xy} = \sigma_x \tan \varphi_w \tag{4.2}$$

Thus

$$C_1 = \gamma b \cot \varphi_w$$
$$C_2 = 0 \tag{4.3}$$

and the asymptotic wall stresses are

$$\sigma_n = \gamma b \cot \varphi_w$$
$$\sigma_t = \gamma b \tag{4.4}$$

Substituting (4.1) into (3.14) and utilizing (4.2) and (4.3), we obtain the following expression for the vertical stress

$$\sigma_y = \frac{\gamma b (1 + \sin^2 \delta)}{\cos^2 \delta \tan \varphi_w} + \frac{2\gamma b}{\cos^2 \delta} \left[\frac{\sin^2 \delta}{\tan^2 \varphi_w} - \cos^2 \delta \frac{x^2}{b^2} \right]^{1/2} \tag{4.5}$$

The solution presented in Figure 4.1a, with two singular points, A and A', is valid only if the upper surface of the material is subjected to pressure $\sigma_{y0} > 0$. As mentioned in Section 3.3.1, for a stress-free upper surface and cohesionless material, the stresses at a singular point are indeterminate. One may assume, however, that between the Rankine zone ABA' and the walls a radial stress field exists where all the stress components are proportional to the radial distance r measured from points A and A'. This is possible because lines AB, AB', and the walls are straight, and variable σ, given by (3.45), is proportional to r along AB and $A'B$. This can be shown from (3.26) and (3.27), with $\sigma_{y0} = 0$ and $y = r \sin \theta_{AB}$, which gives

$$\sigma = \gamma r \frac{\sin \theta_{AB}}{1 + \sin \delta}$$
$$\theta_{AB} = \frac{\pi}{4} + \frac{\delta}{2} \tag{4.6}$$

Equations (3.50) are then solved numerically for κ and η, with the boundary values for η

$$\eta_{AB} = \frac{\pi}{4} - \frac{\delta}{2}$$
$$\eta_{AC} = \frac{1}{2}(\omega - \varphi_w) \tag{4.7}$$

and ω is given by (3.33).

The radial stress field in regions ABC and $A'BC'$ yields stress characteristics that do not intersect at points A and A'. The bounding field characteristics BC and BC', however, differ only slightly when compared with the solution with singular points, and this difference would not be discernible in Figure 4.1a. The solution below lines BC and BC' is constructed in the same manner as for $\sigma_{y0} > 0$. The oscillations in wall stresses are smaller, and stresses approach the asymptotic state given by (4.4) and (4.5).

The solution for wall stresses in the case of the passive state of stress in a bin is significantly different from that of the active case. The α-lines in the passive Rankine zone are inclined to the x-axis at angle (Figure 4.2a)

$$\theta_{AA'} = \frac{\pi}{4} - \frac{\delta}{2} \tag{4.8}$$

whereas the α-lines emanating from wall AC are inclined at angle

$$\theta_{AC} = \frac{\pi}{4} - \frac{\delta}{2} - \frac{1}{2}(\omega + \varphi_w) \tag{4.9}$$

For $\delta \geq \varphi_w > 0$ we have $\theta_{AA'} > \theta_{AC}$, and in the vicinity of corner point A the α-lines overlap. Thus, a smooth transition of the orientation of the α-lines in regions ABC, and β-lines in region $A'BC'$, is not possible, regardless of whether two singular points or the radial stress field are postulated. The overlapping of like characteristics yields multivalued stresses, which can be avoided only by introducing the stress discontinuty lines emanating from points A and A' (Figure 4.2b). The stress discontinuities propagate towards the center line, reflect back to the walls, and again reflect towards the center line. This pattern continues down the bin.

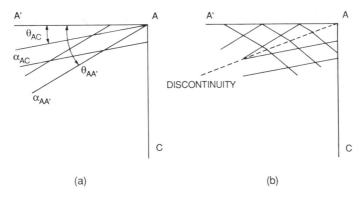

(a)   (b)

Figure 4.2 *(a) Orientation of stress characteristics in the vicinity of point A and (b) stress discontinuity; passive state*

A stress field that is continuous exists only if $\varphi_w = 0$, when all the α- and β-lines are straight, and stresses vary linearly with depth (passive Rankine state).

The algorithm for numerical construction of the characteristics field containing stress discontinuities is complex, and is not discussed here. An example of a characteristics mesh obtained by Horne and Nedderman (1976) for $\delta = 30°$, $\varphi_w = 25°$, and $\sigma_{y0} = 0$, is shown in Figure 4.3a. In this solution, the radial stress field was assumed below the stress discontinuities emanating from points A and A'. Due to reflection of the stress discontinuities at the walls, the wall stresses are locally discontinuous. This is demonstrated in Figure 4.3b which shows the distribution of wall stresses.

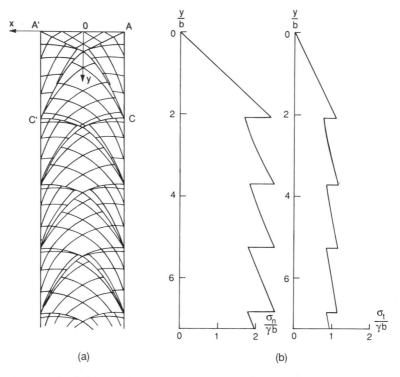

(a)   (b)

Figure 4.3   *(a) Characteristics mesh and (b) wall stresses in a plane bin; passive state, $\delta = 30°$, $\varphi_w = 25°$, $\sigma_{y0} = 0$ (Horne and Nedderman, 1976)*

Although not proven numerically, the stress distribution seems to approach an asymptotic value for a bin of infinite height. This asymptotic solution, independent of the y-coordinate, is again obtained from equilibrium equations (3.13), yield condition (3.14), and wall friction (4.2)$_2$, which give

$$\sigma_n = \gamma b \cot \varphi_w$$
$$\sigma_t = \gamma b$$
$$\sigma_y = \frac{\gamma b(1 + \sin^2 \delta)}{\cos^2 \delta \tan \varphi_w} - \frac{2\gamma b}{\cos^2 \delta} \left[\frac{\sin^2 \delta}{\tan^2 \varphi_w} - \cos^2 \delta \frac{x^2}{b^2} \right]^{1/2} \qquad (4.10)$$

and the asymptotic wall stresses are identical to those corresponding to the active case. Figure 4.4 shows the distribution of asymptotic vertical stresses $\sigma_y/\gamma b$ across the bin width for the active and passive cases, respectively, and for $\delta = 30°$,

$\varphi_w = 25°$. Characteristically, the distribution of vertical stresses is convex for the active case, and concave for the passive case. This trend also holds for any cross-section of a finite bin if local discontinuities in the case of the passive state are ignored.

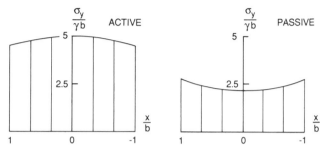

Figure 4.4   *Asymptotic bottom stresses in a plane bin; $\delta = 30°$, $\varphi_w = 25°$*

4.2.2 Stresses in Hoppers

In storage structures with convergent walls, two types of limit state solutions are possible. In the first type, the solution is constructed from the upper surface of the bulk material occupying the hopper in a way similar to that discussed in Section 4.2.1. Only solutions for plane hoppers have been derived successfully. The second type assumes a radial stress field within the whole mass of the bulk material, and both plane and conical hoppers can be considered. We will discuss and present examples of both types of solutions separately, beginning with the first type.

The active limiting stress field depends on the hopper half-included angle θ_w. A stress field that is continuous throughout the hopper can be constructed only if no overlap of stress characteristics occurs. This can be established by comparing the orientation of the β-lines in the active Rankine zone below the upper horizontal surface AA' with those that emanate from the hopper wall AC. In the Rankine zone

$$\theta_{AA'} = \frac{\pi}{4} + \frac{\delta}{2} \tag{4.11}$$

and along the wall

$$\theta_{AC} = \frac{\pi}{4} + \frac{\delta}{2} + \frac{1}{2}(\omega - \varphi_w) - \theta_w \tag{4.12}$$

A continuous transition of the β-lines, whether converging at a singular point A if $\sigma_{y0} > 0$ or non-converging if a radial stress field is selected for $\sigma_{y0} = 0$, is possible only if $\theta_{AA'} < \theta_{AC}$. This will be satisfied if

$$\theta_w \le \frac{1}{2}(\omega - \varphi_w) \tag{4.13}$$

and the pattern of the stress characteristics resembles that for a bin. This is demonstrated in Figure 4.5a, taken from Wilms and Schwedes (1985), for a hopper with

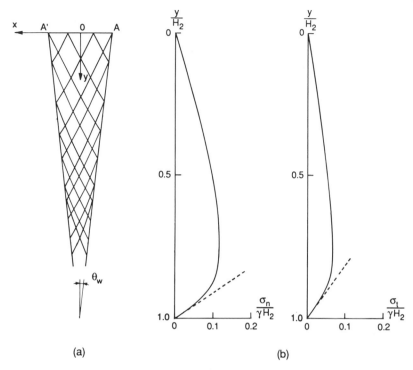

(a)   (b)

Figure 4.5   *(a) Characteristics mesh and (b) wall stresses in a plane*
hopper; active state, $\theta_w = 6°$, $\delta = 40°$, $\varphi_w = 30°$, $\sigma_{y0} = 0$
(Wilms and Schwedes, 1985)

$\theta_w = 6°$, and for $\delta = 40°$, $\varphi_w = 30°$, and $\sigma_{y0} = 0$. The corresponding wall stresses,
shown in Figure 4.5b by the solid lines, initially increase with depth, and then
decrease to zero at the vertex.

A particular distribution of wall stresses, linear with depth, and a mesh of stress
characteristics consisting of straight lines (Rankine state) appears if $\theta_{AA'} = \theta_{AC}$,
i.e., when equality in (4.13) holds.

If inequality (4.13) is not satisfied, and the stress characteristics overlap, stress
discontinuities emanating from corner points A and A' must be introduced, and
they propagate towards the vertex of the hopper by sequential reflections from the
center line and walls. As observed by Horne and Nedderman (1978a), wall stresses
may increase with depth and reach infinity at the vertex. Although infinite stresses
might seem physically unacceptable, the vertex of a hopper is a singular point, and
infinite stresses are acceptable there if the integral of wall stresses taken over the
height of the hopper assumes a finite value (see Section 4.3.2). Further, in any real
hopper the dimension of the outlet is finite, and there the vertical and wall stresses
assume a finite value.

A solution containing stress discontinuities is valid if

$$\frac{1}{2}(\omega - \varphi_w) \le \theta_w \le \frac{\pi}{2} - \frac{1}{2}(\omega + \varphi_w) \tag{4.14}$$

where the right-hand side inequality corresponds to stress discontinuities, emanating from points A and A', coinciding with the horizontal surface AA'. For greater angles θ_w no limiting state of stress solution exists.

A similar analysis of the orientation of the α-lines along the horizontal surface and along the walls for the passive case gives

$$\theta_{AA'} = \frac{\pi}{4} - \frac{\delta}{2} \tag{4.15}$$

and

$$\theta_{AC} = \frac{\pi}{4} - \frac{\delta}{2} - \frac{1}{2}(\omega + \varphi_w) - \theta_w \tag{4.16}$$

Thus, $\theta_{AA'} > \theta_{AC}$, and the α-lines overlap for all values of φ_w. An example of a discontinuous characteristics mesh is shown in Figure 4.6a for $\theta_w = 10°$, $\delta = 30°$, $\varphi_w = 25°$, and $\sigma_{y0} = 0$, (Horne and Nedderman, 1978a). Although the distribution of wall stresses, shown in Figure 4.6b by the solid lines, is discontinuous, the jumps decrease towards the vertex where stresses reach a zero-value. A somewhat similar result, with continuous but oscillatory distribution of wall stresses, was obtained by Pitman (1986). In this work, the finite difference approximation to equations (3.18) was used directly rather than the method of characteristics.

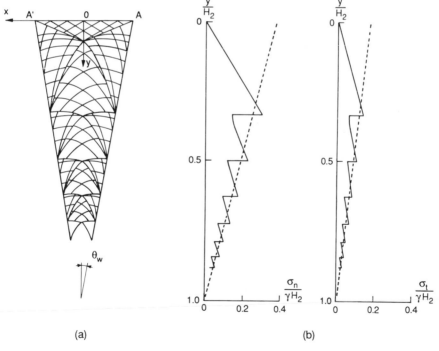

(a)   (b)

Figure 4.6   (a) Characteristics mesh and (b) wall stresses in a plane
hopper; passive state, $\theta_w = 10°$, $\delta = 30°$, $\varphi_w = 25°$,
$\sigma_{y0} = 0$ (Horne and Nedderman, 1978a)

Let us consider now the second type of limit state solutions, i.e., the vertex radial stress fields. This type of field can be postulated for both plane and conical hoppers. In plane hoppers, the solution is constructed by first solving equations (3.54) for two variables κ and η, with the boundary conditions

$$
\begin{aligned}
\theta = 0 \qquad & \eta = (3 + \alpha)\frac{\pi}{4} \\
\theta = \theta_w \qquad & \eta = (3 + \alpha)\frac{\pi}{4} - \frac{\alpha}{2}(\omega - \alpha\varphi_w)
\end{aligned}
\tag{4.17}
$$

where $\alpha = 1$ for the active case and $\alpha = -1$ for the passive case. Similarly, in conical hoppers, equations (3.66) and boundary conditions (4.17) are used. Once the variables η and κ are found, the stresses in the hopper and at the walls are determined from (3.48) and (3.47). Integration of equations (3.54) or (3.66) requires a numerical scheme in which boundary values of κ must be found such that conditions (4.17) are met. Jenike (1964a) provided useful graphs where the resulting dimensionless normal wall stresses $\sigma_n/\gamma b$ for the passive case in plane and conical hoppers are plotted as functions of θ_w, δ, and φ_w; b is the varying half-width of the hopper. Figures 4.7 and 4.8 show examples of these graphs.

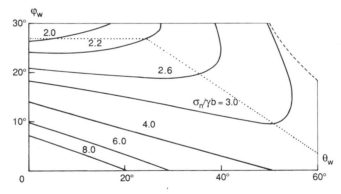

Figure 4.7   *Dimensionless wall normal stresses in a plane hopper as a function of θ_w and φ_w; $\delta = 30°$, passive state (vertex radial stress field, Jenike 1964a)*

The vertex radial stress field cannot be constructed beyond a critical combination of parameters δ, θ_w and φ_w (dashed lines in Figures 4.7 and 4.8). In conical hoppers, according to Jenike, funnel-flow develops above the limit. In plane hoppers, where the critical values of δ, θ_w and φ_w are much higher, Jenike suggested an empirical limit for mass-flow (see Figure 4.7).

Since vertex radial stress solutions yield all stresses that vary linearly with the radial distance r, stress-free or prescribed constant pressure σ_{y0} boundary conditions at the upper surface of material occupying a hopper cannot be satisfied. This is demonstrated in Figures 4.5b and 4.6b by the dashed lines, which show the distributions of wall stresses resulting from the radial stress solutions. In the vicinity of the vertices of hoppers, however, the radial stress solutions closely approximate those corresponding to hoppers with prescribed boundary conditions at the upper

surface. The agreement is better for the passive case, where the radial stress solution locates close to an average of discontinuous distributions over a significant
portion of the hopper height. Further, as the vertex radial stress solutions are exact for an infinitely tall hopper, the agreement becomes closer if the height of the
hopper increases.

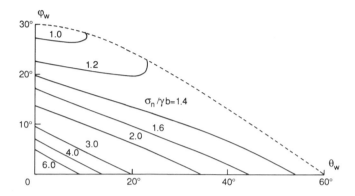

Figure 4.8 *Dimensionless wall normal stresses in a conical hopper as
a function of θ_w and φ_w; $\delta = 30°$, passive state (vertex
radial stress field, Jenike 1964a)*

Jenike (1964a) has extended vertex radial stress fields to hoppers with non-
symmetrically inclined walls, and has provided diagrams for wall normal stresses.
Horne and Nedderman (1978b) performed the analysis of stress concentrations at
transition from the bin to the hopper section. Assuming the active state of stress in
the bin section, and the passive state of stress in the hopper section, these authors
found a peak in wall stresses located slightly below the transition level; this peak
occurs where a stress discontinuity meets the wall.

4.3 DIRECT METHOD OF SLICES SOLUTIONS

There are several solutions for quasi-static bin-loads that are based on the direct
method of slices. The differences in these solutions result from the geometry of
slices selected, and additional assumptions that are necessary to remove the statical
indeterminancy in the global equilibrium equations holding for a slice. We will
discuss those differences in detail, beginning with the derivation of equations that
describe the global equilibrium of a given slice. Next, our attention will focus on
physical motivation of the additional assumptions that have been employed in the
various existing solutions. Finally, several examples of wall stress distributions will
be presented. The analysis will form a basis for our further considerations of the
inertial type of flow which is presented in Chapters 5 and 6. Also, the analysis of
arching given in Chapter 7 will use this method in part.

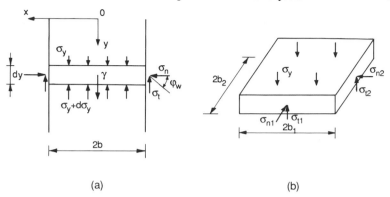

Figure 4.9   *Wall and average vertical stresses acting on a plane slice in (a) plane bin and (b) rectangular bin*

4.3.1 Stresses in Bins

The simplest symmetric slice, for which the average vertical stress is independent of the distribution of tangential stresses, is that of planar finite boundaries that are perpendicular to the walls of the bin. This type of slice will be referred to as the *plane slice*, regardless of whether it spans the walls in a plane, cylindrical or rectangular bin. The corresponding equilibrium equations will depend, however, on the type of bin.

Figure 4.9a shows the arrangement of wall and average vertical stresses acting on a plane slice in a plane bin of width $2b$. The origin of the system of coordinates is located at the upper surface of the bulk material occupying the bin, with the y-axis pointing downward. The forces that act in the y-direction on the slice are:

resultant of average stresses σ_y

$$F_1 = 2b\sigma_y \tag{4.18a}$$

resultant of average stresses $\sigma_y + d\sigma_y$

$$F_2 = -2b(\sigma_y + d\sigma_y) \tag{4.18b}$$

resultant of wall stresses σ_t

$$F_3 = -2dy\sigma_t \tag{4.18c}$$

weight of the slice with γ=const

$$F_4 = \gamma 2b dy \tag{4.18d}$$

On summing up all these forces, we obtain the following equilibrium equation for a slice

$$\frac{d\sigma_y}{dy} + \frac{\sigma_t}{b} - \gamma = 0 \tag{4.19}$$

For a cylindrical bin with radius b, where the slice is a disk, the equilibrium equation becomes

$$\frac{d\sigma_y}{dy} + \frac{2\sigma_t}{b} - \gamma = 0 \tag{4.20}$$

where it is assumed that the tangential stress at the wall, σ_t, is constant over the perimeter of the bin. Alternatively, the tangential stress appearing in (4.20) can be regarded as the average taken over the perimeter. Equations (4.19) and (4.20) can be combined in one form

$$\frac{d\sigma_y}{dy} + \frac{m\sigma_t}{b} - \gamma = 0 \tag{4.21}$$

where m is a pure number assuming the value $m = 1$ for a plane bin, and $m = 2$ for a cylindrical bin.

Consider now a bin with a rectangular cross-section of width $2b_1$ and length $2b_2$ (Figure 4.9b). Depending on the ratio b_1/b_2, the average tangential stresses acting along the walls of a bin can be either approximately the same or significantly different. For instance, if $b_1/b_2 = 1$ and the cross-section is square, equal average tangential stresses should develop at each side. However, if $b_1/b_2 < 1$, the tangential average stress over the shorter side, σ_{t1}, should differ from that over the longer side, σ_{t2}, and the equilibrium equation now becomes

$$\frac{d\sigma_y}{dy} + \frac{b_1\sigma_{t1} + b_2\sigma_{t2}}{b_1 b_2} - \gamma = 0 \tag{4.22}$$

If the difference in stresses σ_{t1} and σ_{t2} is disregarded $(\sigma_{t1} = \sigma_{t2} = \sigma_t)$, equation (4.22) can be written as

$$\frac{d\sigma_y}{dy} + \frac{\sigma_t}{R} - \gamma = 0 \tag{4.23}$$

where R is defined as

$$R = \frac{b_1 b_2}{b_1 + b_2} \tag{4.24}$$

and represents the ratio between the finite area of a slice and the length of its perimeter. Note that for a square bin where $b_1 = b_2 = b$

$$R = \frac{b}{2} \tag{4.25}$$

and, upon substitution into (4.23), we obtain equation (4.20). On the other hand, if $b_2 \gg b_1$, and the bin can be treated as a plane one with $b_1 = b$

$$R = b \tag{4.26}$$

and equation (4.23) becomes identical to (4.19). Applying the definition of R as the ratio of area and perimeter to any cross-section of bin, we can regard equation (4.23) as a universal equilibrium equation holding for any type of bin. The tangential stress σ_t then represents the average of local tangential stresses taken over the whole perimeter of the bin cross-section. The quantity R is often called the *hydraulic radius* of a bin.

As mentioned in Section 3.4.1, in spite of the ordinary differential form of equation (4.23), its integration cannot be performed unless a relationship between the average vertical stress σ_y and the average tangential stress σ_t is known. A discussion of the various assumptions that have been suggested in the literature in order to derive such a relationship will be given in Section 4.3.3. It is demonstrated there that this relationship is usually taken as a linear one, and, in particular, directly proportional, i.e.,

$$\sigma_t = K\sigma_y \tag{4.27}$$

where K is a positive constant. Equilibrium equation (4.23) then can be written as

$$\frac{d\sigma_y}{dy} + \frac{K}{R}\sigma_y - \gamma = 0 \tag{4.28}$$

and is a linear, first-order ordinary differential equation. Integration of this equation yields

$$\sigma_y = e^{-\frac{K}{R}y}\left[\frac{\gamma R}{K}e^{\frac{K}{R}y} + C\right] \tag{4.29}$$

where C is the constant of integration. This constant can be determined from the stress boundary conditions at the upper surface of the bulk material contained in the bin. If the upper surface is subjected to non-zero average vertical stress, e.g., pressure σ_{y0},

$$y = 0 \qquad \sigma_y = \sigma_{y0} \tag{4.30}$$

the integration constant, C, is

$$C = \sigma_{y0} - \frac{\gamma R}{K} \tag{4.31}$$

and the expression for the average vertical stress becomes

$$\sigma_y = \frac{\gamma R}{K} + \left[\sigma_{y0} - \frac{\gamma R}{K}\right]e^{-\frac{K}{R}y} \tag{4.32}$$

In the particular case of a stress-free upper surface, (4.32) reduces to

$$\sigma_y = \frac{\gamma R}{K}\left[1 - e^{-\frac{K}{R}y}\right] \tag{4.33}$$

According to equation (4.33), the vertical stress increases monotonically with increasing depth, is independent of the boundary conditions at the outlet and reaches an asymptotic value

$$y = \infty \qquad \sigma_y = \frac{\gamma R}{K} \tag{4.34}$$

In view of relation (4.27), tangential stress σ_t also increases monotonically, with the asymptotic value

$$y = \infty \qquad \sigma_t = \gamma R \tag{4.35}$$

which is independent of the magnitude of constant K. The normal component of wall stresses, σ_n, can be determined if the inclination of the stress vector along the wall, φ, is given. Assuming that the dry friction along the walls is constant and fully mobilized, $\varphi = \varphi_w$, we have

$$\sigma_t = \sigma_n \tan \varphi_w \tag{4.36}$$

and the asymptotic value for σ_n again is independent of K. Equations (4.34), (4.35), and (4.36) also hold if the upper surface of the material is subjected to a non-zero stress σ_{y0}. In the case of plane and cylindrical bins, respectively, the asymptotic values for stresses are

$$\sigma_y = \frac{\gamma b}{mK}$$

$$\sigma_t = \frac{\gamma b}{m} \tag{4.37}$$

$$\sigma_n = \frac{\gamma b}{m} \cot \varphi_w$$

Thus, the asymptotic values for the tangential and normal stresses are identical to those resulting from the limit state solution (see Section 4.2). This does not apply to the average vertical stress σ_y, whose magnitude depends on constant K.

Figure 4.10 shows distributions of dimensionless vertical and wall stresses in a cylindrical bin, for $K = 0.5$, $\varphi_w = 20°$, $\sigma_{y0} = 0$, and $\sigma_{y0}/\gamma b = 1.5$.

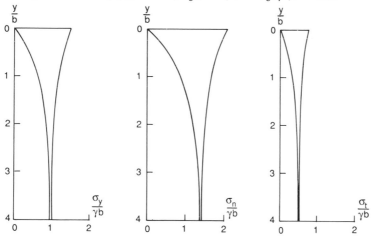

Figure 4.10   *Distributions of vertical and wall stresses in a cylindrical bin; $K = 0.5$, $\varphi_w = 20°$, $\sigma_{y0} = 0$, and $\sigma_{y0}/\gamma b = 1.5$*

Now let us consider the case when stresses σ_y and σ_t are related by a linear relationship

$$\sigma_t = K_1 \sigma_y + K_2 \tag{4.38}$$

and K_1 and K_2 are positive constants. Equation (4.23) now takes the form

$$\frac{d\sigma_y}{dy} + \frac{K_1}{R}\sigma_y + \frac{K_2}{R} - \gamma = 0 \tag{4.39}$$

and remains a linear differential equation, whose solution, with boundary condition (4.30), is

$$\sigma_y = \frac{\gamma R - K_2}{K_1} + \left[\sigma_{y0} - \frac{\gamma R - K_2}{K_1}\right] e^{-\frac{K_1}{R} y} \tag{4.40}$$

and for a stress-free upper surface

$$\sigma_y = \frac{\gamma R - K_2}{K_1} \left[1 - e^{-\frac{K_1}{R} y}\right] \tag{4.41}$$

The asymptotic values of the vertical and wall stresses are

$$\sigma_y = \frac{\gamma R - K_2}{K_1}$$
$$\sigma_t = \gamma R \tag{4.42}$$
$$\sigma_n = \gamma R \cot \varphi_w$$

which means that assumption (4.38) yields asymptotic average wall stresses identical to those resulting from assumption (4.27).

In the derivation of the equilibrium equations for a slice given above, it was assumed that the unit weight is constant regardless of the location of the slice in the bin. This is equivalent to postulating the density of the material to be independent of the magnitude of stresses acting on the slice. As was mentioned in Section 2.3, however, with increasing normal stresses the density of the material increases due to its compaction, whereas shear stresses may cause dilation. An approximate analysis of these effects can be incorporated easily into the equilibrium equations for a slice. For instance, we may consider a case where the unit weight of the bulk material is a linear function of the vertical stress

$$\gamma = \gamma_0 + A\sigma_y \tag{4.43}$$

where A is a positive constant. Thus, an increase in the unit weight with an increase of the vertical stress is postulated. Retaining assumption (4.27), the equlibrium equation is now

$$\frac{d\sigma_y}{dy} + \left[\frac{K}{R} - A\right]\sigma_y - \gamma_0 = 0 \tag{4.44}$$

and its solution with boundary condition (4.30) is similar to (4.32)

$$\sigma_y = \frac{\gamma_0 R}{K - AR} + \left[\sigma_{y0} - \frac{\gamma_0 R}{K - AR}\right] \exp\left(-\frac{K - AR}{R} y\right) \tag{4.45}$$

with the asymptotic values of the vertical and wall stresses given by

$$\sigma_y = \frac{\gamma_0 R}{K - AR}$$
$$\sigma_t = \frac{\gamma_0 K R}{K - AR} \tag{4.46}$$
$$\sigma_n = \frac{\gamma_0 K R}{K - AR} \cot \varphi_w$$

if $K - AR > 0$; the asymptotic wall stresses now depend on constants K and A.

4.3.2 Stresses in Hoppers

The plane slice used for bins also can be selected for plane, conical, and pyramidal hoppers, with its infinitesimal sides parallel to the sloping walls (Figure 4.11a). Other shapes of slices also have been suggested in the literature, and they will be discussed later. In all cases, it is convenient to introduce a system of coordinates that has its origin at the vertex of the hopper rather than at the upper surface of the bulk material. The varying width of a plane hopper, or the radius of the circular cross-section of a conical hopper, can then be expressed as

$$b = y \tan \theta_w \tag{4.47}$$

The vertical components of forces that act on a plane slice in a plane hopper are:

resultant of average stress σ_y

$$F_1 = 2y \tan \theta_w \sigma_y \tag{4.48a}$$

resultant of average stress $\sigma_y + d\sigma_y$ (where higher-order terms are neglected)

$$F_2 = -2 \tan \theta_w (y\sigma_y + yd\sigma_y + dy\sigma_y) \tag{4.48b}$$

resultant of wall stresses σ_n and σ_t

$$F_3 = 2dy(\tan \theta_w \sigma_n + \sigma_t) \tag{4.48c}$$

weight of the slice with γ=const

$$F_4 = -2\gamma y dy \tan \theta_w \tag{4.48d}$$

and the equilibrium equation can be written as

$$\frac{d\sigma_y}{dy} + \frac{1}{y}(\sigma_y - \sigma_n - \sigma_t \cot \theta_w) + \gamma = 0 \tag{4.49}$$

In the case of a conical hopper, we obtain

$$\frac{d\sigma_y}{dy} + \frac{2}{y}(\sigma_y - \sigma_n - \sigma_t \cot \theta_w) + \gamma = 0 \tag{4.50}$$

Equations (4.49) and (4.50) can be written in one form

$$\frac{d\sigma_y}{dy} + \frac{m}{y}(\sigma_y - \sigma_n - \sigma_t \cot \theta_w) + \gamma = 0 \tag{4.51}$$

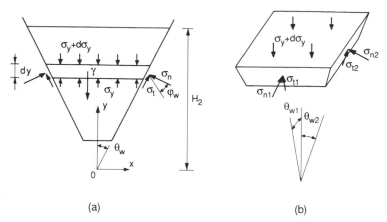

Figure 4.11   *Wall and average vertical stresses acting on a plane slice in (a) plane hopper and (b) pyramidal hopper*

where $m = 1$ for a plane hopper, and $m = 2$ for a conical one.

Equilibrium equations similar in mathematical form to those discussed above can be derived for hoppers whose cross-section is rectangular or polygonal. For example, considering a four-sided pyramidal hopper whose walls are inclined at half-included angles θ_{w1} and θ_{w2} (Figure 4.11b) we obtain

$$\frac{d\sigma_y}{dy} + \frac{1}{y}[2\sigma_y - (\sigma_{n1} + \sigma_{n2}) - (\sigma_{t1}\cot\theta_{w1} + \sigma_{t2}\cot\theta_{w2})] + \gamma = 0 \qquad (4.52)$$

and σ_{n1}, σ_{n2}, σ_{t1}, and σ_{t2} denote the average normal and tangential wall stresses acting on walls inclined at angles θ_{w1} and θ_{w2}, respectively. To illustrate the differences in the solutions for wall stresses in bins and in hoppers, our further analysis will be limited to plane and conical hoppers only.

To integrate equation (4.51), first it is necessary to relate one of the average wall stresses, σ_n or σ_t, to the average vertical stress σ_y. This can be done by employing a linear relationship, similar to (4.27) or (4.38), between σ_y and σ_t, with constants K, $K1$, and $K2$ in general assuming different values. The motivation for such relationships is presented in Section 4.3.4.

Using (4.27) and the dry friction condition at the walls, we can write equilibrium equation (4.51) as

$$\frac{d\sigma_y}{dy} + mN\frac{\sigma_y}{y} + \gamma = 0 \qquad (4.53)$$

where

$$N = 1 - K(\cot\theta_w + \cot\varphi_w) \qquad (4.54)$$

The solution to (4.53) depends on the factor mN. If $mN \neq -1$, then

$$\sigma_y = -\frac{\gamma y}{mN + 1} + Cy^{-mN} \qquad (4.55)$$

The constant of integration, C, can be determined from the stress boundary conditions that hold at the upper surface of the material in a hopper

$$y = H_2 \qquad \sigma_y = \sigma_{y2} \qquad (4.56)$$

where H_2 denotes the distance to the upper surface. Then

$$C = H_2^{mN}\left[\sigma_{y2} + \frac{\gamma H_2}{mN + 1}\right] \tag{4.57}$$

and

$$\sigma_y = -\frac{\gamma y}{mN + 1} + \left[\sigma_{y2} + \frac{\gamma H_2}{mN + 1}\right]\left[\frac{H_2}{y}\right]^{mN} \tag{4.58}$$

or

$$\sigma_y = \frac{\gamma y}{mN + 1}\left\{-1 + \left[\frac{H_2}{y}\right]^{mN+1}\right\} \tag{4.59}$$

if $\sigma_{y2} = 0$. At the vertex of the hopper, $y = 0$, we have

$$
\begin{aligned}
\sigma_y &= 0 \qquad \text{if} \qquad mN < 0 \\
\sigma_y &= \infty \qquad \text{if} \qquad mN > 0
\end{aligned}
\tag{4.60}
$$

and the distribution of the average vertical and wall stresses is drastically different, depending on the sign of the factor mN. This is illustrated in Figure 4.12, for a conical hopper with $\theta_w = 30°$, and $\varphi_w = 20°$, where two values of K were assumed: $K = 0.75$, and $K = 0.22$. It should be noted that wall stresses approaching infinity at the hopper vertex are admissible, for the integral of wall stresses is finite; the vertical component of the resultant of wall stresses equals the weight of the material occupying the hopper, and global equlibrium is satisfied. Furthermore, as was the case with stresses in bins, the distribution of stresses in hoppers is independent of the actual boundary conditions at the outlet level.

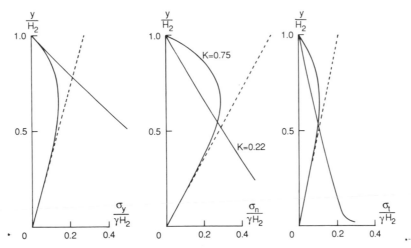

Figure 4.12   *Distributions of vertical and wall stresses in a conical hopper; $\theta_w = 30°$, $\varphi_w = 20°$, $\sigma_{y0} = 0$, $K = 0.75$ and $K = 0.22$*

The solution to equation (4.53) for $mN = -1$, and for boundary condition (4.56), is

$$\sigma_y = \left[\frac{\sigma_{y2}}{H_2} + \gamma \ln \frac{H_2}{y}\right] y \tag{4.61}$$

or

$$\sigma_y = \gamma y \ln \frac{H_2}{y} \tag{4.62}$$

if $\sigma_{y2} = 0$. At the vertex $\sigma_y = 0$.

Besides operating with plane slices, some authors suggested other, curvilinear shapes of slices (cf. Mróz and Szymański, 1971a, Enstad, 1975, 1977). Figures 4.13a and b show slices that are segments of a cylindrical shell and a spherical shell, respectively. The first type is suitable for plane hoppers, and can be named the *cylindrical slice*. The second one applies to conical hoppers, and will be termed the *spherical slice*. The slices can be centered either at the vertex of the hopper, or at some other point along its axis of symmetry. In both cases, only one non-trivial equation describes the equilibrium of the slice, i.e., the equilibrium of forces in the vertical direction. Since for a curvilinear slice the resolution of the resultant force into an average stress is not unique, one has to assume the orientation of the average stress beforehand. For example, the average stress may be taken as normal to the slice, and denoted by σ_r.

With this assumption, and for slices that are centered at the hopper vertex, the forces acting in the vertical direction in a plane hopper are:

resultant of average stress σ_r

$$F_1 = 2r \sin \theta_w \sigma_r \tag{4.63a}$$

resultant of average stress $\sigma_r + d\sigma_r$

$$F_2 = -2 \sin \theta_w \left(r\sigma_r + dr\sigma_r + rd\sigma_r\right) \tag{4.63b}$$

resultant of wall stresses σ_n and σ_t

$$F_3 = 2dr\left(\sin \theta_w \sigma_n + \cos \theta_w \sigma_t\right) \tag{4.63c}$$

weight of the slice

$$F_4 = -2\gamma\theta_w r dr \tag{4.63d}$$

which yields the following equilibrium equation

$$\frac{d\sigma_r}{dr} + \frac{1}{r}\left(\sigma_r - \sigma_n - \sigma_t \cot \theta_w\right) + \frac{\gamma\theta_w}{\sin \theta_w} = 0 \tag{4.64}$$

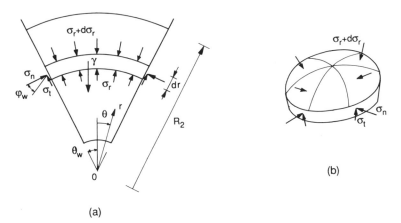

Figure 4.13   *Wall and average radial stresses acting on (a) cylindrical and (b) spherical slice in a hopper*

For a conical hopper, we obtain

$$\frac{d\sigma_r}{dr} + \frac{2}{r}(\sigma_r - \sigma_n - \sigma_t \cot\theta_w) + \frac{2\gamma}{1 + \cos\theta_w} = 0 \qquad (4.65)$$

where it is assumed that γ=const. Using the pure number m defined previously, equations (4.64) and (4.65) can be written as

$$\frac{d\sigma_r}{dr} + \frac{m}{r}(\sigma_r - \sigma_n - \sigma_t \cot\theta_w) + \gamma M = 0 \qquad (4.66)$$

and

$$M = (2 - m)\frac{\theta_w}{\sin\theta_w} - (1 - m)\frac{2}{1 + \cos\theta_w} \qquad (4.67)$$

Utilizing the wall friction condition, and postulating a relationship between σ_r and σ_t that is similar to (4.27), we can write equation (4.66) as

$$\frac{d\sigma_r}{dr} + mN\frac{\sigma_r}{r} + \gamma M = 0 \qquad (4.68)$$

which, upon integration with the boundary condition

$$r = R_2 \qquad \sigma_r = \sigma_{r2} \qquad (4.69)$$

yields for $mN \neq -1$

$$\sigma_r = -\frac{\gamma M r}{mN + 1} + \left[\sigma_{r2} + \frac{\gamma M R_2}{mN + 1}\right]\left[\frac{R_2}{r}\right]^{mN} \qquad (4.70)$$

and for $mN = -1$

$$\sigma_r = \left[\frac{\sigma_{r2}}{R_2} + \gamma M \ln\frac{R_2}{y}\right] r \qquad (4.71)$$

At the vertex of the hopper we have

$$\sigma_r = 0 \quad \text{if} \quad mN < 0$$
$$\sigma_r = \infty \quad \text{if} \quad mN > 0 \tag{4.72}$$

The tangential wall stresses are related to the radial stress σ_r by an equation similar to (4.27), where the constant K may assume a value different from that in the case of a plane slice.

When comparing the solutions corresponding to a plane and a cylindrical or spherical slice, a similarity is seen. Accordingly, the distributions of wall stresses in both cases will be similar to those presented in Figure 4.12. Obviously, when operating with curvilinear slices, the upper surface of the bulk material in a hopper assumes the shape of the slice selected.

The motivation for operating with curvilinear slices may stem from the pattern of principal stress trajectories that develop during storage and discharge of bulk materials from hoppers. This has been raised by Enstad (1975, 1977), who considered slices approximately aligned along those trajectories of the principal stress that span the walls. Referring to Figure 1.5, a convex slice aligned along the principal stress σ_1 is taken for discharge, and a concave slice aligned along the trajectory of σ_2 for storage (Figure 4.14). The bounding surfaces of the slice are subjected to a constant principal stress, either smaller or greater, and no further assumption about the inclination of stresses is necessary. The elemental thickness of the slice is not constant, although the bounding surfaces are cylindrical or spherical with different radii of curvature. This guarantees that neighboring slices perfectly match. A similar approach, with parabolic slices, has been considered recently by Benink (1989). In the following, we only consider the slices suggested by Enstad.

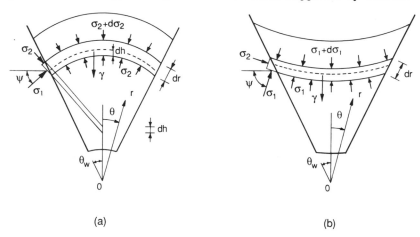

(a)   (b)

Figure 4.14 *Wall and principal stresses acting on (a) convex slice and (b) concave slice in a hopper*

With the help of Figure 4.14a, the vertical components of forces that act on a convex slice in a plane hopper can be expressed as:

resultant of stress σ_2

$$F_1 = 2r \sin \theta_w \sigma_2 \tag{4.73a}$$

resultant of stress $\sigma_2 + d\sigma_2$

$$F_2 = -2 \sin \theta_w \left(r\sigma_2 + dr\sigma_2 + rd\sigma_2 \right) \tag{4.73b}$$

resultant of stresses σ_1 and σ_2 acting at the walls

$$F_3 = 2dr[\sin \psi \cos(\psi - \theta_w)\sigma_1 - \cos \psi \sin(\psi - \theta_w)\sigma_2] \tag{4.73c}$$

weight of the slice with γ=const

$$F_4 = -2\gamma r dr \left[\frac{\psi \sin \theta_w}{\sin^2 \psi} + \frac{\sin(\psi - \theta_w)}{\sin \psi} \right] \sin \theta_w \tag{4.73d}$$

The resulting equilibrium equation for a plane hopper is

$$
\frac{d\sigma_2}{dr} + \frac{1}{r} \left[\sigma_2 + \sigma_2 \frac{\cos \psi \sin(\psi - \theta_w)}{\sin \theta_w} - \sigma_1 \frac{\sin \psi \cos(\psi - \theta_w)}{\sin \theta_w} \right]
$$
$$
+ \gamma \left[\frac{\psi \sin \theta_w}{\sin^2 \psi} + \frac{\sin(\psi - \theta_w)}{\sin \psi} \right] = 0 \tag{4.74}
$$

and for a conical hopper is

$$
\frac{d\sigma_2}{dr} + \frac{2}{r} \left[\sigma_2 + \sigma_2 \frac{\cos \psi \sin(\psi - \theta_w)}{\sin \theta_w} - \sigma_1 \frac{\sin \psi \cos(\psi - \theta_w)}{\sin \theta_w} \right]
$$
$$
+ \gamma \left[\frac{2 \sin \theta_w (1 - \cos \psi)}{\sin^3 \psi} + \frac{\sin(\psi - \theta_w)}{\sin \psi} \right] = 0 \tag{4.75}
$$

A similar derivation for a concave slice (Figure 4.14b) yields the following equations for a plane and a conical hopper, respectively

$$
\frac{d\sigma_1}{dr} - \frac{1}{r} \left[\sigma_1 + \sigma_1 \frac{\sin \psi \cos(\psi - \theta_w)}{\sin \theta_w} - \sigma_2 \frac{\cos \psi \sin(\psi - \theta_w)}{\sin \theta_w} \right]
$$
$$
+ \gamma \left[\frac{(\psi - \pi/2) \sin \theta_w}{\cos^2 \psi} + \frac{\cos(\psi - \theta_w)}{\cos \psi} \right] = 0 \tag{4.76}
$$

$$
\frac{d\sigma_1}{dr} - \frac{2}{r} \left[\sigma_1 + \sigma_1 \frac{\sin \psi \cos(\psi - \theta_w)}{\sin \theta_w} - \sigma_2 \frac{\cos \psi \sin(\psi - \theta_w)}{\sin \theta_w} \right]
$$
$$
+ \gamma \left[\frac{\cos(\psi - \theta_w)}{\cos \psi} - \frac{2 \sin \theta_w (1 - \sin \psi)}{\cos^3 \psi} \right] = 0 \tag{4.77}
$$

Equations (4.74)-(4.77) contain two variables, σ_1 and σ_2. As we will show in Section 4.3.4, the principal stresses can be related proportionally

$$\sigma_1 = K\sigma_2 \tag{4.78}$$

where K is a constant. Also, an expression for angle ψ will be given there. Equations (4.74) and (4.75) take the form

$$\frac{d\sigma_2}{dr} + mG\frac{\sigma_2}{r} + \gamma F = 0 \tag{4.79}$$

where

$$F = \frac{(2-m)\psi \sin\theta_w + 2(m-1)\sin\theta_w\,(1-\cos\psi)}{\sin^{1+m}\psi} + \frac{\sin(\psi-\theta_w)}{\sin\psi}$$
$$G = 1 + \frac{\cos\psi\sin(\psi-\theta_w)}{\sin\theta_w} - \frac{K\sin\psi\cos(\psi-\theta_w)}{\sin\theta_w} \tag{4.80}$$

On integrating (4.79) with the boundary condition

$$r = R_2 \qquad \sigma_2 = \sigma_{22} \tag{4.81}$$

we obtain

$$\sigma_2 = -\frac{\gamma F r}{mG+1} + \left[\sigma_{22} + \frac{\gamma F R_2}{mG+1}\right]\left[\frac{R_2}{r}\right]^{mG} \tag{4.82}$$

if $mG \neq -1$, and

$$\sigma_2 = \left[\frac{\sigma_{22}}{R_2} + \gamma F \ln\frac{R_2}{r}\right] r \tag{4.83}$$

if $mG = -1$.

Similarly, (4.76) and (4.77) can be written in one form, identical to (4.79) with σ_1 replacing σ_2, with constants F and G expressed by

$$F = \frac{(2-m)(\psi-\pi/2)\sin\theta_w - 2(m-1)\sin\theta_w\,(1-\sin\psi)}{\cos^{1+m}\psi} + \frac{\cos(\psi-\theta_w)}{\cos\psi}$$
$$G = -1 - \frac{\sin\psi\cos(\psi-\theta_w)}{\sin\theta_w} + \frac{\cos\psi\sin(\psi-\theta_w)}{K\sin\theta_w} \tag{4.84}$$

and with the solutions given by (4.82) and (4.83).

Clearly, the mathematical form of solutions (4.82) and (4.83) is identical to the solutions given by expressions (4.70) and (4.71), and principal stresses σ_1 or σ_2 at the vertex can attain either zero-value or infinity depending on the sign of the constant mG. The wall stresses σ_n and σ_t can be determined from principal stresses σ_1 and σ_2, and angle ψ

$$\sigma_t = -\frac{\sigma_1-\sigma_2}{2}\sin 2(\psi-\theta_w)$$
$$\sigma_n = \frac{\sigma_1+\sigma_2}{2} + \frac{\sigma_1-\sigma_2}{2}\cos 2(\psi-\theta_w) \tag{4.85}$$

An important result is obtained from the solutions above if the location of the upper surface of the material approaches infinity. The constant of integration in the solutions to equilibrium equations (4.53), (4.68), and (4.79) must assume a zero-value, and the average vertical or radial stresses, and the principal stresses, are expressed by

$$\sigma_y = -\frac{\gamma y}{mN + 1} \tag{4.86}$$

for a plane slice

$$\sigma_r = -\frac{\gamma M r}{mN + 1} \tag{4.87}$$

for a cylindrical or spherical slice that is centered at the vertex of the hopper, and

$$\sigma_2 = -\frac{\gamma F r}{mG + 1} \tag{4.88}$$

for the convex slices assumed by Enstad. Equations (4.86), (4.87), and (4.88) imply that the average vertical or radial stresses, as well as the principal stresses, vary linearly with the distance from the vertex, and the wall stresses will vary the same way. An approximate analytical solution to the vertex radial stress field discussed in Section 4.2 is obtained, and it bounds the solution for a hopper of finite height provided that solution gives a zero-value of stresses at the vertex. This is shown in Figure 4.12 by the dashed lines, which indicate that the stresses in a finite hopper converge to the radial stress field.

The derivations presented above can be modified easily to include the linear relationship between the average vertical and tangential wall stresses given by equation (4.38); a similar expression was considered by Enstad (1981). Further, the unit weight that depends on stresses σ_y and σ_r, or principal stresses σ_1 and σ_2, also can be considered, as well as varying wall friction.

4.3.3 Determination of Constant K for Bins

The fundamental assumption underlying effective applications of the direct method of slices to bin-load analysis involves a relationship between the average stresses acting on the finite dimension of a slice, and stresses that act at the walls of a bin or hopper. In his pioneering work on loads in vertical bins, Janssen (1895) postulated an empirical relationship between the average vertical stress σ_y and the stress normal to the wall, σ_n. Janssen assumed that the ratio between these two stresses is a constant for a given bulk material stored in a bin

$$\frac{\sigma_n}{\sigma_y} = k \tag{4.89}$$

and k is to be determined from measurements. In addition, Janssen postulated a fully mobilized constant dry friction at the interface of the bulk material and the walls of the container, i.e.,

$$\sigma_t = \sigma_n \tan \varphi_w \tag{4.90}$$

Combining (4.89) and (4.90), we obtain

$$\sigma_t = \sigma_y k \tan \varphi_w \tag{4.91}$$

or, defining

$$k \tan \varphi_w = K \tag{4.92}$$

equation (4.91) can be written as

$$\sigma_t = K \sigma_y \tag{4.93}$$

which is identical to (4.27), assumed in Section 4.3.1.

Since the work of Janssen, several attempts aiming at an expression for K, based on postulating a mechanical model for bulk solids, have been presented in the literature. A critical assessement of some of these expressions is given, for example, by Cowin (1979). Most derivations hinge on postulating that the bulk material stored in or discharged from a bin is at a limiting state of stress. In other words, the material is regarded as a rigid-perfectly plastic solid, and the state of stress satisfies the yield condition. In addition, effective Mohr-Coulomb yield condition (2.30) is usually taken as appropriate for analyzing stresses in the bulk material regardless of whether it is temporarily stored or discharged. The assumption of the limiting state of stress in the bulk material alone, however, is insufficient for deriving a relationship between the stresses appearing in the equilibrium equations for a slice. The yield condition is expressed in terms of local stresses, whereas the stresses in the equilibrium equations are averages taken over the area or the perimeter of a slice.

There are two possibilities of overcoming the inconsistency in operating with local and average stresses. In the first one, the average stresses are identified with the local stress components, which is equivalent to postulating a uniform distribution of the vertical stresses over the finite dimension of a slice. Consequently, the notion of average stresses is actually rejected. An alternative is to assume a distribution of the stress vectors over the finite dimension of a slice, from which the average stress can be calculated. In both cases, the tangential and normal stresses acting along the walls must be constant over the perimeter of the slice.

Consider first a plane slice in a plane bin, with a uniform distribution of vertical stresses σ_y (Figure 4.15a). The shear stresses σ_{yx} that act over the finite side of the slice are distributed antisymmetrically, although the actual distribution is unknown. However, at the endpoints of the slice, shear stresses σ_{yx} must equal tangential stresses σ_t, and horizontal stress σ_x must equal normal stress σ_n. Thus, at these points, the components of the state of stress in the plane of the slice are σ_y, $\sigma_x = \sigma_n$, $\sigma_{xy} = \sigma_{yx} = \sigma_t$, and they uniquely define the limiting state of stress for a material whose yielding is independent of the intermediate principal stress σ_z. This also holds for a plane slice in a cylindrical bin, where the stresses that cause yielding are σ_y, $\sigma_x = \sigma_n$, $\sigma_{xy} = \sigma_{yx} = \sigma_t$, and circumferential stress σ_w is assumed to be the intermediate principal stress.

Figure 4.16 shows corresponding Mohr's circles for the active and passive cases, respectively. The inclination of the stress vector at the wall results from the assumed

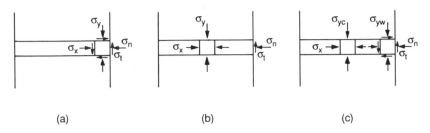

Figure 4.15   *(a) Yielding at the wall, (b) yielding at the center and (c)
yielding at the center and at the wall*

dry friction at the interface, and is usually taken as fully mobilized. Using the
trigonometric identities resulting from Figure 4.16 and yield condition (2.30), it
appears that the relationship between wall tangential stress σ_t and vertical stress
σ_y is directly proportional. The proportionality factor K, defined by equation
(4.27), is

$$K = \frac{\sin \delta \sin(\omega - \alpha\varphi_w)}{1 + \alpha \sin \delta \cos(\omega - \alpha\varphi_w)} \qquad (4.94)$$

where ω is defined by (3.33), and $\alpha = 1$ for the active case, and $\alpha = -1$ for the
passive case. Note that in the literature expressions for k rather than K are usually
derived. Since the derivation above considers the state of stress at the walls, it can
be referred to as being based on the *yielding at the walls* hypothesis.

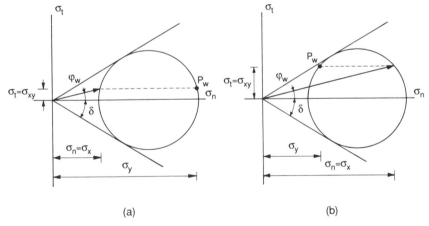

Figure 4.16   *Mohr's circles for yielding at the walls for a plane slice in
a bin, (a) active state and (b) passive state*

Consider now a point located at the center of the slice (Figure 4.15b). By
reason of symmetry, vertical stress σ_y is a principal stress. If the remaining horizontal principal stress were known at this point, the state of stress would again
be uniquely defined. An assumption that is often utilized here (cf. Walker, 1966,
Walters, 1973a, 1973b) is that horizontal stress σ_x or σ_r is constant along the slice,
and thus equals normal stress σ_n at the wall.

Figure 4.17 shows corresponding Mohr's circles for the active and passive states, respectively. At the endpoints of the slice, besides normal stresses σ_y and σ_n, there are non-zero shear stresses $\sigma_{xy} = \sigma_{yx} = \sigma_t$, and the resulting Mohr's circle is located outside the yield locus. Although this result violates the concept of the limiting state of stress, it may still be accepted in view of the approximate nature of the direct method of slices itself. The resulting expressions relating the vertical and tangential stresses, σ_y and σ_t, are again directly proportional, with proportionality constant K given by

$$K = \frac{1 - \alpha \sin \delta}{1 + \alpha \sin \delta} \tan \varphi_w \tag{4.95}$$

which can be regarded as being derived from the hypothesis of *yielding at the center*.

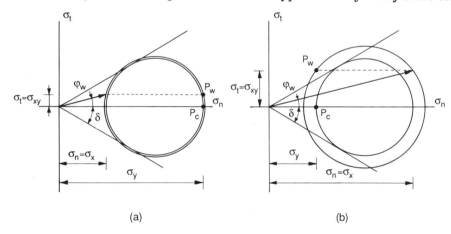

(a)   (b)

Figure 4.17   *Mohr's circles for yielding at the center for a plane slice in a bin, (a) active state and (b) passive state*

A third possibility is to assume *yielding at the center and at the walls* (Figure 4.15c). This hypothesis assumes that the state of stress at the center and at the walls is limiting, therefore, it is represented by two Mohr's circles tangent to the yield locus (Figure 4.18). If the stress normal to the cross-section of the slice, σ_x or σ_r, is taken as constant along the slice, vertical stress σ_y cannot be constant over the slice. The simplest assumption is to postulate a linear distribution of the vertical stress. The average vertical stress that appears in the equilibrium equations for a slice is than given by

$$\sigma_y = \frac{\sigma_{yw} + \sigma_{yc}}{2} \tag{4.96}$$

if the bin is plane, and

$$\sigma_y = \frac{2\sigma_{yw} + \sigma_{yc}}{3} \tag{4.97}$$

if the bin is cylindrical; σ_{yw} and σ_{yc} denote vertical stresses at the wall and at the center, respectively. Using (4.96), (4.97), and yield condition (2.30), a directly proportional relationship between σ_y and σ_t is obtained, with

$$K = \frac{1 - \alpha \sin \delta}{\cot \varphi_w + \alpha(1 - \alpha \sin \delta) \cot(\omega - \alpha \varphi_w)} \qquad (4.98)$$

for a plane bin, and

$$K = \frac{3 \sin \delta (1 - \alpha \sin \delta) \sin(\omega - \alpha \varphi_w)}{3 - \alpha \sin \delta + \sin \delta (\alpha - 3 \sin \delta) \cos(\omega - \alpha \varphi_w)} \qquad (4.99)$$

for a cylindrical bin.

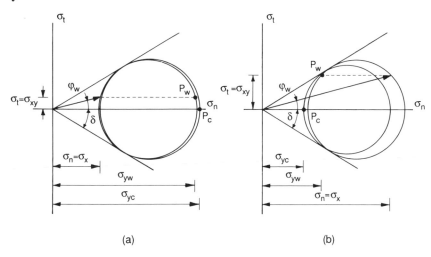

(a)   (b)

Figure 4.18 *Mohr's circles for yielding at the center and at the walls for a plane slice in a bin, (a) active state and (b) passive state*

A hypothesis that could be regarded as a generalization of the latter one is due to Walker (1966). This author suggested expressing the variation of the vertical stress by the *distribution factor D*. The distribution factor is defined as

$$D = \frac{\sigma_{yw}}{\sigma_y} \qquad (4.100)$$

Considering the limiting state at the wall (Figure 4.16), we have

$$\sigma_t = B\sigma_{yw} \qquad (4.101)$$

where

$$B = \frac{\sin \delta \sin(\omega - \alpha \varphi_w)}{1 + \alpha \sin \delta \cos(\omega - \alpha \varphi_w)} \qquad (4.102)$$

which, combined with (4.90), yields the proportionality factor in (4.27)

$$K = BD \qquad (4.103)$$

The actual value of constant K depends on distribution factor D, which can be either directly postulated or derived from a given distribution of the stress vectors acting over the finite dimension of a slice. Note that for $D = 1$ the distribution of vertical stresses is uniform. Walker (1966) and also Walters (1973a) suggested assuming that the shear stress σ_{yx} is distributed linearly over the slice, and at every point along the slice the stress state satisfies the yield condition. With the assumption that the horizontal stress is constant along the slice, $\sigma_x = \sigma_n$, the distribution of the vertical stress along the x-coordinate is given by

$$\sigma_y = \frac{(1 + \sin^2 \delta)\sigma_n}{\cos^2 \delta} + \alpha \frac{2}{\cos^2 \delta} \left[\sigma_n^2 \sin^2 \delta - \sigma_t^2 \cos^2 \delta \frac{x^2}{b^2} \right]^{1/2} \tag{4.104}$$

Calculating the average vertical stress, using (4.100) and (4.102), and utilizing some trigonometric identities, we arrive at the following formula for D in a cylindrical bin

$$D = \frac{\cos \varphi_w (1 + \sin^2 \delta) + 2\alpha (\sin^2 \delta - \sin^2 \varphi_w)^{1/2}}{\cos \varphi_w \left\{ (1 + \sin^2 \delta) + \alpha \sin \delta \frac{4}{3C} [1 - (1 - C)^{3/2}] \right\}} \tag{4.105}$$

$$C = \frac{\tan^2 \varphi_w}{\tan^2 \delta} \tag{4.106}$$

Although the derivations of the relationship between the average vertical and tangential wall stresses presented above are based on different hypotheses regarding the location of a point, or points, where the state of stress in the slice is limiting, all yield the relationship directly proportional, with the proportionality factor K. Other derivations (cf. Vardoulakis, Graf and Gudehus, 1981, Drescher and Vardoulakis, 1982) confirm this finding. The reason for this is yield condition (2.30), which proportionally relates the principal stresses at yielding regardless of their actual magnitude. One might expect, therefore, that a more general linear relationship (4.38) will result if a yield condition described by two parameters is assumed for yielding of a bulk material. This has been demonstrated by Enstad (1981), for instance, who used effective yield condition (2.31).

It should be noted here, however, that not every hypothesis of yielding leads to linear relationship (4.38). For example, assuming yielding at the walls (Figure 4.19a), it is apparent that wall stress σ_t becomes a non-linear function of vertical stress σ_y. A linear relationship is obtained for the hypothesis of yielding at the center of a slice (Figure 4.19b). Then,

$$K_1 = \frac{1 - \alpha \sin \phi}{1 + \alpha \sin \phi} \tan \varphi_w$$

$$K_2 = -c \frac{2\alpha \cos \phi}{1 + \alpha \sin \phi} \tan \varphi_w \tag{4.107}$$

and equation (4.38) holds for any location of the slice in a bin, provided $\varphi_w \leq \phi$. If, however, $\varphi_w > \phi$, dry friction exists only along a portion of the wall, and expressions (4.107) apply, whereas along the remaining part sticking friction occurs. The location of the separating point must be found from the solution for the wall stresses (cf. Kwaszczyńska, Mróz and Drescher, 1969). In the region of sticking friction

$$K_1 = \frac{1 - \alpha \sin \phi}{1 + \alpha \sin \phi} \tan \phi$$

$$K_2 = c \frac{1 - \alpha \sin \phi}{1 + \alpha \sin \phi}$$

(4.108)

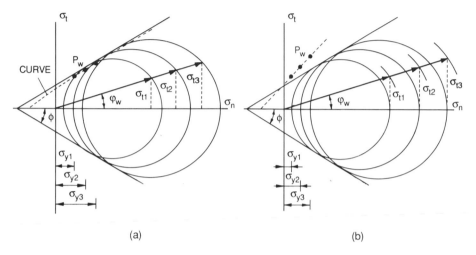

(a)   (b)

Figure 4.19 *Mohr's circles for yield condition (2.31), (a) yielding at the wall and (b) yielding at the center*

4.3.4 Determination of Constant K for Hoppers

The idea of postulating yielding at a given point, or points, in a slice spanning walls in a bin can be applied equally to plane or curvilinear slices in a hopper. For effective yield condition (2.30), the relationship between vertical stress σ_y and tangential stress σ_t that appears in the equilibrium equations presented in Section 4.3.2 is again directly proportional. The corresponding proportionality factor K, however, depends on the assumed shape of the slice. For plane slices, we have:

yielding at the walls (Figure 4.20)

$$K = \frac{\sin \delta \sin(\omega - \alpha \varphi_w)}{1 + \alpha \sin \delta \cos(\omega - \alpha \varphi_w - 2\alpha \theta_w)}$$

(4.109)

yielding at the center (Figure 4.21)

$$K = \frac{1 - \alpha \sin \delta \cos 2\theta_w}{1 + \alpha \sin \delta} \tan \varphi_w$$

(4.110)

yielding at the center and at the walls (Figure 4.22)

$$K = \frac{\sin \delta (1 - \alpha \sin \delta) \sin(\omega - \alpha \varphi_w)}{1 - \sin^2 \delta \cos(\omega - \alpha \varphi_w - 2\alpha \theta_w)} \tag{4.111}$$

for a plane hopper, and

$$K = \frac{3 \sin \delta (1 - \alpha \sin \delta) \sin(\omega - \alpha \varphi_w)}{3 - \alpha \sin \delta + \sin \delta (\alpha - 3 \sin \delta) \cos(\omega - \alpha \varphi_w - 2\alpha \theta_w)} \tag{4.112}$$

for a conical hopper.

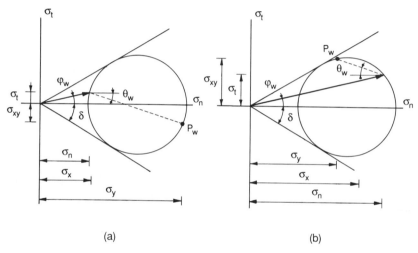

(a)   (b)

Figure 4.20   *Mohr's circles for yielding at the walls for a plane slice in a hopper, (a) active state and (b) passive state*

Retaining the assumptions of a linear distribution of the shear stress along the slice, and of the limiting state at every point of the slice, we arrive at the following expression for the distribution factor in a conical hopper

$$D = \frac{\cos \eta (1 + \sin^2 \delta) + 2\alpha (\sin^2 \delta - \sin^2 \eta)^{1/2}}{\cos \eta \left\{ (1 + \sin^2 \delta) + \alpha \sin \delta \frac{4}{3C} [1 - (1 - C)^{3/2}] \right\}} \tag{4.113}$$

where

$$C = \frac{\tan^2 \eta}{\tan 2\delta} \tag{4.114}$$

and angle η can be found from

$$\tan \eta = \frac{\sin \delta \sin(\omega - \alpha \varphi_w - 2\alpha \theta_w)}{1 - \alpha \sin \delta \cos(\omega - \alpha \varphi_w - 2\alpha \theta_w)} \tag{4.115}$$

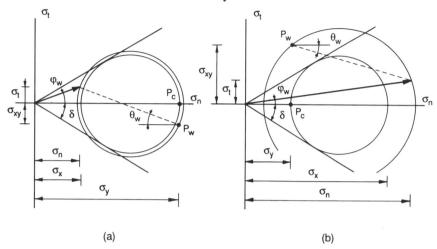

(a)　　　　　　　　　　　　　　　　　　　(b)

Figure 4.21 *Mohr's circles for yielding at the center for a plane slice in a hopper, (a) active state and (b) passive state*

The constant B in (4.103) is given by (4.109).

Consider now a cylindrical or spherical slice centered at the vertex of a hopper. Figure 4.23a shows Mohr's circle for the hypothesis of yielding at the walls and the passive state of stress. Inspection of this figure reveals that the ratio between tangential stress σ_t and radial stress σ_r is identical to the ratio between tangential stress σ_t and vertical stress σ_y in a vertical bin (Figure 4.23b); this is also true for the active case. Thus, the proportionality factor K is given by equation (4.94). The reason for this is the same inclination of stresses σ_r and σ_y with respect to the walls of a container; in both cases these stresses are parallel to the walls. Similarly, constant K is given by equation (4.95), if the hypothesis of yielding at the center is selected. However, for the hypothesis of yielding at the center and at the walls, proportionality constant K depends on the type of hopper. For a plane hopper equation (4.98) applies, whereas for a conical hopper K is given by

$$K \frac{\tan \varphi_w}{\dfrac{1 + \alpha \sin \delta}{1 - \alpha \sin \delta} + \dfrac{1}{\theta_w (1 - \cos \theta_w)(1 - \alpha \sin \delta)[1 - \alpha \sin \delta \cos(\omega - \alpha \varphi_w)]}} \tag{4.116}$$

Finally, we will give expressions for constant K and angle ψ for slices assumed by Enstad (1975, 1977). According to his hypothesis, the slice is in a uniform, limiting state of stress. Then, from yield condition (2.30) and expression (4.78), we have

$$K = \frac{1 + \sin \delta}{1 - \sin \delta} \tag{4.117}$$

Assuming, in addition, fully developed dry friction at the walls of a hopper, angle ψ at the left wall is given by

$$\psi = (1 + \alpha)\frac{\pi}{4} - \frac{\alpha}{2}(\omega - \alpha \varphi_w) + \theta_w \tag{4.118}$$

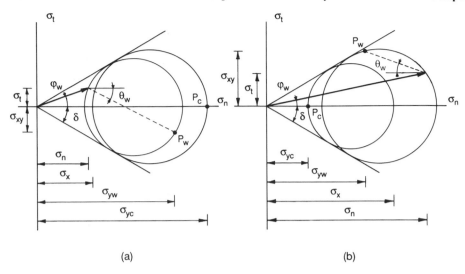

Figure 4.22 *Mohr's circles for yielding at the center and at the walls for a plane slice in a hopper, (a) active state and (b) passive state*

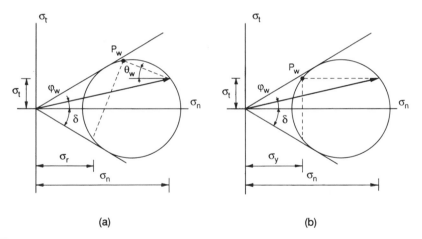

Figure 4.23 *Mohr's circles for yielding at the walls, (a) cylindrical slice in a hopper and (b) plane slice in a bin*

where the active state is assumed for the concave slice and the passive state for the convex slice, respectively .

4.3.5 Distribution of Wall Stresses

It is apparent that the diversity of the expressions for proportionality factors K, K_1, and K_2 in the equilibrium equations for a slice affects the magnitude of these constants. In general, all the expressions for K are functions of effective angle of internal friction δ, mobilized wall friction angle φ_w, and, in the case of hoppers, may also depend on half-included angle θ_w. Furthermore, the magnitude of K depends on whether the active or passive state is selected. A comprehensive analysis of all the expressions and parameters affecting the magnitude of K, and possible limitations in the range of these parameters, reaches beyond the objective of this work. It should be remembered also that all the derivations are based on hypotheses that from the formal point of view are equally admissible, and whose correctness can be tested only against the measurements of wall stresses. On the other hand, however, one might try to assign a plausible physical motivation in favor of a given hypothesis. For instance, the location of a point, or points, where yielding is assumed, could be related to the mechanism of deformation that takes place during the various operational phases. An example would be sliding along the walls during discharge from bins, where yielding at the walls can actually occur. In hoppers, however, yielding spreads over the whole mass of the material, and a more appropriate hypothesis would be that of yielding at the center and at the walls, or yielding everywhere, as has been assumed by Walker (1966) or Enstad (1975, 1977).

In the following, some examples of stress distributions resulting from different hypotheses for K are given. All results are presented as distributions of dimensionless stresses defined in Section 4.2.

Figure 4.24 shows wall normal stresses in a plane bin for the active and passive cases, respectively. The material parameters selected were $\delta = 40°$, $\varphi_w = 20°$, $\sigma_{y0} = 0$, and the various yielding hypotheses are indicated by the number of the corresponding equation for K. It is seen that, in the passive case, the wall stresses approach the limiting values more rapidly than in the active case. Also, in the passive case, the highest stresses result from the hypothesis of yielding at the center, and smallest stresses from yielding at the walls. The opposite holds for the active case.

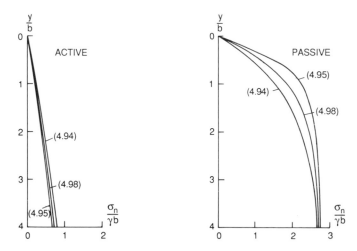

Figure 4.24   *Influence of the yielding hypothesis on wall stresses in a plane bin; $\delta = 40°$, $\varphi_w = 20°$, $\sigma_{y0} = 0$*

The stress distributions in Figure 4.24 were obtained with the assumption that either the active or passive state develops within the whole mass of the bulk material. It is also possible to consider a case where the passive state exists in the lower section of a bin, while the material in the upper portion is in the active state (cf. Nanninga, 1956, Walters, 1973a). This may model a partial drawdown of the material from a bin. Continuity in vertical stress σ_y is preserved across the boundary between the active and passive states; the stresses in the lower portion are obtained from (4.32), with the origin located at the boundary, and with stress σ_{y0} resulting from the solution in the active zone. Due to the difference in constant K for both regions, the wall stresses experience a jump given by

$$[\sigma_t] = (K_p - K_a)\sigma_y$$
$$[\sigma_n] = (K_p - K_a)\cot\varphi_w\sigma_y \tag{4.119}$$

where K_a and K_p stand for constant K in the active and passive regions, respectively. This is demonstrated in Figure 4.25 for the hypothesis of yielding at the walls, where the envelope of jumps is indicated by the dashed line.

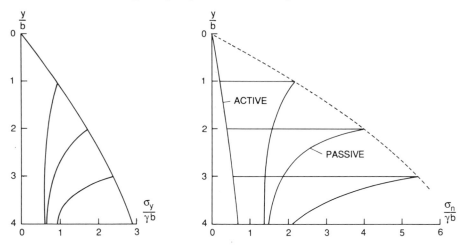

Figure 4.25 *Distribution of stresses in a cylindrical bin with active/passive state of stress; $\delta = 40°$, $\varphi_w = 20°$, $\sigma_{y0} = 0$, yielding at the walls*

A comparison of wall normal stresses resulting from different hypotheses for constant K in a plane hopper with $\theta_w = 30°$ is shown in Figure 4.26, where the active or passive state is assumed within the whole mass of the material, and its parameters are the same as in Figure 4.24. For the passive case, the stresses approach zero-values at the vertex, while for the active case they become infinite at the vertex. However, for small angles $\delta \approx \varphi_w$, all yielding hypotheses give zero stresses at the vertex (dashed line). This illustrates a greater sensitivity of the solutions to the material parameters in hoppers than in bins, where asymptotic wall stresses do not depend on the parameters selected.

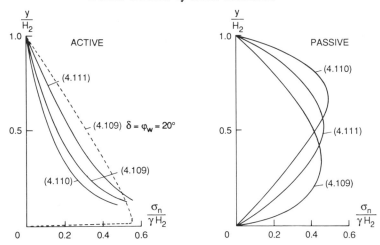

Figure 4.26 *Influence of the yielding hypothesis on wall stresses in a plane hopper;* $\theta_w = 30°$, $\delta = 40°$, $\varphi_w = 20°$, $\sigma_{y2} = 0$

Figure 4.27 shows discontinuous wall stresses that occur across a boundary separating the active and passive state regions. The jumps in wall stresses are again given by equations (4.119).

Finally, the stresses in a bin/hopper container are depicted in Figure 4.28. These were obtained for plane slices, $\theta_w = 30°$, $\delta = 40°$, and $\varphi_w = 20°$. At the transition from the bin to the hopper section the vertical stresses are continuous, with the active state and yielding at the wall assumed in the bin section, and the passive state and yielding at the center in the hopper. Note that the presence of a peak in wall stresses at the transition point is a consequence of postulating different states, active and passive, in each section of the bin/hopper, and the peak will appear, regardless of the hypothesis for K.

4.3.6 Stresses in Non-Symmetric Hoppers

The application of the direct method of slices to bin-load analysis is not limited to symmetric and vertical bins and hoppers. Bins and hoppers that are equipped with flow correcting devices also can be analyzed successfully by this method. In the following, we will briefly discuss some solutions that illustrate the potential of this method in problems other than the classical ones considered in the previous sections.

It has been observed experimentally (cf. Johanson, 1966, 1967/68) that placement of conical inserts in bins or hoppers that operate in the funnel-flow mode substantially improves the flow pattern, which becomes more stable, and changes to the mass-flow mode. Obviously, the presence of an insert affects the stress field within the bulk material and at the walls, and the solutions discussed in Sections 4.3.1 and 4.3.2 are no longer applicable. Further, the stresses that the bulk material exerts on the insert are of interest in the design of the suspension of the insert and

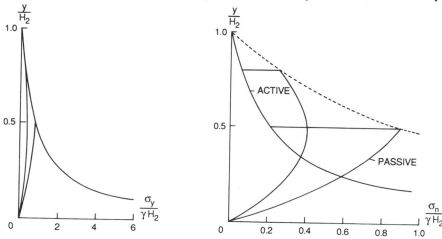

Figure 4.27   *Distribution of stresses in a conical hopper with the active/passive state of stress; $\theta_w = 30°$, $\delta = 40°$, $\varphi_w = 20°$, $\sigma_{y2} = 0$, yielding at the walls*

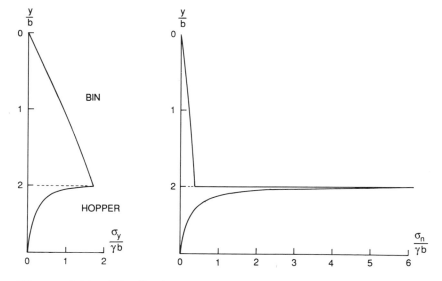

Figure 4.28   *Distribution of stresses in a cylindrical/conical bin/hopper; $\theta_w = 30°$, $\delta = 40°$, $\varphi_w = 20°$, $\sigma_{y0} = 0$*

its structural stability.

Figure 4.29a shows a conical hopper with an insert placed right at the top. The half-included insert angle θ_i is assumed to be equal to the half-included hopper angle θ_w. Selecting a plane slice, which is actually a ring enclosed between the hopper and the insert, and assuming a symmetrical distribution of stresses with respect to the hopper axis, we conclude that the only non-trivial equilibrium equation applies to the vertical direction. For the system of coordinates with its origin at the insert tip and the y-coordinate pointing downward, the global equilibrium equation is

$$\frac{d\sigma_y}{dy} - \frac{2}{H_2 - 2y}\sigma_y + \frac{2}{H_2(H_2 - 2y)}[(H_2 - y)(\sigma_{nw} + \sigma_{tw}\cot\theta_w)$$
$$+ y(\sigma_{ni} + \sigma_{ti}\cot\theta_w)] - \gamma = 0 \tag{4.120}$$

where subscripts w and i refer to the wall and the insert, respectively. To remove the statical indeterminancy in (4.120), a relationship between the average vertical stress σ_y and the stresses at the wall and the insert is required. Following our discussion in Section 4.3.4, a linear relationship is postulated, with the proportionality constant determined from a hypothesis of yielding. For example, we might assume the hypothesis of yielding at the center and at the walls, which, for the same friction angle φ_w at the wall and the insert, and $\theta_w = \theta_i$, gives one proportionality factor K for the wall and insert stresses. Equation (4.120) then simplifies to

$$\frac{d\sigma_y}{dy} - 2N\frac{\sigma_y}{H_2 - 2y} - \gamma = 0 \tag{4.121}$$

where N is given by (4.54).

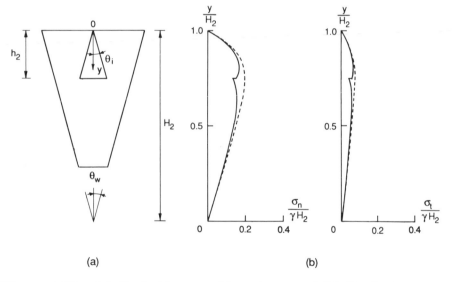

(a)   (b)

Figure 4.29   *(a) Conical hopper with an insert and (b) distribution of wall stresses; $\theta_w = \theta_i = 15°$, $\delta = 40°$, $\varphi_w = 20°$, $\sigma_{y0} = 0$, yielding at the center and at the walls*

The solution to equation (4.121), for $2N \neq -1$, is

$$\sigma_y = -\frac{\gamma(H_2 - 2y)}{2(N + 1)} + C(H_2 - 2y)^{-N} \tag{4.122}$$

where the constant of integration C is determined from the boundary condition

$$y = 0 \qquad \sigma_y = \sigma_{y2} \tag{4.123}$$

which gives

$$C = \sigma_{y2} H_2^N + \frac{\gamma H_2^{N+1}}{2(N+1)} \tag{4.124}$$

and

$$\sigma_y = -\frac{\gamma(H_2 - 2y)}{2(N+1)} + \left[\sigma_{y2} + \frac{\gamma H_2}{2(N+1)}\right] \left[\frac{H_2}{H_2 - 2y}\right]^N \tag{4.125}$$

Solution (4.125) applies only to the depth of a hopper equal to the height of insert h_2. For greater depth, an approximate solution for wall stresses can be obtained from (4.58), where σ_{y0} is taken as the average of vertical stresses resulting from (4.125). Figure 4.29b shows the distribution of wall stresses for a hopper with $\theta_w = 15°$, and for $\delta = 40°$, $\varphi_w = 20°$, and the passive state throughout. The proportionality constant K was calculated by means of (4.112). For comparison, the distribution of wall stresses in the absence of an insert is shown as a dashed line. Clearly, placement of an insert reduces the wall stresses.

A more general case, with different angles θ_w and θ_i, was considered by Polderman, Scott and Boom (1985).The general form of the equilibrium equation then can be written as

$$\frac{d\sigma_y}{dy} + \frac{dA}{dy}\frac{\sigma_y}{A} + \frac{P_w}{A}(\sigma_{nw}\tan\theta_w + \sigma_{tw}) + \frac{P_i}{A}(\sigma_{ni}\tan\theta_i + \sigma_{ti}) - \gamma = 0 \tag{4.126}$$

where A is the area of the upper surface of a slice, and P_w and P_i are the wall and insert perimeters, respectively. To remove the statical indeterminancy in (4.126), Polderman *et al.* modified the concept of the distribution factor, equation (4.100), by postulating a linear distribution of shear stress σ_{yx} over the ring slice. Due to the complexity of the explicit form of equation (4.126), and of D, only a numerical solution was constructed.

In conical hoppers with conical inserts, regardless of their actual geometry and the hypothesis of yielding selected, only one non-trivial equation describes the equilibrium of a slice. This is because the existence of an insert merely reduces the area of a slice, which becomes a ring, rather than a disk. In a plane hopper, however, a wedge-type insert separates the material into two independent slices, whose equilibrium should be considered separately. If $\theta_w = \theta_i$ and the same friction holds at the wall and insert surfaces, again, one equilibrium equation applies to each slice. If, however, $\theta_w \neq \theta_i$, or a different surface friction exists, the equilibrium in the horizontal direction and the equilibrium of moments are no longer identically satisfied.

The analysis of wall stresses in plane, non-symmetric hoppers was presented by Michalowski (1983). This author considered a plane slice with different inclination of infinitesimal sides, subjected to a linear distribution of normal stresses σ_y and to average shear stresses σ_{yx} (Figure 4.30a). From the equilibrium of forces in the x- and y-directions, and from the equilibrium of moments taken with respect to the

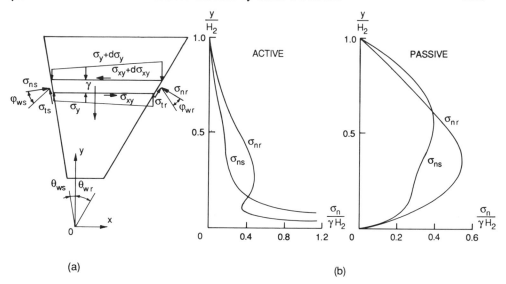

Figure 4.30   *(a) Stresses acting on a plane slice in a non-symmetric plane hopper and (b) distribution of wall stresses; $\theta_{ws} = 10°$, $\theta_{wr} = 40°$, $\delta = 30°$, $\varphi_{ws} = \varphi_{wr} = 15°$, $\sigma_{y2} = 0$, yielding at the walls (Michalowski, 1983)*

center of the slice, the following set of linear differential equations is obtained

$$y\frac{d\sigma_{ys}}{dy} + \sigma_{ys}A_1 + \sigma_{yr}B_1 - \frac{6}{b}\sigma_{yx} + \gamma y = 0$$

$$y\frac{d\sigma_{yr}}{dy} + \sigma_{ys}A_2 + \sigma_{yr}B_2 + \frac{6}{b}\sigma_{yx} + \gamma y = 0 \qquad (4.127)$$

$$y\frac{d\sigma_{yx}}{dy} - \sigma_{ys}A_3 + \sigma_{yr}B_3 + \sigma_{yx} = 0$$

where the subscripts s and r refer to the left and right walls of a hopper, respectively, and constants A and B are functions of the wall friction, slope of the walls, and proportionality constants relating wall stresses to vertical stresses at both walls of a hopper; b is the ratio of the length of a slice to its distance from the vertex. The solution to set (4.127) is expressed in terms of complex numbers, with the real solution for two integration constants assumed to be conjugate complex numbers. Then, the solution can be written as

$$\sigma_{ys} = \gamma D_1 y + E_1 y^{r_1} + F_1 y^\alpha \cos(\beta \ln y) + G_1 y^\alpha \sin(\beta \ln y)$$
$$\sigma_{yr} = \gamma D_2 y + E_2 y^{r_1} + F_2 y^\alpha \cos(\beta \ln y) + G_2 y^\alpha \sin(\beta \ln y) \qquad (4.128)$$
$$\sigma_{yx} = \gamma D_3 y + E_3 y^{r_1} + F_3 y^\alpha \cos(\beta \ln y) + G_3 y^\alpha \sin(\beta \ln y)$$

where D, E, F, and G are some constants, r_1 is the real root of the characteristic equation of set (4.127), and α and β are the real and imaginary parts of the remaining two complex roots. Explicit expressions for all the constants are given in the work of Michalowski (1983).

The presence of trigonometric functions in solution (4.128) causes the wall stresses to undergo fluctuations. This was demonstrated by Michalowski in an example of a non-symmetric hopper with $\theta_{ws} = 10°$, $\theta_{wr} = 40°$, $\varphi_{ws} = \varphi_{wr} = 15°$, $\delta = 30°$, and for the hypothesis of yielding at the walls. The results depicted in Figure 4.30 demonstrate more pronounced fluctuations for the active state.

4.4 INDIRECT METHOD OF SLICES SOLUTIONS

As outlined in Section 3.4.2, the indirect method of slices hinges on integrating the local equilibrium equations along a specified coordinate, and on postulating a distribution of some components of stress along this coordinate. To illustrate the application of the indirect method of slices to bin-load analysis, we will present solutions for a plane bin and a plane hopper (Savage and Yong, 1970). Cylindrical bins and conical hoppers were considered by Savage and Sayed (1981). Further, the effective angle of internal friction δ, and the unit weight γ, are assumed to be constant throughout the bulk material filling a container.

4.4.1 Stresses in Bins

For a vertical plane bin, the local equilibrium equations in the system of coordinates in Figure 4.31a are

$$\frac{\partial \sigma_x}{\partial x} + \frac{\partial \sigma_{xy}}{\partial y} = 0$$

$$\frac{\partial \sigma_{yx}}{\partial x} + \frac{\partial \sigma_y}{\partial y} = \gamma$$

(4.129)

Due to symmetry of local and wall stresses with respect to the vertical y-axis, the integration of the equilibrium equations over the whole width of bin $2b$ leads to only one non-trivial equation along the y-coordinate; this equation is identical to that resulting from the direct method of slices (see Section 4.3.1). To use the indirect method of slices properly, the integration should be performed over a distance where the boundary conditions are different. In a vertical bin with friction present at the walls, the stresses that act at the center and at the walls are different, regardless of their distribution. Thus, integration over half of width b gives a one-strip approximation of the equilibrium equations (4.129)

$$\int_0^b \frac{\partial \sigma_{xy}}{\partial y} dx + \sigma_{xb} - \sigma_{x0} = 0$$

$$\int_0^b \frac{\partial \sigma_y}{\partial y} dx + \sigma_{xyb} - \sigma_{xy0} = \gamma b$$

(4.130)

The variation of vertical stresses σ_y and shear stresses σ_{xy} is postulated as a

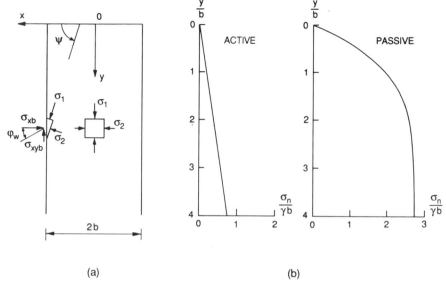

(a)   (b)

Figure 4.31   *(a) Principal stresses in a plane bin and (b) distribution*
of wall stresses; $\delta = 40°$, $\varphi_w = 20°$, $\sigma_{y0} = 0$

parabolic and a linear function of x, respectively

$$\sigma_y = \sigma_{y0}(y) + a(y)\left[\frac{x}{b}\right]^2$$
$$\sigma_{xy} = \sigma_{xyb}(y)\left[\frac{x}{b}\right]$$

$$(4.131)$$

On substituting (4.131) into (4.130) and integrating, we obtain

$$\frac{b}{2}\frac{d\sigma_{xyb}}{dy} + \sigma_{xb} - \sigma_{x0} = 0$$
$$b\frac{d\sigma_{y0}}{dy} + \frac{b}{3}\frac{da}{dy} + \sigma_{xyb} = \gamma b$$

$$(4.132)$$

Equations (4.132) contain five unknown functions, which number can be reduced if the yield condition and the boundary conditions at $x = 0$ and $x = b$ are
used. By reason of symmetry the vertical and horizontal stresses, σ_y and σ_x, are
principal stresses at $x = 0$, and, from yield condition (2.30)

$$\sigma_{y0} = \sigma_{x0}\frac{1 + \alpha\sin\delta}{1 - \alpha\sin\delta}$$

$$(4.133)$$

where $\alpha = 1$ for the active case, and $\alpha = -1$ for the passive case. For constant and
fully mobilized dry friction at the wall, the angle of inclination ψ of major principal
stress σ_1 at the left wall with respect to the x-axis is

$$\psi = (1 + \alpha)\frac{\pi}{4} - \frac{\alpha}{2}(\omega - \alpha\varphi_w)$$

$$(4.134)$$

With the help of Mohr's circle representing the limiting stress state at the wall, it is possible to express wall stresses σ_{yb} and σ_{xyb} as functions of angle ψ

$$\sigma_{yb} = \sigma_{xb}\frac{1 - \sin\delta\cos 2\psi}{1 + \sin\delta\cos 2\psi}$$

$$\sigma_{xyb} = \sigma_{yb}\frac{\sin\delta\sin 2\psi}{1 - \sin\delta\cos 2\psi}$$

(4.135)

Using (4.131), (4.133), and (4.135), we can write equations (4.132) as

$$\frac{b\sin\delta\sin 2\psi}{2(1 - \sin\delta\cos 2\psi)}\frac{d\sigma_{yb}}{dy} + \left[\frac{1 + \sin\delta\cos 2\psi}{1 - \sin\delta\cos 2\psi} - \frac{1 - \alpha\sin\delta}{1 + \alpha\sin\delta}\right]\sigma_{yb} + a\frac{1 - \alpha\sin\delta}{1 + \alpha\sin\delta} = 0$$

(4.136)

$$b\frac{d\sigma_{yb}}{dy} - \frac{2b}{3}\frac{da}{dy} + \frac{\sin\delta\sin 2\psi}{1 - \sin\delta\cos 2\psi}\sigma_{yb} = \gamma b$$

where the number of unknowns is reduced to two: σ_{yb} and a. It is convenient to combine equations (4.136) to obtain one second-order equation, which can be analytically integrated

$$A\frac{d^2\sigma_{yb}}{dy^2} + B\frac{d\sigma_{yb}}{dy} + C\sigma_{yb} = \gamma$$

(4.137)

where

$$A = \frac{b(1 + \alpha\sin\delta)\sin\delta\sin 2\psi}{3(1 - \alpha\sin\delta)(1 - \sin\delta\cos 2\psi)}$$

$$B = 1 + \frac{4\sin\delta(\alpha + \cos 2\psi)}{3(1 - \alpha\sin\delta)(1 - \sin\delta\cos 2\psi)}$$

(4.138)

$$C = \frac{\sin\delta\sin 2\psi}{b(1 - \sin\delta\cos 2\psi)}$$

and the only unknown is σ_{yb}. If the upper surface of a bin is free from surcharge, the boundary conditions are

$$y = 0 \qquad \sigma_{yb} = 0 \qquad \frac{d\sigma_{yb}}{dy} = 0$$

(4.139)

The boundary condition for the stress derivative results from the first equations in (4.131) and (4.136). The solution to equation (4.137) is given by

$$\sigma_{yb} = \frac{\gamma}{C} + De^{r_1 y} + Ee^{r_2 y}$$

(4.140)

where

$$r_{1,2} = -\frac{B}{2A} \pm \frac{B}{2A}\left[1 - \frac{4AC}{B^2}\right]^{1/2}$$

$$D = \frac{\gamma}{C}\left[\frac{r_2}{r_1 - r_2}\right] \qquad E = -\frac{r_1}{r_2}D$$

(4.141)

and the roots r_1 and r_2 are real for cases of practical interest. The function $a = a(y)$, eliminated from (4.136), can be determined from the first equation in (4.136), i.e.,

$$a = -\left[\frac{1 + \alpha \sin \delta}{1 - \alpha \sin \delta}\right]\left[\frac{b \sin \delta \sin 2\psi}{2(1 - \sin \delta \cos 2\psi)}\frac{d\sigma_{yb}}{dy} + \frac{2 \sin \delta (\alpha + \cos 2\psi)}{(1 + \alpha \sin \delta)(1 - \sin \delta \cos 2\psi)}\sigma_{yb}\right]$$
$$(4.142)$$

The distribution of stress components σ_y and σ_{xy} over the width and height of a bin and along its walls can be calculated using (4.131), (4.134), (4.135), (4.140), and (4.142). The horizontal stresses σ_x can be determined then from the yield condition expressed in terms of stress state components (e.g., condition (3.14) with $c = 0$ and $\phi = \delta$). Although the solution satisfies the yield condition everywhere, the equilibrium equations are satisfied only in a global sense.

The distribution of wall stresses over the height of a bin, for the active and passive cases, and for $\delta = 40°$, $\varphi_w = 20°$, is depicted in Figure 4.31b. The asymptotic values for the wall stresses are

$$\sigma_t = \gamma b$$
$$\sigma_n = \gamma b \cot \varphi_w$$
$$(4.143)$$

and they are identical to those obtained from the previously discussed solutions, i.e., from the limit state solution, and from the direct method of slices solution. The asymptotic vertical stresses are given by

$$\sigma_y = \gamma b \left\{\frac{1 - \sin \delta \cos 2\psi}{\sin \delta \sin 2\psi} + \frac{2(\alpha + \cos 2\psi)}{(1 - \alpha \sin \delta) \sin 2\psi}\left(1 - \left[\frac{x}{b}\right]^2\right)\right\}$$
$$(4.144)$$

Although the mathematical form of equation (4.144) differs from equations (4.5) and (4.10), the values of σ_y when calculated from these equations and from (4.144) appear to be the same.

4.4.2 Stresses in Hoppers

The analysis of wall stresses in a vertical and a symmetrical plane hopper closely follows the analysis of a plane bin. In particular, equations (4.129), and (4.130), still hold if the system of coordinates is chosen as in Figure 4.32a. Note that the system of coordinates differs from that selected for hoppers in the direct method of slices analysis. If the variation of vertical stresses σ_y and shear stresses σ_{xy} is given by (4.131), the only difference in the resulting ordinary differential equations is due to the sloping walls of the hopper, i.e., due to varying width

$$b = b_0 \left[1 - \frac{y}{H_2}\right]$$
$$\frac{db}{dy} = -\tan \theta_w$$
$$(4.145)$$

where b_0 is the half-width at $y = 0$, and H_2 is the hopper height measured from its vertex. Substituting (4.131) into (4.130), making use of (4.145), and performing integration, we obtain

$$\frac{b}{2}\frac{d\sigma_{xyb}}{dy} + \frac{\tan\theta_w}{2}\sigma_{xyb} + \sigma_{xb} - \sigma_{x0} = 0$$

$$b\frac{d\sigma_{yb}}{dy} + \frac{b}{3}\frac{da}{dy} + \sigma_{xyb} + \frac{2a}{3}\tan\theta_w = \gamma b$$

(4.146)

The angle ψ is given by

$$\psi = (1 + \alpha)\frac{\pi}{4} - \frac{\alpha}{2}(\omega - \alpha\varphi_w) + \theta_w$$

(4.147)

Utilizing (4.133) and (4.135), we obtain the following set of ordinary differential equations

$$\frac{b\sin\delta\sin 2\psi}{2(1 - \sin\delta\cos 2\psi)}\frac{d\sigma_{yb}}{dy} + \left[\frac{\sin\delta\sin 2\psi\tan\theta_w}{2(1 - \sin\delta\cos 2\psi)} + \frac{1 + \sin\delta\cos 2\psi}{1 - \sin\delta\cos 2\psi}\right.$$

$$\left. - \frac{1 - \alpha\sin\delta}{1 + \alpha\sin\delta}\right]\sigma_{yb} + a\frac{1 - \alpha\sin\delta}{1 + \alpha\sin\delta} = 0$$

(4.148)

$$b\frac{d\sigma_{yb}}{dy} - \frac{2b}{3}\frac{da}{dy} + \frac{\sin\delta\sin 2\psi}{1 - \sin\delta\cos 2\psi}\sigma_{yb} + \frac{2a}{3}\tan\theta_w = \gamma b$$

Combining equations (4.148) we obtain a second-order differential equation

$$bA\frac{d^2\sigma_{yb}}{dy^2} + B\frac{d\sigma_{yb}}{dy} + \frac{C}{b}\sigma_{yb} = \gamma$$

(4.149)

where

$$A = \frac{(1 + \alpha\sin\delta)\sin\delta\sin 2\psi}{3(1 - \alpha\sin\delta)(1 - \sin\delta\cos 2\psi)}$$

$$B = \frac{1}{3} + \frac{(1 + \alpha\sin\delta)}{3(1 - \alpha\sin\delta)(1 - \sin\delta\cos 2\psi)}[2(1 + \sin\delta\cos 2\psi) - \sin\delta\sin 2\psi\tan\theta_w]$$

(4.150)

$$C = \frac{\sin\delta\sin 2\psi}{1 - \sin\delta\cos 2\psi} - \frac{\sin\delta\tan\theta_w}{3(1 - \alpha\sin\delta)(1 - \sin\delta\cos 2\psi)}$$

$$\times [(1 + \alpha\sin\delta)\sin 2\psi\tan\theta_w + 4(\alpha + \cos 2\psi)]$$

and b is given by (4.145). For boundary conditions (4.139), the solution to equation (4.149) is

$$\sigma_{yb} = \frac{\gamma H_2 F}{D + E}\left\{1 - \frac{y}{H_2} - \frac{1}{r_1 - r_2}\left((1 - r_2)\left[1 - \frac{y}{H_2}\right]^{r_1} - (1 - r_1)\left[1 - \frac{y}{H_2}\right]^{r_2}\right)\right\}$$

(4.151)

where

$$D = -\frac{B}{A}\cot\theta_w \qquad E = \frac{C}{A}\cot^2\theta_w \qquad F = \frac{1}{A}\cot\theta_w$$

$$(4.152)$$

$$r_{1,2} = -\frac{D-1}{2} \pm \frac{1}{2}\left[(D-1)^2 - 4E\right]^{1/2}$$

with roots real for cases of practical interest. The function $a = a(y)$ is given by

$$a = -\left[\frac{1+\alpha\sin\delta}{1-\alpha\sin\delta}\right]\left[\frac{b\sin\delta\sin 2\psi}{2(1-\sin\delta\cos 2\psi)}\frac{d\sigma_{yb}}{dy} + \frac{\sin\delta\sin 2\psi\tan\theta_w}{2(1-\sin\delta\cos 2\psi)}\sigma_{yb}\right.$$
$$\left. + \frac{1+\sin\delta\cos 2\psi}{1-\sin\delta\cos 2\psi}\sigma_{yb} - \frac{1-\alpha\sin\delta}{1+\alpha\sin\delta}\sigma_{yb}\right]$$

$$(4.153)$$

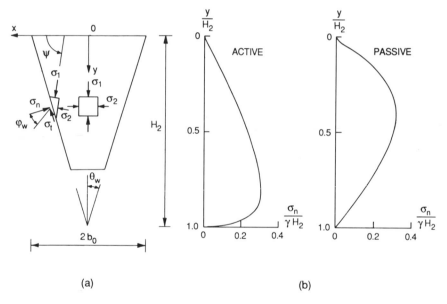

(a)   (b)

Figure 4.32   *(a) Principal stresses in a plane hopper and (b) distribution of wall stresses; $\theta_w = 10°$, $\delta = 20°$, $\varphi_w = 15°$, $\sigma_{y0} = 0$*

The stress components σ_y, σ_x and σ_{xy} can be determined from (4.131), (4.135), (4.147), (4.151), (4.153), and from the yield condition. The normal and shear stresses along the walls, σ_n and σ_t, are given by

$$\sigma_n = \sigma_{xyb}\frac{\sin 2(\psi - \theta_w)}{\sin 2\psi\tan\varphi_w}$$

$$(4.154)$$

$$\sigma_t = \sigma_n\tan\varphi_w$$

The solution for σ_{yb} in an infinitely tall hopper is

$$\sigma_{yb} = \frac{\gamma F y^*}{D+E}$$

$$(4.155)$$

where y^* is the vertical distance measured from the vertex. Since all stresses are proportional to σ_{yb}, which is a linear function of y^*, a radial stress distribution is obtained.

The solution given by (4.151) is valid only if angle $\psi < \pi/2$; for $\psi \geq \pi/2$ stress σ_{yb} becomes negative (tensile). For the passive case, the latter may occur for very large values for θ_w, δ, and φ_w; for the active case it occurs even for moderate values of these parameters. Within the acceptable range of parameters, solutions for both the passive and active cases yield wall stresses that initially increase with the depth of a hoppper and then decrease to zero at the vertex. This is demonstrated in Figure 4.32b, which shows the distribution of wall stresses for $\theta_w = 10°$, $\delta = 20°$, and $\varphi_w = 15°$.

4.5 KINEMATICAL METHOD OF LIMIT ANALYSIS SOLUTIONS

In this Section we will present, after Mróz and Drescher (1969), some applications of the kinematical method of limit analysis for approximate determination of wall stresses that develop during quasi-static discharge of bulk materials from bins and hoppers.

The starting point of the method is a kinematically admissible velocity field that models an incipient or steady flow of a bulk material throughout a container. We will select fields consisting of translational-motion regions that are separated by velocity discontinuities. This type of velocity field was discussed in Section 3.5, and is particularly suitable for the analysis of flow in plane bins and hoppers with the regions being triangular in the plane of flow. It also can be applied to bins and hoppers rectangular or polygonal in cross-section with tetrahedral translational-motion regions. In cylindrical bins or conical hoppers, however, where an axisymmetric velocity field is most likely to occur, a rigid-block type velocity field is not permissible, since axisymmetric deformation requires non-zero circumferential strains. In other words, a velocity field where the particles move with different velocities must be considered. This type of velocity field requires more elaborate and careful analysis, as will be explained in Section 8.2.2. Accordingly, the analysis of wall stresses presented in this section will be limited to plane bins and plane hoppers only.

Further, the mechanical properties of the bulk material will be assumed to be constant throughout the mass, i.e., effective angle of internal friction δ of the Mohr-Coulomb yield condition and wall friction angle φ_w are taken as constants.

4.5.1 Stresses in Bins

Referring to the example discussed in Section 3.5, the mechanism of failure consisting of four translational-motion regions permits only evaluation of the total forces acting on the walls and bottom of a bin, and no information regarding the stress distribution can be inferred from such a solution. However, by increasing the number of blocks over the height of a bin, the forces that act on each segment of the wall can be determined easily, and eventually, approximately at least, the stress distribution can be found.

Figure 4.33a illustrates a kinematically admissible incipient failure mechanism where several geometrically similar triangles are assumed. Thus, only two angles, α_1 and α_2, define the geometry of the failure mechanism, which in turn greatly simplifies the derivation of expressions for the forces that act along the walls of a bin. It suffices, indeed, to consider element $ACC'A'$ and use the resulting expressions recursively. These expressions can be derived by considering the equilibrium of forces for each triangular region within element $ACC'A'$. Alternatively, we may first determine the force acting over sector CC' by equating the energies dissipated and supplied for failure, and then make use of the equilibrium of forces for the whole element $ACC'A'$. In the following derivation of the wall stresses in bins the first approach is used, whereas the second one will be utilized for analyzing stresses in hoppers.

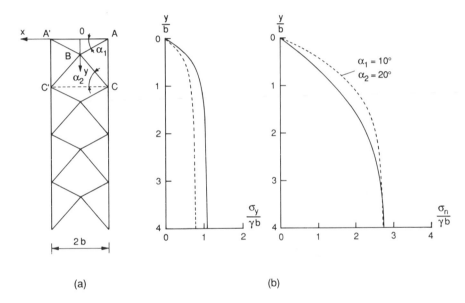

(a)   (b)

Figure 4.33   *(a) Incipient failure mechanism and (b) wall stresses in a plane bin; $\delta = 30°$, $\varphi_w = 20°$, $\sigma_{y0} = 0$*

Figure 4.34a shows half of element $ACC'A'$, where the forces that act on each triangle are indicated by vectors. These forces are inclined to the normals of velocity discontinuity lines AB and BC at effective angle of internal friction δ. At wall segment AC, the resultant force is inclined to the normal at wall friction angle φ_w. The interaction between element $EACD$ and the neighboring elements located above and below is represented by resultant forces F_{EA} and R_{CD}, respectively.

Figure 4.34b shows the force polygon of all forces that act within and along the boundaries of element $EACD$. Since in incipient flow the change in the density of the material is disregarded, γ=const, the weights of each triangular region are given by

$$W_{EAB} = \frac{\gamma b^2}{2} \tan \alpha_1$$

$$W_{ABC} = \frac{\gamma b^2}{2} (\tan \alpha_1 + \tan \alpha_2) \qquad (4.156)$$

$$W_{BCD} = \frac{\gamma b^2}{2} \tan \alpha_2$$

From the force polygon we obtain

$$F_{ACn} = F_{EA} \frac{\tan(\alpha_1 + \delta) + \tan(\alpha_2 + \delta)}{1 + \tan \varphi_w \tan(\alpha_2 + \delta)}$$
$$+ \frac{\gamma b^2}{2} \left[\frac{\tan \alpha_1 \tan(\alpha_1 + \delta) + \tan \alpha_2 \tan(\alpha_2 + \delta) + 2 \tan \alpha_1 \tan(\alpha_2 + \delta)}{1 + \tan \varphi_w \tan(\alpha_2 + \delta)} \right]$$

$$(4.157)$$

$$F_{ACt} = F_{ACn} \tan \varphi_w$$

and

$$R_{CD} = F_{EA} - F_{ACn} \tan \varphi_w + \gamma b^2 (\tan \alpha_1 + \tan \alpha_2) \qquad (4.158)$$

Expressions (4.157) and (4.158) are used recursively, with the calculation beginning at the uppermost element, where force F_{EA} results from the stress boundary conditions at the upper surface of the bulk material; for a stress-free surface $F_{EA} = 0$. Assuming that along each sector AC the normal and tangential stresses, σ_n and σ_t, vary continuously, we obtain an approximate distribution of these stresses over the height of the bin.

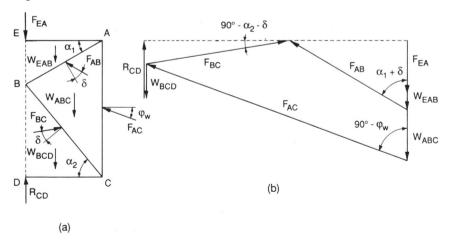

Figure 4.34 *(a) Forces acting on a typical element in a plane bin and (b) polygon of forces*

The dashed lines in Figure 4.33b show the distribution of average vertical stresses, and the normal wall stresses, for $\delta = 30°$ and $\varphi_w = 20°$. The α-angles assumed were $\alpha_1 = 10°$ and $\alpha_2 = 20°$, and they are within the range of values that guarantee finite velocities in each of the rigid-motion regions (see Section 3.5.4)

$$0 < \alpha_1 < \frac{\pi}{2} - \delta - \varphi_w$$

$$0 < \alpha_2 < \frac{\pi}{2} - \delta \tag{4.159}$$

According to the theorems of limit analysis, a kinematically admissible solution furnishes a lower bound to the true reaction R_{CD}. Thus, angles α_1 and α_2 should be determined from the condition of the maximum of R_{CD}. Referring to our discussion of the limit state and the differential slice solutions, we concluded there that stresses at a given depth of the bin are unaffected by the location of the outlet, i.e., of the total height of a bin. In other words, for a given width of a bin, the distribution of stresses down to a given depth can be obtained from a solution for an infinitely tall bin. For the stresses resulting from the kinematic method of limit analysis to comply with this requirement, the maximization procedure for the α-angles should be performed for an infinitely tall bin rather than for a finite one with a finite number of geometrically similar elements. It is seen from Figure 4.33b that the distributions of wall stresses rapidly approach asymptotic values at infinity. These asymptotic values are obtained from equation (4.158) by setting $F_{EA} = R_{CD}$, which gives

$$\sigma_t = \gamma b$$

$$\sigma_n = \gamma b \cot \varphi_w \tag{4.160}$$

and they are identical to those corresponding to the limit state and differential slice solutions. Note that the asymptotic values are independent of the α-angles. The expression for the asymptotic average vertical stress is obtained from the first equation in (4.157) and equation (4.158)

$$\sigma_y = \frac{\gamma b}{2} \left[\frac{\tan \alpha_2 \tan(\alpha_2 + \delta) - \tan \alpha_1 \tan(\alpha_1 + \delta)}{\tan(\alpha_1 + \delta) + \tan(\alpha_2 + \delta)} \right.$$
$$\left. + \frac{2 \cot \varphi_w (\tan \alpha_1 + \tan \alpha_2)}{\tan(\alpha_1 + \delta) + \tan(\alpha_2 + \delta)} \right] \tag{4.161}$$

and depends on the α-angles selected to be optimized to provide a maximum of σ_y. For $\delta = 30°$ and $\varphi_w = 20°$, the optimal angles are $\alpha_1 \approx 14°$, $\alpha_2 \approx 46°$, and $\sigma_y/\gamma b = 1.10$, which is slightly below the value $\sigma_y/\gamma b = 1.12$, calculated from the average of σ_y corresponding to the exact asymptotic solution (see Section 4.2.1). The distribution of the wall stresses corresponding to the optimal values of α_1 and α_2 is shown in Figure 4.33b by the solid lines.

4.5.2 Stresses in Hoppers

The derivation of expressions for the wall stresses in a plane hopper that is given below first makes use of the energy balance. Next, the wall forces are determined from the global equilibrium of a selected portion of the collapse mechanism.

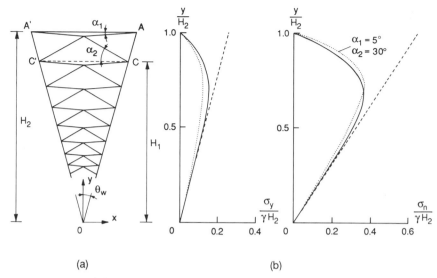

(a)   (b)

Figure 4.35   (a) Incipient failure mechanism and (b) wall stresses in a
plane hopper; $\theta_w = 15°$, $\delta = 30°$, $\varphi_w = 20°$, $\sigma_{y2} = 0$

Figure 4.35a shows the assumed incipient failure mechanism, where, again, two
angles α_1 and α_2 define its geometry. Figure 4.36 shows the typical element and
the corresponding hodograph, respectively. The jumps in velocities are inclined to
discontinuity lines AC and BC at angle δ, whereas at wall AC the jump is inclined
at angle φ_w. The angles α_1 and α_2 must satisfy inequalities

$$0 < \alpha_1 < \frac{\pi}{2} - \delta - \varphi_w - \theta_w$$

$$0 < \alpha_2 < \frac{\pi}{2} - \delta \tag{4.162}$$

Since for a material that does not possess cohesion the rate of energy dissipated
in failure is zero (see [3.102]), the energy balance involves only the rate of external
energy due to the weights of the triangular regions and forces F_{EA} and R_{CD}. The
velocities of each region are given by

$$v_{EAB} = v_0$$

$$v_{ABC} = v_0 \frac{\cos(\alpha_1 + \delta)}{\cos(\alpha_1 + \delta + \varphi_w + \theta_w)} \tag{4.163}$$

$$v_{BCD} = v_0 \frac{\cos(\alpha_1 + \delta)\cos(\alpha_2 + \delta - \varphi_w - \theta_w)}{\cos(\alpha_2 + \delta)\cos(\alpha_1 + \delta + \varphi_w + \theta_w)}$$

and the weights of the regions are

$$W_{EAB} = \frac{\gamma}{2} H_2^2 \tan^2 \theta_w \tan \alpha_1$$

$$W_{ABC} = \frac{\gamma}{2} \frac{H_2^2 \tan^2 \theta_w \sin(\alpha_1 + \alpha_2)\cos(\alpha_1 + \theta_w)}{\cos^2 \alpha_1 \cos(\alpha_2 - \theta_w)} \tag{4.164}$$

$$W_{BCD} = \frac{\gamma}{2} \frac{H_2^2 \tan^2 \theta_w \cos^2(\alpha_1 + \theta_w)\sin \alpha_2 \cos \alpha_2}{\cos^2 \alpha_1 \cos^2(\alpha_2 - \theta_w)}$$

where H_2 is the height of the upper surface of the element. The rate of external energy computed as the dot product of weights $W_{EAB}, W_{ABC}, W_{BCD}$, forces F_{EA}, R_{CD}, and the corresponding velocities $v_{EAB}, v_{ABC}, v_{BCD}$, is

$$\dot{w} = v_0 \frac{\gamma H_2^2 \tan^2 \theta_w}{2 \cos \alpha_1 \cos(\alpha_2 - \theta_w)} \left[\sin \alpha_1 \cos(\alpha_2 - \theta_w) \right.$$
$$+ \frac{\sin(\alpha_1 + \alpha_2) \cos(\alpha_1 + \theta_w) \cos(\alpha_1 + \delta) \cos(\varphi_w + \theta_w)}{\cos \alpha_1 \cos(\alpha_1 + \delta + \varphi_w + \theta_w)}$$
$$\left. + \frac{\sin \alpha_2 \cos \alpha_2 \cos(\alpha_1 + \delta) \cos^2(\alpha_1 + \theta_w) \cos(\alpha_2 + \delta - \varphi_w - \theta_w)}{\cos \alpha_1 \cos(\alpha_2 - \theta_w) \cos(\alpha_2 + \delta) \cos(\alpha_1 + \delta + \varphi_w + \theta_w)} \right]$$
$$+ v_0 F_{EA} - v_0 R_{CD} \frac{\cos(\alpha_1 + \delta) \cos(\alpha_2 + \delta - \varphi_w - \theta_w)}{\cos(\alpha_2 + \delta) \cos(\alpha_1 + \delta + \varphi_w + \theta_w)} \tag{4.165}$$

By setting $\dot{w} = \dot{d} = 0$, and rearranging (4.165), we arrive at

$$R_{CD} = \frac{\gamma H_2^2 \tan^2 \theta_w}{2} \left[\frac{\cos(\alpha_2 + \delta) \cos(\alpha_1 + \delta + \varphi_w + \theta_w) \tan \alpha_1}{\cos(\alpha_1 + \delta) \cos(\alpha_2 + \delta - \varphi_w - \theta_w)} \right.$$
$$+ \frac{\cos(\alpha_2 + \delta) \sin(\alpha_1 + \alpha_2) \cos(\alpha_1 + \theta_w) \cos(\varphi_w + \theta_w)}{\cos^2 \alpha_1 \cos(\alpha_2 - \theta_w) \cos(\alpha_2 + \delta - \varphi_w - \theta_w)}$$
$$\left. + \frac{\cos^2(\alpha_1 + \theta_w) \sin \alpha_2 \cos \alpha_2}{\cos^2 \alpha_1 \cos^2(\alpha_2 - \theta_w)} \right]$$
$$+ F_{EA} \frac{\cos(\alpha_2 + \delta) \cos(\alpha_1 + \delta + \varphi_w + \theta_w)}{\cos(\alpha_1 + \delta) \cos(\alpha_2 + \delta - \varphi_w - \theta_w)} \tag{4.166}$$

The force that acts along the segment of wall AC can be determined from the global equilibrium of forces acting on element $EACD$

$$F_{ACn} = (F_{EA} + W_{EAB} + W_{ABC} + W_{BCD} - R_{CD}) \frac{\cos \varphi_w}{\sin(\varphi_w + \theta_w)} \tag{4.167}$$

$$F_{ACt} = F_{ACn} \tan \varphi_w$$

Again, equations (4.166) and (4.167) are used recursively, beginning from the uppermost element. Following the argument that the wall stresses do not depend on the location of the outlet (see Sections 4.3 and 4.4), the recursive procedure is carried out down to the vertex of the hopper.

In Figure 4.35b the distributions of wall and vertical stresses for a hopper with angle $\theta_w = 15°$, and $\delta = 30°$, $\varphi_w = 20°$, $\alpha_1 = 5°$, and $\alpha_2 = 30°$, are shown by the dotted lines. In the vicinity of the vertex of the hopper, the vertical and wall stresses approach a linear distribution. This means that the asymptotic solution is radial.

To derive expressions for the radial stress field we observe that the average vertical stressses acting on the horizontal sections of the element, EA and CD, must be proportional to the distance measured from the vertex. Thus,

$$R_{CD} = F_{EA} \left[\frac{H_1}{H_2} \right]^2 \tag{4.168}$$

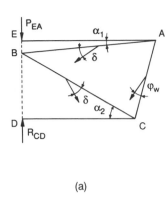

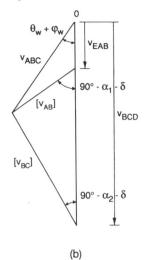

(a)

(b)

Figure 4.36 *(a) Failure mechanism for a typical element in a plane hopper and (b) hodograph*

where ratio H_1/H_2 is given by

$$\frac{H_1}{H_2} = \frac{\cos\alpha_2 \cos(\alpha_1 + \theta_w)}{\cos\alpha_1 \cos(\alpha_2 - \theta_w)} \tag{4.169}$$

Substituting (4.168) into (4.166), solving for F_{EA}, and dividing the result by the length of sector EA, we obtain

$$\sigma_y = \frac{\gamma \tan\theta_w M_1 y}{2M_2} \tag{4.170}$$

where y is substituted for H_2, and

$$M_1 = \frac{\cos(\alpha_2 + \delta) \cos(\alpha_1 + \delta + \varphi_w + \theta_w) \tan\alpha_1}{\cos(\alpha_1 + \delta) \cos(\alpha_2 + \delta - \varphi_w - \theta_w)}$$
$$+ \frac{\cos(\alpha_2 + \delta) \sin(\alpha_1 + \alpha_2) \cos(\alpha_1 + \theta_w) \cos(\varphi_w + \theta_w)}{\cos^2\alpha_1 \cos(\alpha_2 - \theta_w) \cos(\alpha_2 + \delta - \varphi_w - \theta_w)}$$
$$+ \frac{\cos^2(\alpha_1 + \theta_w) \sin\alpha_2 \cos\alpha_2}{\cos^2\alpha_1 \cos^2(\alpha_2 - \theta_w)} \tag{4.171}$$

$$M_2 = \frac{\cos^2\alpha_2 \cos^2(\alpha_1 + \theta_w)}{\cos^2\alpha_1 \cos^2(\alpha_2 - \theta_w)} - \frac{\cos(\alpha_2 + \delta) \cos(\alpha_1 + \delta + \varphi_w + \theta_w)}{\cos(\alpha_1 + \delta) \cos(\alpha_2 + \delta - \varphi_w - \theta_w)}$$

The wall forces, and, eventually, the wall stresses, are obtained from (4.167) and (4.168), which give

$$F_{ACn} = \left\{ \sigma_y \tan\theta_w \left(1 - \left[\frac{H_1}{H_2}\right]^2 \right) y + W_{EAB} + W_{ABC} + W_{BCD} \right\} \frac{\cos\varphi_w}{\sin(\varphi_w + \theta_w)} \tag{4.172}$$

$$F_{ACt} = F_{ACn} \tan\varphi_w$$

The dashed lines in Figure 4.35b show the distributions of stresses corresponding to the radial stress field giving values that are slightly lower than those corresponding to the exact radial solution, where the α-angles were determined from the condition of the maximum of σ_y. For $\theta_w = 15°$, $\delta = 30°$, and $\varphi_w = 20°$, the optimal angles are $\alpha_1 \approx 5°$, and $\alpha_2 \approx 51°$. Using these α-angles, the stresses in a finite hopper are shown as solid lines.

Small differences in wall stresses between the exact radial stress solution and the solution obtained by the kinematic method of limit analysis can be attributed to constancy of the unit weight assumed in both cases. In the latter method, a constant unit weight of the material throughout the failure mechanism can be assumed only if the flow is regarded as incipient. In the steady flow, where the velocity discontinuities are regarded as stationary shocks, the material crossing a discontinuity experiences dilation, and the unit weight is different in each rigid-motion region. Now we will consider an example of steady flow in a finite height hopper with material continuously supplied from above.

Figure 4.37a shows an arrangement of triangular blocks. Although this arrangement is identical to that shown in Figure 4.35a, the velocities in blocks adjacent to the hopper walls are no longer inclined at angle φ_w, but are parallel to the walls. Steady flow of a material requires that particle trajectories coincide with velocities. For a velocity inclined to the wall, a stationary region would exist adjacent to the wall and the flow would be limited to a region narrowing towards the outlet. This is demonstrated in Figure 4.37a, where the dashed line defines the narrowing region of flow. Thus, funnel flow develops, and wall stresses cannot be determined. To analyze mass flow, therefore, it is imperative to postulate velocities parallel to walls.

For a symmetrical half of a typical element $ACC'A'$, the velocities v_{EAB}, v_{ABC}, and v_{BCD} are given by (4.163) with $\varphi_w = 0$. Utilizing equation (3.92), we can express the unit weights of each region as

$$\gamma_{EAB} = \gamma_0$$
$$\gamma_{ABC} = \gamma_0 \frac{\cos \alpha_1 \cos(\alpha_1 + \delta + \theta_w)}{\cos(\alpha_1 + \delta)\cos(\alpha_1 + \theta_w)}$$
$$\gamma_{BCD} = \gamma_0 \frac{\cos \alpha_1 \cos(\alpha_2 + \delta)\cos(\alpha_2 - \theta_w)\cos(\alpha_1 + \delta + \theta_w)}{\cos \alpha_2 \cos(\alpha_1 + \delta)\cos(\alpha_1 + \theta_w)\cos(\alpha_2 + \delta - \theta_w)}$$

(4.173)

and the total weights of the regions are given by (4.164), where γ is substituted by the appropriate equation in (4.173). The rate of external energy in region $EACD$ is

$$\dot{w} = v_{EAB}F_{EA} + v_{EAB}W_{EAB} + v_{ABC}W_{ABC}\cos\theta_w + v_{BCD}W_{BCD} - v_{BCD}R_{CD}$$
(4.174)

Since the motion of region ABC is parallel to wall AC, the dissipation along the wall is no longer zero, as was the case of incipient flow and velocity v_{ABC} inclined at angle φ_w. However, for constant wall friction along AC, the resultant of wall stresses, F_{AC}, is inclined at angle φ_w to the normal to AC, and the dissipation can be expressed as

$$\dot{d} = v_{ABC}F_{ACt}$$
(4.175)

It is evident that the energy balance equation contains two unknowns, R_{CD} and F_{ACt}, and an additional equation is required to determine R_{CD}. This additional equation can be obtained from the global equilibrium of forces acting on region $EACD$, which gives

$$F_{ACt} = \frac{F_{EA} + W_{EAB} + W_{ABC} + W_{BCD} - R_{CD}}{\sin\theta_w \cot\varphi_w + \cos\theta_w} \tag{4.176}$$

Substituting (4.176) into (4.175), equating the rate of external energy and the rate of energy dissipation, and, after rearranging, we obtain

$$R_{CD} = \left(F_{EA} + W_{EAB}\right)\frac{v_{ABC} - v_{EAB}A}{v_{ABC} - v_{BCD}A} + W_{ABC}\frac{v_{ABC}\left(1 - A\cos\theta_w\right)}{v_{ABC} - v_{BCD}A} + W_{BCD} \tag{4.177}$$

where

$$A = \sin\theta_w \cot\varphi_w + \cos\theta_w \tag{4.178}$$

The wall forces, F_{ACn} and F_{ACt}, are given by (4.167).

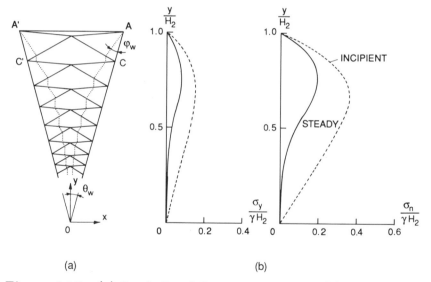

(a)   (b)

Figure 4.37   *(a) Steady flow failure mechanism and (b) wall stresses in a plane hopper;* $\theta_w = 15°$, $\delta = 30°$, $\varphi_w = 20°$, $\sigma_{y2} = 0$

The solid lines in Figure 4.37b show the distribution of the dimensionless wall and vertical stresses corresponding to the steady flow in a hopper with $\theta_w = 15°$, and $\delta = 30°$, $\varphi_w = 20°$, $\alpha_1 = 5°$, and $\alpha_2 = 51°$. These were obtained by using equations (4.177) and (4.167) recursively. For comparison, the dashed lines demonstrate the distribution of stresses if the incipient flow is assumed (equations [4.166] and [4.167]). All stresses in the steady flow are significantly smaller than in the incipient flow, as the unit weight of the material decreases towards the vertex. Unrealistically small unit weights in the vicinity of the vertex, where the stresses approach a zero vertical asymptote, make the steady flow solution meaningful only over a limited depth of the hopper.

4.6 CLOSING REMARKS

As demonstrated in the preceding sections, the three groups of analytical methods described in Chapter 3 are suitable for determination of quasi-static wall and bottom stresses in bins and hoppers. All solutions are approximate, however, due to the assumptions involved.

The limit state methods utilize only the assumption of the limiting state of stress throughout the mass of the bulk material, and the resulting stresses satisfy the local equilibrium equations everywhere. In this regard, the limit state methods solutions seem to be most accurate, as the differential slice methods satisfy equilibrium only in a global sense. However, neither of these two groups of methods makes direct reference to the kinematic counterpart of the solution, and the solutions cannot be regarded as complete. On the other hand, the kinematical method of limit analysis operating on velocities gives only an approximate distribution of wall stresses.

The lack of a direct coupling between the static and kinematic solutions that is inherent in the quasi-static approach may make some statically rigorous solutions unacceptable if viewed from the rigid-perfectly plastic model concept. A complete solution requires verification that plastic yielding does occur, i.e., that the velocities of particles satisfy the flow rule. An example of properly addressing this question is the vertex radial stress field considered by Jenike (1964b), who constructed a kinematically admissible vertex radial velocity field obeying the non-associative flow rule. Recently, Jenike (1987) extended the vertex radial stress and velocity solutions to the von Mises-Schleicher yield condition. Kinematic solutions have not been presented in the case of stress solutions constructed from the upper surface of the bulk material occupying a container. The difficulty one might encounter here results from the presence of the stress discontinuities.

The limit state solutions are extremely sensitive to the geometry of the boundary from which the solution is constructed. A slightly curved upper or lower boundary in a bin or hopper may significantly affect the pattern of the stress characteristics and, thus, the stress field (cf. Michalowski, 1984). The solutions based on other methods are less susceptible to boundary geometry, as the approximations involved allow for various additional simplifications.

All solutions lead to bottom stresses that are greater than zero. This is fully acceptable if the outlet of a bin or hopper is closed or drawdown controlled by a feeder. During a free gravitational discharge, however, the stresses at the level of the outlet should attain a zero-value as no support is provided by the material leaving a bin or hopper. If the vertex radial stress field is considered, the resulting stresses at the bulk material upper surface also may violate the actual boundary conditions. Further, the stress distributions are independent of the location of the outlet regardless of whether constructed from an upper boundary or as the vertex radial stress fields.

In spite of criticism that can be raised against all the wall and bottom stress solutions presented, they have been generally accepted as valuable engineering approximations for bin-load evaluation in bin and hopper structural design. In particular, they adequately capture the influence of wall friction on wall stress distribution: the wall stresses in bins do not increase unlimitedly with depth, and in hoppers the stresses tend to a zero-value at the hopper vertex if the passive state is considered.

A comparison of the various solutions for a bin and a hopper is given below. Figure 4.38a shows wall normal stresses in a plane bin and the active state of stress for a bulk material with $\delta = 30°$ and wall friction angle $\varphi_w = 20°$. The limit state solutions shown in this figure, and also in the next one, were taken from Horne and Nedderman (1976, 1978a). Two yielding hypotheses were used in the direct method of slices: a) yielding at the walls, b) yielding at the center. A similar comparison for the passive state of stress is shown in Figure 4.38b.

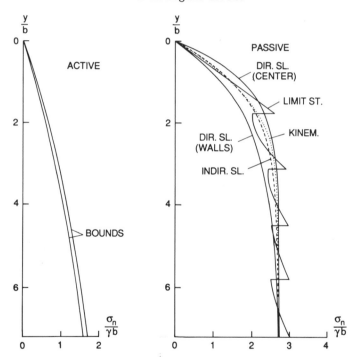

Figure 4.38   *Comparison of various solutions for wall normal stresses in a plane bin; $\delta = 30°$, $\varphi_w = 20°$, $\sigma_{y0} = 0$*

The differences in wall normal stresses are small for the active case, where all methods predict continuous stress distributions. Therefore, only bounds to the stress distributions are given in Figure 4.38a. In the passive case, however, the limit state solution gives discontinuous stresses that oscillate around other solutions. The differences diminish with the depth of the bin, as all methods predict the same asymptotic stresses at infinity.

A comparison of the solutions for a plane hopper with $\theta_w = 5°$, $\delta = 30°$, $\varphi_w = 22°$, and the active state is given in Figure 4.39a. The difference in wall stresses is again very small, and only bounds are indicated in this figure. For larger hopper angles θ_w, however, the limit state solution yields discontinuous wall stresses. Figure 4.39b shows the results for $\theta_w = 10°$, $\delta = 30°$, and $\varphi_w = 25°$, for the passive state. In both figures, plane slices were selected in the direct method of slices. In general, excluding the limit state discontinuous solutions, the differences in the various solutions pertain only to the location of maximum wall stresses. This is because the integral of all stress distributions is the same for hoppers with the same height.

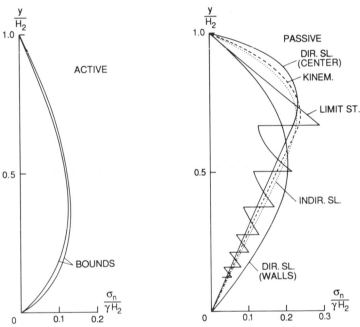

Figure 4.39   *Comparison of various solutions for wall normal stresses in a finite plane hopper; active case: $\theta_w = 5°$, $\delta = 30°$, $\varphi_w = 22°$, $\sigma_{y2} = 0$; passive case, $\theta_w = 10°$, $\delta = 30°$, $\varphi_w = 25°$, $\sigma_{y2} = 0$*

5 BIN-LOADS IN STEADY INERTIAL MASS FLOW

5.1 INTRODUCTION

The analysis of bin-loads carried out in Chapter 4 disregarded the contribution of inertial forces that may develop in a bulk material occupying a bin or hopper. This might be satisfactory for filling and storage operations when the particles undergo negligibly small accelerations. During discharge, however, the particles may reach finite velocities that vary with time and position, which in turn may induce significant inertial forces. The accelerations in the vicinity of an outlet may become comparable to those corresponding to free fall if the outflow is not controlled by a receiving assembly.

In this chapter, a particular inertial process of the flow of bulk materials from storage structures will be discussed: namely, flow in which the velocities may vary with position but not with time. This kind of flow is called *steady*, as distinct from *unsteady* flow where the velocities also vary with time. A steady flow may prevail in a tall bin or hopper where the lowering of the upper surface of the material does not affect the velocities in the lower section. It will also occur in short bins and hoppers if drawdown is compensated for by resupplying material from above. Further, the viscous effects associated with rapid flow will be disregarded, and the rigid-perfectly plastic model for bulk materials subject to large strains will form the basis of our analysis. On account of the discharge process that is considered, the passive rather than the active state is meaningful.

The analysis will be limited to the direct method of differential slices, and will closely follow our discussion in Section 4.3. Only bins and hoppers that are either plane or circular in cross-section will be considered.

5.2 DIRECT METHOD OF SLICES SOLUTIONS

Within the framework of the direct method of differential slices, the components of stresses acting on a slice are transformed into appropriate resultant forces that contribute to the equilibrium of all forces. Similarly, any mass forces distributed along the slice are transformed into the resultant mass force. If the particles are stationary, the mass forces resulting from the gravitational acceleration equal the unit weight, $\gamma = \rho g$. For moving particles subject to an acceleration field, the inertial forces develop as the product of the mass and acceleration. The inertial forces may increase or decrease the mass forces due to the unit weight, depending on whether the particles decelerate or accelerate. To determine the inertial forces, the acceleration field of the particles must be known. Since the accelerations can always be determined if the velocity field is given, we shall begin with postulating simple, steady-velocity fields; this approach can be regarded as kinematical. In Section 5.2.3, we will discuss briefly a more complex approach in which the velocity field derives from the constitutive behavior of the bulk material.

5.2.1 Stresses in Bins for Incompressible Flow

Several experimental observations indicate (cf. Takahashi and Yanai, 1973, Perry, Rothwell and Woodfin, 1976) that in symmetrical, plane and cylindrical mass-flow bins the velocities of particles away from the outlet are approximately vertical and constant over the height (Figure 5.1). If the process of flow is regarded as steady, a rigid-body type velocity field produces no accelerations. Thus, inertial forces do not occur, and the problem becomes quasi-static. Since no information as to the velocity of particles can be deduced from a quasi-static solution, the problem is kinematically indeterminate.

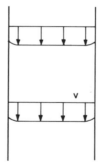

Figure 5.1   *Velocities in a tall bin*

5.2.2 Stresses in Hoppers for Incompressible Flow

In a plane or conical hopper the sloping walls and diminishing cross-section towards the outlet force the particles to move with different velocities. A typical velocity field obtained from tests on mass-flow model hoppers is shown schematically in Figure 5.2a. Although the velocities vary significantly across the hopper width, and discontinuities are observed (cf. Pariseau, 1969/70, Blair-Fish and Bransby, 1973, Michalowski, 1984, 1987), the directions of the velocities are approximately radial (cf. Bransby and Blair-Fish, 1975, Drescher, Cousens and Bransby, 1978). A radial velocity field is defined by

$$v_r = v_r(r, \theta) \qquad v_\theta = 0 \qquad (5.1)$$

for a plane hopper, and

$$v_r = v_r(r, \theta, \omega) \qquad v_\theta = 0 \qquad v_\omega = 0 \qquad (5.2)$$

for a conical one, where the system of coordinates is shown in Figure 5.2b (see also Figure 3.12). A particular radial velocity field is now selected, in which the velocities are independent of the θ, or θ and ω-coordinate, and thus constant for a given radius r (Figure 5.2b)

$$\begin{aligned} v_r &= v_r(r) \qquad v_\theta = 0 \\ v_r &= v_r(r) \qquad v_\theta = 0 \qquad v_\omega = 0 \end{aligned} \qquad (5.3)$$

Finally, we will assume that the volume of the material does not change during flow, i.e., the flow is incompressible and the density ρ of the material is constant. This assumption may not be confirmed by experiments; it is retained here to simplify the analysis. As will be shown in the next section, a physically sounder assumption greatly complicates the analysis.

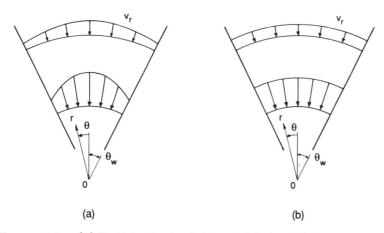

(a)   (b)

Figure 5.2   *(a) Radial velocity field and (b) simplified velocity field in a hopper*

In a steady incompressible flow, the volume of the bulk material passing per unit time through an arbitrary cross-section of the hopper must be constant. This results from the principle of mass conservation (3.8). Denoting this volume by V_1, and selecting cross-section of hopper $r =$const., the following expression results for V_1 in a plane hopper

$$V_1 = -2 \int_0^{\theta_w} v_r r \, d\theta = -2 v_r r \theta_w \qquad (5.4)$$

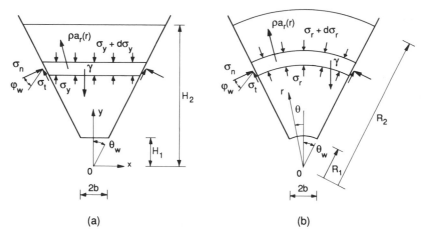

Figure 5.3 *(a) Plane and (b) cylindrical slices in a hopper*

and in a conical hopper

$$V_1 = -2\pi \int_0^{\theta_w} v_r r^2 \sin\theta \, d\theta = -2\pi v_r r^2 (1 - \cos\theta_w) \tag{5.5}$$

Relations (5.4) and (5.5) can be rewritten as

$$v_r = -\frac{V_1}{2r\theta_w} = \frac{A_1}{r}$$
$$v_r = -\frac{V_1}{2\pi r^2 (1 - \cos\theta_w)} = \frac{A_2}{r^2} \tag{5.6}$$

where A_1 and A_2 are constants to be determined later. The acceleration in a steady flow is given by the convective part of the material time derivative of velocity, and for radial flow is expressed as

$$a_r = \frac{Dv_r}{Dt} = v_r \frac{\partial v_r}{\partial r} = v_r \frac{dv_r}{dr} \tag{5.7}$$

Using (5.6) and (5.7), we obtain

$$a_r = -\frac{A_1^2}{r^3}$$
$$a_r = -\frac{2A_2^2}{r^5} \tag{5.8}$$

With the help of a pure number m, defined as $m = 1$ for a plane hopper, and $m = 2$ for a conical hopper, expressions (5.8) can be written in one form as

$$a_r = -\frac{mA_m^2}{r^{2m+1}} \tag{5.9}$$

It is seen from (5.9) that the radial accelerations a_r increase towards the hopper vertex, and so will increase the inertial forces, which are the product of acceleration and mass, ρa_r. Since the direction of inertial forces opposes acceleration, they actually point along the positive r-coordinate.

Consider now the equilibrium of forces acting on a slice, including the inertial forces resulting from the acceleration field (5.9). Two cases similar to those discussed in Section 4.3.2 are presented: a plane slice, and a cylindrical or spherical slice centered at the vertex (Figure 5.3). In the first case, the arrangement of forces and the system of coordinates chosen are shown in Figure 5.3a. Due to the assumed radial velocity field and the constancy of the resulting accelerations for a given radius r, the accelerations vary along a plane slice according to

$$a_r = -mA_m^2 \left[\frac{\sin\theta}{x}\right]^{2m+1} \tag{5.10}$$

Integrating the y-components of the inertial forces along the slice and adding them to the sum of all other forces in the y-direction, we obtain the following differential equation for a plane hopper

$$\frac{d\sigma_y}{dy} + \frac{1}{y}(\sigma_y - \sigma_n - \sigma_t \cot\theta_w) + \gamma - \frac{\rho A_1^2}{2y^3}(\cos^2\theta_w + \theta_w \cot\theta_w) = 0 \tag{5.11}$$

On the other hand, for a conical hopper we have

$$\frac{d\sigma_y}{dy} + \frac{2}{y}(\sigma_y - \sigma_n - \sigma_t \cot\theta_w) + \gamma - \frac{\rho A_2^2}{y^5}(1 + \cos^2\theta_w)\cos^2\theta_w = 0 \tag{5.12}$$

Alternatively, using the pure number m defined previously, we can write both equations (5.11) and (5.12) as

$$\frac{d\sigma_y}{dy} + \frac{m}{y}(\sigma_y - \sigma_n - \sigma_t \cot\theta_w) + \gamma - \frac{\rho D_m L}{y^{2m+1}} = 0 \tag{5.13}$$

where

$$\begin{aligned}
D_m &= A_m^2 \\
L &= \frac{1}{3-m}\left[\cos^2\theta_w + (2-m)\theta_w \cot\theta_w + (m-1)\cos^4\theta_w\right]
\end{aligned} \tag{5.14}$$

Equation (5.13) cannot be integrated directly because it contains three unknown stresses acting on a slice, i.e., σ_y, σ_n, and σ_t. However, this statical indeterminacy can be removed in exactly the same fashion as for quasi-static flow (see Section 4.3.2). In fact, the presence of inertial forces affects the equilibrium of forces only and not the relation between the stresses acting on a slice. Thus, postulating

$$\begin{aligned}
\sigma_t &= K\sigma_y \\
\sigma_n &= \sigma_t \cot\varphi_w
\end{aligned} \tag{5.15}$$

we can write equation (5.13) as

$$\frac{d\sigma_y}{dy} + mN\frac{\sigma_y}{y} + \gamma - \frac{\rho D_m L}{y^{2m+1}} = 0 \tag{5.16}$$

where

$$N = 1 - K(\cot \varphi_w + \cot \theta_w) \tag{5.17}$$

Differential equation (5.16) is linear, and can be integrated easily. Two solutions are possible, depending on the magnitude of the factor mN. If $mN \neq -1$, we have

$$\sigma_y = \rho D_m L \frac{y^{-2m}}{m(N-2)} - \gamma\frac{y}{mN+1} + \frac{C}{y^{mN}} \tag{5.18}$$

Note, that for the range $0 \leq \theta_w \leq \pi/2$ and $0 \leq \varphi_w \leq \pi/2$, the factor $N-2$ appearing in the first right-hand side term of equation (5.18) is always less than zero.

Solution (5.18), in contrast to the quasi-static solution from Section 4.3.2, contains two unknown constants C and D_m. The former is an integration constant, whereas the latter is related through (5.14)$_1$ to the unknown constant A_m of the radial velocity field (5.6). It is thus possible to determine these constants from the boundary conditions that exist not only at the upper surface but also at the lower surface of the material occupying the hopper. There are two possibilities for selecting the boundary conditions. In the first case, we may assume that at both surfaces the vertical stresses σ_y are known, i.e.,

$$\begin{aligned} y &= H_1 & \sigma_y &= \sigma_{y1} \\ y &= H_2 & \sigma_y &= \sigma_{y2} \end{aligned} \tag{5.19}$$

where H_1 denotes the distance from the vertex of the hopper to the lower surface of the material within, and H_2 the distance from the vertex to the upper surface. In particular, we will assume that both surfaces are stress-free, and

$$\sigma_{y1} = \sigma_{y2} = 0 \tag{5.20}$$

This case may correspond to a free gravitational discharge from a hopper. An alternative is to select boundary conditions of the mixed-type, with stresses given at one surface and velocity at another. The boundary conditions are now

$$\begin{aligned} y &= H_1 & v_r &= v_{r1} \\ y &= H_2 & \sigma_y &= \sigma_{y2} \end{aligned} \tag{5.21}$$

or

$$\begin{aligned} y &= H_1 & \sigma_y &= \sigma_{y1} \\ y &= H_2 & v_r &= v_{r2} \end{aligned} \tag{5.22}$$

where v_{r1} and v_{r2} are the velocities at a given point of the flat surface, say at the center. Conditions (5.21) with $\sigma_{y2} = 0$ may exist if the gravitational discharge from a hopper is controlled by a feeder, and the velocity of discharge at the outlet is known.

Using boundary conditions (5.19), we determine constants C and D_m as

$$C = \frac{\gamma H_1^{mN+1}}{mN+1}\left[1 - \frac{H^{mN+1}-1}{H^{m(N-2)}-1}\right] + \sigma_{y1}H_1^{mN} - \frac{\sigma_{y2}H_2^{mN}-\sigma_{y1}H_1^{mN}}{H^{m(N-2)}-1}$$

$$(5.23)$$

$$D_m = \frac{\gamma m(N-2)}{\rho L(mN+1)}H_1^{2m+1}\left[\frac{H^{mN+1}-1}{H^{m(N-2)}-1}\right] + \frac{m(N-2)(\sigma_{y2}H_2^{mN}-\sigma_{y1}H_1^{mN})}{\rho L\left[H_2^{m(N-2)}-H_1^{m(N-2)}\right]}$$

where $H = H_2/H_1$. For condition (5.20), the last right-hand side terms in (5.23) disappear, and the vertical stresses σ_y are given explicitly by

$$\sigma_y = \frac{\gamma}{mN+1}\left\{\frac{H^{mN+1}-1}{H^{m(N-2)}-1}\left[\frac{H_1^{2m+1}}{y^{2m}} - \frac{H_1^{mN+1}}{y^{mN}}\right] + \frac{H_1^{mN+1}}{y^{mN}} - y\right\} \quad (5.24)$$

If boundary conditions (5.21) or (5.22) are selected, the constant A_m, and therefore D_m, can be evaluated directly from expressions (5.6). The remaining constant C for conditions (5.21) is

$$C = \sigma_{y2}H_2^{mN} - \rho D_m L \frac{H_2^{m(N-2)}}{m(N-2)} + \gamma\frac{H_2^{mN+1}}{mN+1} \quad (5.25)$$

An analogous expression holds for conditions (5.22), with σ_{y1} and H_1 replacing σ_{y2} and H_2, respectively.

The solution to equation (5.16) for $mN = -1$ becomes slightly simpler, and

$$\sigma_y = -\rho D_m L\frac{y^{-2m}}{1+2m} - \gamma y \ln y + Cy \quad (5.26)$$

with

$$C = \frac{\sigma_{y1}}{H_1} + \frac{(\sigma_{y2}H_1 - \sigma_{y1}H_2)(H_1H_2)^{2m} + \gamma(H_1H_2)^{1+2m}\ln H}{(H_2^{1+2m} - H_1^{1+2m})H_1^{1+2m}} + \gamma \ln H_1$$

$$(5.27)$$

$$D_m = \frac{(1+2m)}{\rho L}\left[\frac{(\sigma_{y2}H_1 - \sigma_{y1}H_2)(H_1H_2)^{2m} + \gamma(H_1H_2)^{1+2m}\ln H}{H_2^{1+2m} - H_1^{1+2m}}\right]$$

for boundary conditions (5.19), and

$$C = \frac{\sigma_{y2}}{H_2} + \rho D_m L\frac{H_2^{-(1+2m)}}{1+2m} + \gamma \ln H_2 \quad (5.28)$$

if (5.21) holds.

Expressions (5.18), (5.24), and (5.26) derived above determine the distribution of the vertical stress σ_y over the height of a hopper. The normal, and the tangential stresses along the walls are related to σ_y by equations (5.15).

Consider now a cylindrical or spherical slice (Figure 5.3b). Following the procedure and notation outlined above, and noting that the inertial forces are constant along a cylindrical or spherical slice as seen from (5.9), we derive the resulting differential equation for the radial stress σ_r as

$$\frac{d\sigma_r}{dr} + mN\frac{\sigma_r}{r} + \gamma M - \frac{\rho m D_m}{r^{2m+1}} = 0 \tag{5.29}$$

where

$$M = (2 - m)\frac{\theta_w}{\sin \theta_w} - (1 - m)\frac{2}{1 + \cos \theta_w} \tag{5.30}$$

Again, two solutions are possible depending on the factor mN. For $mN \neq -1$

$$\sigma_r = \rho D_m \frac{r^{-2m}}{N - 2} - \gamma M \frac{r}{mN + 1} + C r^{-mN} \tag{5.31}$$

and for $mN = -1$

$$\sigma_r = -\rho m D_m \frac{r^{-2m}}{1 + 2m} - \gamma M r \ln r + C r \tag{5.32}$$

Constants C and D_m can be determined from the boundary conditions analogous to (5.19), (5.20), (5.21) or (5.22), with R_1, R_2, σ_{r1}, and σ_{r2} appropriately substituted for H_1, H_2, σ_{y1}, and σ_{y2} (Figure 5.3b). The expressions for constants C and D_m resemble those given above, and they are shown below merely for the sake of completeness. For $mN \neq -1$ and for conditions (5.19)

$$C = \frac{\gamma M R_1^{mN+1}}{mN + 1}\left[1 - \frac{R^{mN+1} - 1}{R^{m(N-2)} - 1}\right] + \sigma_{r1} R_1^{mN} - \frac{\sigma_{r2} R_2^{mN} - \sigma_{r1} R_1^{mN}}{R^{m(N-2)} - 1} \tag{5.33}$$

$$D_m = \frac{\gamma M(N - 2)}{\rho(mN + 1)} R_1^{2m+1}\left[\frac{R^{mN+1} - 1}{R^{m(N-2)} - 1}\right] + \frac{(N - 2)(\sigma_{r2} R_2^{mN} - \sigma_{r1} R_1^{mN})}{\rho[R_2^{m(N-2)} - R_1^{m(N-2)}]}$$

where $R = R_2/R_1$, and for (5.21)

$$C = \sigma_{r2} R_2^{mN} - \rho D_m \frac{R_2^{m(N-2)}}{N - 2} + \gamma M \frac{R_2^{mN+1}}{mN + 1} \tag{5.34}$$

If $mN = -1$, then, accordingly,

$$C = \frac{\sigma_{r2}}{R_1} + \frac{(\sigma_{r2} R_1 - \sigma_{r1} R_2)(R_1 R_2)^{2m} + \gamma M(R_1 R_2)^{1+2m} \ln R}{(R_2^{1+2m} - R_1^{1+2m}) R_1^{1+2m}} + \gamma M \ln R_1 \tag{5.35}$$

$$D_m = \frac{1 + 2m}{\rho m}\left[\frac{(\sigma_{r2} R_1 - \sigma_{r1} R_2)(R_1 R_2)^{2m} + \gamma M(R_1 R_2)^{1+2m} \ln R}{R_2^{1+2m} - R_1^{1+2m}}\right]$$

or

$$C = \frac{\sigma_{r2}}{R_2} + \rho D_m m \frac{R_2^{-(1+2m)}}{1+2m} + \gamma M \ln R_2 \qquad (5.36)$$

The normal and tangential stresses along the walls are again related to the radial stresses by equations similar to (5.15). However, the constant K may be assumed to have a different value than in the case of a plane slice (see Section 4.3.4). The above solution for a cylindrical or spherical slice was given by Mróz and Szymański (1971a).

A greater number of parameters enter the steady inertial solutions for vertical or radial stresses in plane and conical hoppers than in the case of quasi-static flow. These additional parameters are the distance or radius to the lower surface, the boundary stresses, and the boundary velocities.

Figure 5.4 shows an example of the distributions of vertical and wall stresses over the height of a conical hopper. These were obtained using equation (5.24) for $\theta_w = 30°$, $K = 0.75$, $\varphi_w = 20°$, and for the ratio $H_2/H_1 = 4$. For comparison, the distributions of stresses resulting from the quasi-static solution (4.59) are shown by the dashed lines. Since in solution (5.24) stress-free boundary conditions were used, the stresses at the outlet vanish accordingly. This is not the case with the quasi-static solution, where zero-stresses occur at the hopper vertex. Further, the stresses due to inertial flow are lower than the quasi-static stresses because the inertial forces oppose the gravitational forces.

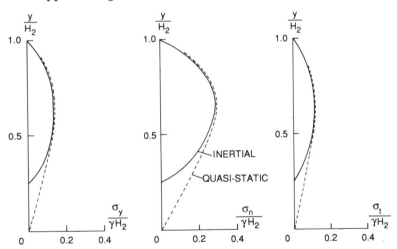

Figure 5.4   *Stress distributions in inertial and quasi-static flow in a conical hopper; $\theta_w = 30°$, $\varphi_w = 20°$, $K = 0.75$, $H_2/H_1 = 4$*

It is interesting to consider the limiting case when the location of the upper surface approaches infinity, i.e., when

$$\lim_{H_2 \to \infty} \left[\frac{H_1}{H_2} \right] = 0 \qquad H_1 < \infty \qquad (5.37)$$

or

$$\lim_{R_2 \to \infty} \left[\frac{R_1}{R_2} \right] = 0 \qquad R_1 < \infty \tag{5.38}$$

Asymptotic solutions exist if we select boundary conditions (5.19) with (5.20). Also, the exponents of H or R in the expressions for constants C and D_m must be negative. The latter holds, providing $mN < -1$. Then, for a plane slice

$$C = 0$$
$$D_m = \frac{\gamma m(N-2)}{\rho L(mN+1)} H_1^{2m+1} \tag{5.39}$$

and for a cylindrical or spherical slice

$$C = 0$$
$$D_m = \frac{\gamma m(N-2)}{\rho(mN+1)} R_1^{2m+1} \tag{5.40}$$

Substituting (5.39) and (5.40) into the expressions for σ_y and σ_r, we arrive at

$$\sigma_y = \frac{\gamma y}{mN+1} \left\{ \left[\frac{H_1}{y} \right]^{2m+1} - 1 \right\}$$
$$\sigma_r = \frac{\gamma M r}{mN+1} \left\{ \left[\frac{R_1}{r} \right]^{2m+1} - 1 \right\} \tag{5.41}$$

Neglecting the inertial forces, i.e., assuming $D_m = 0$, we see that the vertical and the radial stresses vary linearly with distance

$$\sigma_y = -\frac{\gamma y}{mN+1}$$
$$\sigma_r = -\frac{\gamma M r}{mN+1} \tag{5.42}$$

Note that equations (5.42) are identical with those given in Section 4.3.2.

The distribution of stresses for the upper surface of the material approaching infinity is shown in Figure 5.5. Here, the geometry of the hopper and slice, and the parameters selected, are the same as in Figure 5.4. Clearly, solution (5.41) asymptotically approaches quasi-static radial solution (5.42).

5.2.3 Stresses in Dilating/Contracting Flow

In the analysis presented in Section 5.2.2, the fundamental assumption underlying the solution to inertial steady flow was a radial velocity field (5.3), with constant density ρ. The assumption of an incompressible flow actually contradicts the observed behavior of the material, which, even in the critical state, shows that density

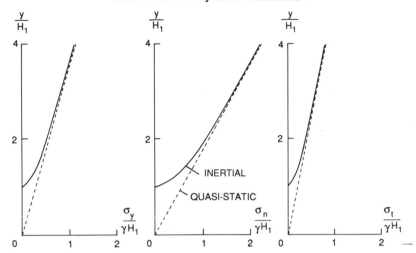

Figure 5.5   *Stress distributions in inertial and quasi-static flow in an infinitely tall conical hopper; $\theta_w = 30°$, $\varphi_w = 20°$, $K = 0.75$*

depends on the state of stress (see Section 2.3). We will now examine some possible modifications to the above assumption.

    We will begin by incorporating the variation of density with stress in a way similar to that presented in Section 4.3. In other words, we assume that the density and the vertical or radial stress are related by

$$\rho = f(\sigma_y) \qquad \text{or} \qquad \rho = g(\sigma_r) \tag{5.43}$$

whereas the velocity field remains incompressible. This is obviously incorrect, since for non-uniform stress distribution volume changes must occur to produce different densities at various locations of the flowing mass; the principle of mass conservation is violated. Nonetheless, we retain this assumption of uncoupled density and velocity fields to illustrate the changes in the governing equations. Following the derivation of equations (5.16) or (5.29), we observe that only the third and fourth terms will change in these equations. Depending on the form of relation (5.43), equations (5.16) or (5.29) may remain linear or become non-linear. For a simple linear relation used in Section 4.3

$$\rho = \rho_0 + A\sigma_y \tag{5.44}$$

equation (5.16) becomes

$$\frac{d\sigma_y}{dy} + \sigma_y \left[\frac{mN}{y} + Ag - A\frac{D_m L}{y^{2m+1}} \right] + \rho_0 \left[g - \frac{D_m L}{y^{2m+1}} \right] = 0 \tag{5.45}$$

where g is the acceleration of gravity. Although differential equation (5.45) is linear, due to the form of its non-constant coefficients, a numerical integration is required to obtain a solution.

Consider now a radial velocity field which leads to a prescribed contraction or dilation of the bulk material. The variation of the density is compatible with the velocity field, yet unrelated to the state of stress. This approach is a simple extension of the kinematical one discussed at the begining of this chapter. There is experimental evidence (cf. Brown and Richards, 1970, van Zuilichem, van Egmond and de Swart, 1974, Drescher, Cousens and Bransby 1978,) that initially compacted bulk materials experience appreciable dilation in the vicinity of an outlet. If we postulate a dilating radial velocity field that is independent of the θ-coordinate, the volume V_1 defined by (5.4) or (5.5) becomes a function of r. For example, the dilation increases uniformly towards the outlet if

$$V_1 = V_{10} \left[\frac{r_0}{r} \right]^n \tag{5.46}$$

where V_{10} is the volume at some distance r_0, and the exponent n is greater than zero. A negative exponent n would lead to contraction. Using expression (5.4), (5.5), and (5.7), we derive the equations

$$v_r = \frac{A_m}{r^{m+n}}$$
$$a_r = -\frac{(m+n)A_m^2}{r^{2(m+n)+1}} \tag{5.47}$$

From the principle of mass conservation (3.8) and equation (5.46), the density ρ can be expressed as

$$\rho = \rho_0 \left[\frac{r}{r_0} \right]^n \tag{5.48}$$

where ρ_0 is the density at r_0. Equations (5.47) and (5.48) enable us to determine the gravitational and inertial forces at any location in the hopper. Restricting our analysis to a cylindrical or spherical slice, the resulting differential equation for the radial stress σ_r becomes

$$\frac{d\sigma_r}{dr} + mN\frac{\sigma_r}{r} + BMr^n - \frac{B(m+n)D_m}{gr^{2m+n+1}} = 0 \tag{5.49}$$

where

$$B = \frac{\rho_0 g}{r_0^n} \tag{5.50}$$

and the other symbols are as previously defined. Equation (5.49) can be integrated easily, and, for boundary conditions (5.20) and $mN + n \neq -1$, it yields

$$\sigma_r = \frac{BM}{mN+n+1} \left\{ \frac{R^{mN+n+1}-1}{R^{m(N-2)-n}-1} \left[\frac{R_1^{2m+2n+1}}{r^{2m+n}} - \frac{R_1^{mN+n+1}}{r^{mN}} \right] \right.$$
$$\left. + \frac{R_1^{mN+n+1}}{r^{mN}} - r^{n+1} \right\} \tag{5.51}$$

The influence of the exponent n on the stress distribution is shown in Figure 5.6, where $\theta_w = 30°$, $\varphi_w = 20°$, $K = 0.75$, and $R_2/R_1 = 4$. Because in dilating flow

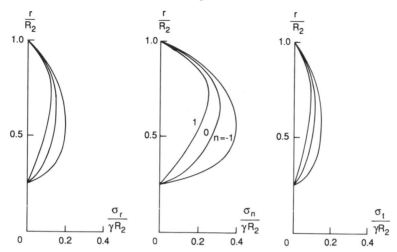

Figure 5.6   *Stress distributions in inertial flow in a conical hopper for dilatant, incompressible, and contractant material; $\theta_w = 30°$, $\varphi_w = 20°$, $K = 0.75$, $R_2/R_1 = 4$*

($n = 1$) the density decreases towards the outlet, the resulting stresses are lower than those in an incompressible flow ($n = 0$). The opposite holds for contracting flow ($n = -1$).

Finally, we will outline, after Savage and Sayed (1979), an approach in which the stress field and the radial velocity field (5.3) are coupled by a constitutive law of the bulk material. Although these authors used a simplified indirect method of slices, their approach applies equally well to the direct method. The starting point is equation (5.43) relating average stress to density. Savage and Sayed assumed a non-linear relationship

$$\sigma_r = D \left[\frac{\rho - \rho_1}{\rho_2 - \rho} \right] \tag{5.52}$$

where ρ_1 and ρ_2 correspond to the minimum and to the maximum possible density of the material, respectively, and D is a material constant. Since in the coupled approach the dependence of the radial velocity field (5.3) on r is unknown, and the material may dilate or contract due to varying stress, an additional equation is required to determine this dependence. This additional equation is provided by the continuity equation (3.9), which for a polar system of coordinates is

$$v_r \frac{d\rho}{dr} + \rho \frac{dv_r}{dr} + \frac{\rho v_r}{r} = 0 \tag{5.53}$$

With equations (5.52), (5.53), (5.7), and the differential equation that results from vertically summing up all the forces acting on a slice, we complete the set of equations governing the flow. This set consists of non-linear equations, and a numerical integration scheme is required. The work by Savage and Sayed focuses on the rate of flow, and no stress distribution is presented there.

5.2.4 Rate of Flow

Probably the most significant feature of the inertial analysis of discharge is the possibility of determining the velocities of particles and thus the rate of flow. We refer here to a free gravitational discharge where the rate of flow is not controlled by a feeder. For the radial velocity field (5.3) in a hopper, the volume flow rate is given by

$$q = V_1 \tag{5.54}$$

whereas the mass flow rate is given by

$$Q = \rho V_1 \tag{5.55}$$

The volume V_1 is determined by equations (5.4) or (5.5), which hold for both incompressible and dilatant or contractant flow. The variables that depend on the kind of flow are the radial velocity v_r and the density ρ. In the kinematical approach, where the velocity field is uncoupled from the stress field, the radial velocities are given by equation $(5.47)_1$ with an appropriate exponent n; $n = 0$ corresponds to incompressible flow. The constant A_m appearing in equation $(5.47)_1$, which is directly related to the constant D_m by equation $(5.14)_1$, depends on the type of slice, the magnitude of the factor $mN + n$, and the boundary tractions. Below, explicit expressions are given for the volume flow rate q in incompressible flow.

For a plane slice and $mN \neq -1$

$$q = 2[(m-1)(1 - \cos\theta_w)\pi + (2-m)\theta_w]$$

$$\times \left\{ \frac{\gamma m(N-2)}{\rho L(mN+1)} H_1^{2m+1} \left[\frac{H^{mN+1} - 1}{H^{m(N-2)} - 1} \right] + \frac{m(N-2)(\sigma_{y2}H_2^{mN} - \sigma_{y1}H_1^{mN})}{\rho L[H_2^{m(N-2)} - H_1^{m(N-2)}]} \right\}^{1/2} \tag{5.56}$$

and for $mN = -1$

$$q = 2[(m-1)(1 - \cos\theta_w)\pi + (2-m)\theta_w]$$

$$\times \left[\frac{1 + 2m}{\rho L} \frac{(\sigma_{y2}H_1 - \sigma_{y1}H_2)(H_1 H_2)^{2m} + \gamma(H_1 H_2)^{1+2m} \ln H}{H_2^{1+2m} - H_1^{1+2m}} \right]^{1/2} \tag{5.57}$$

In the case of a cylindrical or spherical slice and $mN \neq -1$

$$q = 2[(m-1)(1 - \cos\theta_w)\pi + (2-m)\theta_w]$$

$$\times \left\{ \frac{\gamma M(N-2)}{\rho(mN+1)} R_1^{2m+1} \left[\frac{R^{mN+1} - 1}{R^{m(N-2)} - 1} \right] + \frac{(N-2)(\sigma_{r2}R_2^{mN} - \sigma_{r1}R_1^{mN})}{\rho[R_2^{m(N-2)} - R_1^{m(N-2)}]} \right\}^{1/2} \tag{5.58}$$

and for $mN = -1$

$$q = 2[(m-1)(1-\cos\theta_w)\pi + (2-m)\theta_w]$$

$$\times \left[\frac{1+2m}{\rho m} \frac{(\sigma_{r2}R_1 - \sigma_{r1}R_2)(R_1 R_2)^{2m} + \gamma M(R_1 R_2)^{1+2m}\ln R}{R_2^{1+2m} - R_1^{1+2m}} \right]^{1/2} \tag{5.59}$$

In the case of a plane slice, the expressions for the volume flow rate in a dilatant or contractant flow contain integrals whose solutions are expressed in terms of an infinite series. They become much simpler if a cylindrical or spherical slice is selected; if $mN + n \neq -1$, then

$$q = 2[(m-1)(1-\cos\theta_w)\pi + (2-m)\theta_w]$$

$$\times \left\{ \frac{\gamma(mN - 2m - n)}{\rho(m+n)} \left(\frac{M R_1^{2m+2n+1}}{mN + n + 1} \left[\frac{R^{mN+n+1} - 1}{R^{mN-2m-n} - 1} \right] \right. \right.$$

$$\left. \left. + \frac{\sigma_{r2}R_2^{mN} - \sigma_{r1}R_1^{mN}}{B(R_2^{mN-2m-n} - R_1^{mN-2m-n})} \right) \right\}^{1/2} \tag{5.60}$$

and if $mN + n = -1$

$$q = 2[(m-1)(1-\cos\theta_w)\pi + (2-m)\theta_w]$$

$$\times \left\{ \frac{\gamma(1+2m+2n)}{\rho B(m+n)} \left[\frac{(\sigma_{r2}R_1^{1+n} - \sigma_{r1}R_2^{1+n})(R_1 R_2)^{2m+n}}{R_2^{1+2m+2n} - R_1^{1+2m+2n}} \right. \right.$$

$$\left. \left. + \frac{BM(R_1 R_2)^{1+2m+2n}\ln R}{R_2^{1+2m+2n} - R_1^{1+2m+2n}} \right] \right\}^{1/2} \tag{5.61}$$

Figure 5.7a demonstrates the influence of the constant K on the dimensionless volume flow rate $q/[4b^2\sqrt{(2bg)}]$ for incompressible flow in conical hoppers of various half-included angles θ_w and a constant ratio $B = (R_2 - R_1)/2b = 5$; $2b = 2R_1\sin\theta_w$ is the dimension of the outlet. Figure 5.7b depicts the influence of the wall friction angle φ_w; here a constant ratio $\sigma_r/\sigma_n = \tan\varphi_w/K = 0.35$ is assumed, and the spherical slice and the stress-free boundary conditions are selected. It is seen from Figures 5.7a and 5.7b that the flow rate decreases with increasing angle θ_w, i.e., with hopper walls that are less steep. This result agrees with the experimental observations (cf. Williams, 1977, Nguyen, Brennen and Sabersky, 1979). Also, the flow rate is lower for a higher angle φ_w and higher K. However, as the constant K may vary with angles φ_w and θ_w, the above results are merely an illustration of some particular cases.

5.3 CLOSING REMARKS

In the direct method of differential slices, incorporating inertial effects into a steady flow is relatively simple, provided the kinematical approach is used. The differential equations governing the variation of vertical or radial stress contain an additional

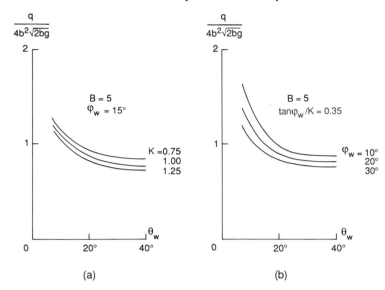

Figure 5.7 *Rate of volume flow of an incompressible material in a conical hopper, (a) influence of K and (b) influence of φ_w*

term due to inertial forces. Although in the present analysis only particular velocity fields were considered, there is virtually no limitation to the form of these fields. This equally applies to the flow in bins and hoppers. For example, a continuously dilating or contracting velocity field can be assumed for the flow in a bin, which in turn will result in non-zero inertial forces. Also, any variation of the velocity across a slice is admissible. However, the selection of a complex velocity field may not be justified in view of the lack of coupling between the velocities, or rather the resulting strain-rates, and the stresses predicted by a constitutive law. As demonstrated by Savage and Sayed (1979), a physically sounder coupled approach leads inevitably to a complex set of governing equations. This also has been shown by Spink and Nedderman (1978), who considered an inertial steady flow through a plane hopper in the presence of gas filtration. It should be remembered, however, that any coupled approach in the direct method of slices retains the approximations involved in this method. Since average rather than local stresses are considered, it is not possible to make proper use of a local constitutive law.

The results pertaining to incompressible flow through a hopper indicate that, with respect to quasi-static flow, the inertial forces reduce the wall stresses. This is not surprising, since the accelerations increase towards the outlet. The magnitude of wall stresses and the rate of flow strongly depend on the boundary conditions selected at the upper and outlet levels. Since both velocity and stress boundary conditions can be chosen there, a more realistic modeling of discharge can be incorporated into the analysis. With an increase of outlet boundary stresses the wall stresses also increase. At the limit, if the boundary stresses were set equal to those corresponding to the quasi-static solution, there would be no difference between inertial and quasi-static stress distribution. In fact, the differential equations governing quasi-static and inertial flow differ by one term which is dependent on variable y or r. The solution to both equations is identical, providing equal boundary conditions are set. It also can be shown that if mixed-type boundary conditions are selected, the resulting stress distribution would be located between a quasi-static distribution and an inertial one with stress-free conditions. Setting arbitrarily high velocities at the outlet, we obtain tensile vertical or radial stresses that are inadmissible. The above results are not affected by the shape of the slice, whether plane or circular, nor by the geometry of the hopper, whether plane or conical.

Other solutions to inertial steady flow were presented by Savage (1965), Mróz and Szymański (1971b), Davidson and Nedderman (1973), Brennen and Pearce (1978), Williams (1977), Nguyen, Brennen and Sabersky (1979), and Meric and Tabarrok, (1982). In these solutions, various approximation and perturbation methods were utilized to solve the equations of motion. Their main objective was to determine the rate of flow.

6 BIN-LOADS IN UNSTEADY INERTIAL MASS FLOW

6.1 INTRODUCTION

The discharge of bulk materials from bins and hoppers, whether free gravitational or controlled by a receiving assembly, is rarely accompanied by a simultaneous supply of material from above. As a result, the upper surface of the material moves downward as the material is drawn from the bin or hopper. In such a process, the velocities of particles may vary not only with location, but also with time. A *transient* or *unsteady* inertial flow takes place, as opposed to the steady flow considered in Chapter 5, where the velocities were assumed to be constant with time.

In this chapter, we will present some solutions to the process of unsteady inertial mass flow from bins and hoppers that illustrate the differences with respect to steady processes. The analysis will make use of the direct method of differential slices, and only the passive state will be considered. All other assumptions regarding the material model that were used in the preceding chapters will remain in effect.

6.2 DIRECT METHOD OF SLICES SOLUTIONS

In analyzing unsteady inertial flow by the direct method of slices, the only difference with respect to steady flow results from additional acceleration, and thus inertial force, due to the change of the velocities with time, i.e., due to non-zero local time derivatives of the velocities. However, this difference is essential, as the variation of the velocities with time cannot, in general, be specified beforehand even if the kinematical approach discussed in Chapter 5 is adopted. The variation of the velocities with time is to be found from the solution unless the problem is trivialized by postulating this variation beforehand. In addition to adopting a kinematical approach, we will also assume that at the onset of discharge all the material occupying a bin or hopper begins to flow simultaneously. In other words, a gradual flow spreading upward from the outlet (cf. Bransby and Blair-Fish, 1975), or propagation of dilatancy waves which may occur in dense materials (cf. Cowin and Comfort, 1982), is disregarded.

6.2.1 Stresses and Rate of Incompressible Flow in Bins

Assuming that in unsteady flow in a bin the velocities of particles remain vertical and spatially constant, we observe that their variation in time will produce accelerations that are equal for every particle flowing downward. For a plane bin the velocity field is given by

$$v_x = 0 \qquad v_y = v_y(t) \tag{6.1}$$

and for a cylindrical bin by

$$v_x = 0 \qquad v_y = v_y(t) \qquad v_\omega = 0 \tag{6.2}$$

For velocity fields (6.1) or (6.2) that are independent of spatial coordinates, the volume of the material that flows in a given time interval $\Delta t = t - t_0$ through any horizontal cross-section is

$$V_1 = 2b \int_{t_0}^{t} v_y(\tau)\, d\tau \tag{6.3}$$

for a plane bin of width $2b$, and

$$V_1 = \pi b^2 \int_{t_0}^{t} v_y(\tau)\, d\tau \tag{6.4}$$

for a cylindrical bin of radius b. For a spatially constant flow given by (6.1) or (6.2), volume V_1 equals the volume enclosed between the initial position of the upper surface, $h(t_0)$, and the current location, $h(t)$ (Figure 6.1a). Denoting this volume by V_2, we have

$$V_2 = 2b[h(t) - h(t_0)] \tag{6.5}$$

for a plane bin, and

$$V_2 = \pi b^2[h(t) - h(t_0)] \tag{6.6}$$

for a cylindrical bin. The continuity of flow requires not only $V_1 = V_2$, but also equality of their time increments

$$\frac{dV_1}{dt} = \frac{dV_2}{dt} \tag{6.7}$$

Differentiating (6.3), (6.4), (6.5), and (6.6) with respect to time, and using (6.7), we arrive at an obvious result

$$v_y(t) = \frac{dh(t)}{dt} \tag{6.8}$$

The accelerations resulting from velocity field (6.1) or (6.2), and (6.8), are given only by the local time derivative of the material time derivative of velocity

$$a_y = \frac{\partial v_y(t)}{\partial t} = \frac{d^2 h}{dt^2} \tag{6.9}$$

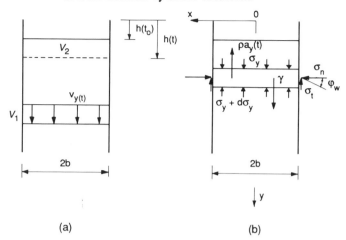

Figure 6.1   *(a) Unsteady incompressible flow in a bin and (b) stresses acting on a slice*

where $h = h(t)$. Accelerations a_y, constant for all particles, produce spatially constant inertial forces ρa_y.

Once the inertial forces are known, the equilibrium in the y-direction of all forces acting on a slice gives the following equation for a plane bin (Figure 6.1b)

$$\frac{d\sigma_y}{dy} + \frac{\sigma_t}{b} - \gamma + \rho\frac{d^2h}{dt^2} = 0 \qquad (6.10)$$

and for a cylindrical bin

$$\frac{d\sigma_y}{dy} + \frac{2\sigma_t}{b} - \gamma + \rho\frac{d^2h}{dt^2} = 0 \qquad (6.11)$$

Equations (6.10) and (6.11) can be written as one equation, if a pure number $m = 1$ for a plane bin, and $m = 2$ for a cylindrical bin is used

$$\frac{d\sigma_y}{dy} + \frac{m\sigma_t}{b} - \gamma + \rho\frac{d^2h}{dt^2} = 0 \qquad (6.12)$$

Retaining the assumption that the stresses σ_y, σ_n, and σ_t are interrelated by (see [5.15])

$$\sigma_t = K\sigma_y$$
$$\sigma_n = \sigma_t \cot \varphi_w \qquad (6.13)$$

we can write equation (6.12) as

$$\frac{d\sigma_y}{dy} + \frac{mK}{b}\sigma_y - \gamma + \rho\frac{d^2h}{dt^2} = 0 \qquad (6.14)$$

With respect to σ_y, equation (6.14) is linear, with the solution

$$\sigma_y = \exp\left(-\frac{mK}{b}y\right)\left\{\frac{b}{mK}\left[\gamma - \rho\frac{d^2h}{dt^2}\right]\exp\left(\frac{mK}{b}y\right) + C\right\} \qquad (6.15)$$

Solution (6.15) contains two unknown functions of time, $h = h(t)$ and $C = C(t)$, which can be determined from the boundary conditions and initial conditions. Mixed-type boundary conditions can be selected as

$$y = h(t) \qquad \sigma_y = \sigma_{yh}(t)$$
$$y = H \qquad v_y = v_y(t) \tag{6.16}$$

or

$$y = h(t) \qquad v_y = v_y(t)$$
$$y = H \qquad \sigma_y = \sigma_{yH}(t) \tag{6.17}$$

Alternatively, stresses can be specified at both surfaces of the material

$$y = h(t) \qquad \sigma_y = \sigma_{yh}(t)$$
$$y = H \qquad \sigma_y = \sigma_{yH}(t) \tag{6.18}$$

with

$$\sigma_{yh} = \sigma_{yH} = 0 \tag{6.19}$$

for a free gravitational discharge. Note that selecting mixed-type boundary conditions with specified function $v_y(t)$ renders the problem trivial, as the accelerations and thus the inertial forces are directly known. In particular, if $v_y(t)=$const, the problem becomes quasi-static with varying height of the material. However, if we consider a bin as an upper part of a bin/hopper structure, then the velocity at the bottom of the bin section will result from the solution of flow in a hopper.

For free gravitational discharge with boundary conditions (6.19), function $C = C(t)$ is given by

$$C = \frac{b}{mK}\left[\rho\frac{d^2h}{dt^2} - \gamma\right]\exp\left(\frac{mK}{b}H\right) \tag{6.20}$$

and the function $h = h(t)$ is given by the following second-order differential equation

$$\frac{d^2h}{dt^2} = g \tag{6.21}$$

where g is the acceleration of gravity. Selecting the initial conditions as

$$t = t_0 \qquad h = h_0 \qquad v_y = 0 \tag{6.22}$$

on integrating (6.21) we obtain

$$h = g\frac{t^2}{2} + h_0 \tag{6.23}$$

which, in view of (6.1) or (6.2), corresponds to free fall of the material as a rigid block. Substituting (6.21) into (6.20) we have

$$C = 0 \tag{6.24}$$

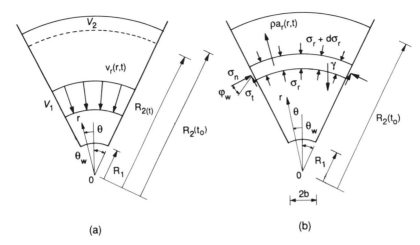

(a)   (b)

Figure 6.2   *(a) Radial unsteady incompressible flow in a hopper and*
(b) stresses acting on a slice

and the vertical average stress σ_y becomes

$$\sigma_y = 0 \tag{6.25}$$

Thus, no stresses are induced in the material and no stresses act at the walls. Non-zero stresses will occur if mixed-type boundary conditions are assumed or the bin is connected with a hopper.

6.2.2 Stresses and Rate of Incompressible Flow in Hoppers

The analysis of unsteady inertial flow in a hopper will be limited to a velocity field that is radial, depends on the r-coordinate only, and is incompressible. Solution to this problem was given by Wol-Gajewska (1978).

The velocity field for a plane hopper is given by

$$v_r = v_r(r,t) \qquad v_\theta = 0 \tag{6.26}$$

and for a conical hopper by

$$v_r = v_r(r,t) \qquad v_\theta = 0 \qquad v_\omega = 0 \tag{6.27}$$

As in bin flow, lowering of the upper surface of the material can be related to the volume of the material flowing downward in a time interval $\Delta t = t - t_0$. To preserve the problem as spatially one-dimensional, the shape of the upper surface must remain, however, geometrically similar. It is imperative, therefore, to select the upper surface for a plane hopper as a portion of a cylindrical surface, and for a conical hopper as a portion of a spherical surface (Figure 6.2a). In other words, there is a coupling between the shape of the upper surface and the velocity field assumed. This is a significant difference with respect to steady inertial mass flow, where the velocity field and the shape of the upper surface are uncoupled.

The volume of the material that flows through any cylindrical cross-section is

$$V_1 = -2 \int_{t_0}^{t} \int_{0}^{\theta_w} r v_r(r, \tau) d\theta d\tau = -2r\theta_w \int_{t_0}^{t} v_r(r, \tau) d\tau \tag{6.28}$$

and through a spherical cross-section is

$$V_1 = -2\pi \int_{t_0}^{t} \int_{0}^{\theta_w} r^2 \sin\theta\, v_r(r, \tau) d\theta d\tau = -2\pi r^2 (1 - \cos\theta_w) \int_{t_0}^{t} v_r(r, \tau) d\tau \tag{6.29}$$

Lowering of the upper surface yields

$$V_2 = 2 \int_{0}^{\theta_w} \int_{0}^{R_2(t_0)} r dr d\theta - 2 \int_{0}^{\theta_w} \int_{0}^{R_2(t)} r dr d\theta = \theta_w \left[R_2^2(t_0) - R_2^2(t) \right] \tag{6.30}$$

for a plane hopper, and

$$V_2 = 2\pi \int_{0}^{\theta_w} \int_{0}^{R_2(t_0)} r^2 \sin\theta\, dr d\theta - 2\pi \int_{0}^{\theta_w} \int_{0}^{R_2(t)} r^2 \sin\theta\, dr d\theta$$

$$= \frac{2\pi}{3} (1 - \cos\theta_w) \left[R_2^3(t) - R_2^3(t) \right] \tag{6.31}$$

for a conical hopper. Differentiating (6.28), (6.29), (6.30), and (6.31) with respect to time, and using (6.7), which still holds, we obtain the following expressions for the radial velocity in a plane and conical hopper, respectively

$$v_r(r, t) = \frac{R_2(t)}{r} \frac{dR_2(t)}{dt}$$

$$v_r(r, t) = \frac{R_2^2(t)}{r^2} \frac{dR_2(t)}{dt} \tag{6.32}$$

and since $dR_2(t)/dt < 0$ the velocity points downward. Using the pure number m defined in Section 6.2.1, we can write equations (6.32) as

$$v_r(r, t) = \frac{R_2^m}{r^m} \frac{dR_2}{dt} \tag{6.33}$$

where $R_2 = R_2(t)$. The acceleration $a_r = a_r(r, t)$ in unsteady inertial flow is given by both the local and the convective part of the material time derivative of velocity

$$a_r = \frac{Dv_r}{Dt} = \frac{\partial v_r}{\partial t} + v_r \frac{\partial v_r}{\partial r}$$

$$= \frac{m}{r} \left[\frac{dR_2}{dt} \right]^2 \left\{ \left[\frac{R_2}{r} \right]^{m-1} - \left[\frac{R_2}{r} \right]^{2m} \right\} + \left[\frac{R_2}{r} \right]^m \frac{d^2 R_2}{dt^2} \tag{6.34}$$

Because the shape of the upper surface is either cylindrical or spherical, the only admissible shape of a slice is also cylindrical or spherical, respectively. The equilibrium in the vertical direction of all forces acting on a slice gives, for a plane hopper (Figure 6.2b),

$$\frac{d\sigma_r}{dr} + \frac{1}{r}(\sigma_r - \sigma_n - \sigma_t \cot\theta_w) + \frac{\gamma\theta_w}{\sin\theta_w} + \frac{\rho}{r}\left[\frac{dR_2}{dt}\right]^2\left\{1 - \left[\frac{R_2}{r}\right]^2\right\}$$

$$+ \frac{\rho}{r}R_2\frac{d^2R_2}{dt^2} = 0 \tag{6.35}$$

and for a conical hopper

$$\frac{d\sigma_r}{dr} + \frac{2}{r}(\sigma_r - \sigma_n - \sigma_t \cot\theta_w) + \frac{2\gamma}{1+\cos\theta_w} + \frac{2\rho}{r}\left[\frac{dR_2}{dt}\right]^2\left\{\frac{R_2}{r} - \left[\frac{R_2}{r}\right]^4\right\}$$

$$+ \rho\left[\frac{R_2}{r}\right]^2\frac{d^2R_2}{dt^2} = 0 \tag{6.36}$$

Utilizing equations (6.13) that relate stresses σ_r, σ_n, and σ_t and the pure number m, we write equations (6.35) and (6.36) as

$$\frac{d\sigma_r}{dr} + mN\frac{\sigma_r}{r} + \gamma M + \frac{m\rho}{r}\left[\frac{dR_2}{dt}\right]^2\left\{\left[\frac{R_2}{r}\right]^{m-1} - \left[\frac{R_2}{r}\right]^{2m}\right\}$$

$$+ \rho\left[\frac{R_2}{r}\right]^m\frac{d^2R_2}{dt^2} = 0 \tag{6.37}$$

where N and M are given by

$$N = 1 - K(\cot\varphi_w + \cot\theta_w)$$
$$M = (2-m)\frac{\theta_w}{\sin\theta_w} - (1-m)\frac{2}{1+\cos\theta_w} \tag{6.38}$$

With respect to σ_r, equation (6.37) is linear, with the solution

$$\sigma_r = -\frac{\rho r^{1-m}}{m(N-1)+1}\left\{mR_2^{m-1}\left[\frac{dR_2}{dt}\right]^2 + R_2^m\frac{d^2R_2}{dt^2}\right\}$$

$$+ \frac{\rho R_2^{2m}r^{-2m}}{N-2}\left[\frac{dR_2}{dt}\right]^2 - \frac{\gamma Mr}{mN+1} + Cr^{-mN} \tag{6.39}$$

if $mN \neq -1$, and $m(N-1) \neq -1$ (see comment to equation [5.18]). The two unknown functions of time, $R_2 = R_2(t)$ and $C = C(t)$, can be determined from the boundary conditions specified at R_1 and R_2, and from the initial conditions at $t = 0$. Mixed-type boundary conditions are

$$\begin{array}{ll} r = R_1 & v_r = v_r(t) \\ r = R_2(t) & \sigma_r = \sigma_{r2}(t) \end{array} \tag{6.40}$$

$$r = R_1 \qquad \sigma_r = \sigma_{r1}(t)$$
$$r = R_2(t) \qquad v_r = v_r(t) \tag{6.41}$$

and stress boundary conditions are

$$r = R_1 \qquad \sigma_r = \sigma_{r1}(t)$$
$$r = R_2(t) \qquad \sigma_r = \sigma_{r2}(t) \tag{6.42}$$

For free gravitational discharge, where

$$\sigma_{r1} = \sigma_{r2} = 0 \tag{6.43}$$

function $C = C(t)$ is

$$C = -\frac{\rho R_2^{2m} R_1^{m(N-2)}}{N-2} \left[\frac{dR_2}{dt}\right]^2 + \frac{\gamma M R_1^{mN+1}}{mN+1}$$
$$+ \frac{\rho R_1^{m(N-1)+1}}{m(N-1)+1} \left\{ mR_2^{m-1} \left[\frac{dR_2}{dt}\right]^2 + R_2^m \frac{d^2 R_2}{dt^2} \right\} \tag{6.44}$$

whereas the function $R_2 = R_2(t)$ can be determined from the second-order differential equation

$$\frac{d^2 R_2}{dt^2} \frac{R_2}{m(N-1)+1} \left\{ 1 - \left[\frac{R_1}{R_2}\right]^{m(N-1)+1} \right\}$$
$$+ \left[\frac{dR_2}{dt}\right]^2 \left\{ \frac{m - m\left[\frac{R_1}{R_2}\right]^{m(N-1)+1}}{m(N-1)+1} - \frac{1 - \left[\frac{R_1}{R_2}\right]^{m(N-2)}}{N-2} \right\}$$
$$+ \frac{gM R_2}{mN+1} \left\{ 1 - \left[\frac{R_1}{R_2}\right]^{mN+1} \right\} = 0 \tag{6.45}$$

The solution to equation (6.45) cannot be found analytically, and a numerical method must be used. The initial conditions can be taken as

$$t = 0 \qquad R_2 = R_{20} \qquad \frac{dR_2}{dt} = 0 \tag{6.46}$$

If $mN = -1$, the solution to equation (6.37) is

$$\sigma_r = \frac{\rho r^{1-m}}{m} \left\{ mR_2^{m-1} \left[\frac{dR_2}{dt}\right]^2 + R_2^m \frac{d^2 R_2}{dt^2} \right\}$$
$$- \frac{\rho m R_2^{2m} r^{-2m}}{2m+1} \left[\frac{dR_2}{dt}\right]^2 - \gamma M r \ln r + Cr \tag{6.47}$$

and for boundary conditions (6.43), functions $C = C(t)$ and $R_2 = R_2(t)$ can be obtained from

$$C = -\frac{\rho R_1^{-m}}{m}\left\{mR_2^{m-1}\left[\frac{dR_2}{dt}\right]^2 + R_2^m\frac{d^2R_2}{dt^2}\right\}$$

$$+ \frac{\rho m R_2^{2m} R_1^{-(2m+1)}}{2m+1}\left[\frac{dR_2}{dt}\right]^2 + \gamma M \ln R_1 \tag{6.48}$$

$$\frac{d^2R_2}{dt^2}\frac{R_2}{m}\left\{\left[\frac{R_2}{R_1}\right]^m - 1\right\} + \left[\frac{dR_2}{dt}\right]^2$$

$$\times \left\{\frac{m}{2m+1}\left(1 - \left[\frac{R_2}{R_1}\right]^{2m+1}\right) + \left[\frac{R_2}{R_1}\right]^m - 1\right\} + gMR_2\ln\frac{R_2}{R_1} = 0 \tag{6.49}$$

If $m(N-1) = -1$, and boundary conditions (6.43) hold, then

$$\sigma_r = -\rho r^{1-m}\ln r\left\{mR_2^{m-1}\left[\frac{dR_2}{dt}\right]^2 + R_2^m\frac{d^2R_2}{dt^2}\right\}$$

$$- \frac{\rho m}{m+1}R_2^{2m}r^{-2m}\left[\frac{dR_2}{dt}\right]^2 - \frac{\gamma M}{m}r + Cr^{1-m} \tag{6.50}$$

$$C = \rho\ln R_1\left\{mR_2^{m-1}\left[\frac{dR_2}{dt}\right]^2 + R_2^m\frac{d^2R_2}{dt^2}\right\}$$

$$+ \frac{\rho m}{m+1}R_2^{2m}R_1^{-m-1}\left[\frac{dR_2}{dt}\right]^2 + \frac{\gamma M}{m}R_1^m \tag{6.51}$$

$$\frac{d^2R_2}{dt^2}R_2\ln\frac{R_2}{R_1} + \left[\frac{dR_2}{dt}\right]^2\left\{\ln\frac{R_2}{R_1} + \frac{m}{m+1}\left(1 - \left[\frac{R_2}{R_1}\right]^{m+1}\right)\right\}$$

$$- \frac{gM}{m}R_2\left\{\left[\frac{R_2}{R_1}\right]^m - 1\right\} = 0 \tag{6.52}$$

Due to the non-analytical form of the solutions for radial stress σ_r, the wall stresses σ_n and σ_t also cannot be expressed in a closed form. Thus only an example is given in which the second-order differential equation for $R_2 = R_2(t)$ was solved numerically. The following parameters were selected: $\theta_w = 30°$, $\varphi_w = 20°$, $K = 0.75$, and $R_{20}/R_1 = 4$, where R_{20} is the initial outer radius. Stress boundary conditions (6.42), (6.43) and initial conditions (6.46) were also assumed. The dimensionless radial and wall stresses are plotted in Figure 6.3 as a function of the dimensionless radius r/R_{20} and dimensionless time $t\sqrt{(g/R_1)}$. It is interesting to compare this solution with the solution of steady flow, in which the upper surface is

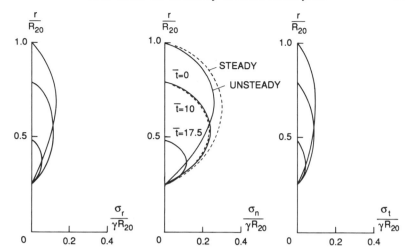

Figure 6.3   *Stress distributions in unsteady inertial flow in a conical hopper;* $\theta_w = 30°$, $\varphi_w = 20°$, $K = 0.75$, $R_{20}/R_1 = 4$

assumed to coincide with the current location in unsteady flow. As shown in Figure 6.3, the difference is significant only in the initial stage of flow; approximation by the steady flow gives higher stresses.

An important result that cannot be obtained directly from the steady-state solution pertains to the duration of discharge and change in velocities with which the bulk material flows through a hopper with time. The total time of discharge can be calculated as the difference in time between the onset of flow and the instant when $R_2(t) = R_1$. Figure 6.4a shows the variation of the location of the upper surface with time. When $R_2/R_1 = 1$, the flow ends. The change in dimensionless flow velocity at the outlet, $v_r/\sqrt{(gR_1)}$, with time is presented in Figure 6.4b. It is clearly seen that at the beginning of flow the velocity rapidly increases, which is followed by a nearly constant flow velocity regime. At the end of discharge, the velocity slightly decreases, though it remains greater than zero. Since volume discharge is proportional to velocity, Figure 6.4b also illustrates the change in the rate of flow. The result above is in agreement with the well-known experimental finding that the rate of discharge remains virtually independent of the height of the material occupying the hopper (cf. Ketchum, 1929, Brown and Richards, 1959, Beverloo, Leniger and van de Velde, 1961, Nedderman, Tüzün, Savage and Houlsby, 1982). The dashed line in Figure 6.4b shows the variation of the flow velocity when unsteady flow is approximated by a sequence of steady flow solutions with varying location of the upper surface. It is seen that this approximation overestimates the velocities only at the beginning of flow.

6.3. CLOSING REMARKS

In spite of the approximations involved, the direct method of slices combined with the kinematical approach provides a means for analyzing wall stresses during un-

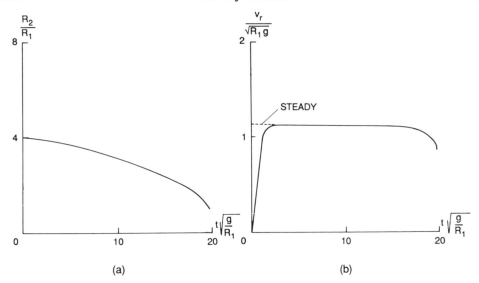

Figure 6.4   *(a) Location of the upper surface and (b) velocity at the outlet with time; conical hopper, $\theta_w = 30°$, $\varphi_w = 20°$, $K = 0.75$, $R_{20}/R_1 = 4$*

steady discharge from bins and hoppers. Although the results for the flow in bins might seem unrealistic, they were presented merely to illustrate the method.

For the flow in hoppers, the method predicts acceptable results for both the wall stresses and the rate of flow. On the other hand, approximation of unsteady discharge by a sequence of steady flow solutions introduces a significant error only in the initial phase of flow. The wall stresses and the velocity of discharge so obtained are greater than those predicted by the unsteady solution, with the difference rapidly decreasing in the course of discharge. A nearly constant rate of flow over a significant time period of discharge process agrees well with the experimental finding that the rate of discharge remains virtually independent of the height of the material occupying a hopper.

The discussion was limited to incompressible flow separately in bins and hoppers. It is possible, however, to consider storage structures with a lower portion sloping towards the outlet; then, the stresses in the bin section no longer are zero.

7 ARCHING

7.1 INTRODUCTION

In this chapter, we will present methods that can be used for analyzing formation of arches and domes during drawdown of bulk materials from bins and hoppers. The arches or domes can form in both mass- and funnel-flow storage structures, and their shape varies from shallow, nearly circular, to deep, parabolic-type arches. Arching can occur only if the strength of the bulk material adjacent to the exposed surface of an arch or dome is high enough to sustain stresses that develop due to the weight of the material. The strength of the bulk material depends on stresses that act prior to or during discharge, since arching is observed either upon first opening the outlet, or at some stage of flow. These stresses may consolidate the initially loose material and increase its strength. Since the consolidating stresses, and the stresses that develop above an arch or dome depend, among other factors, on the geometry of a bin or hopper, by appropriate selection of their geometry arching can be avoided. In particular, a sufficiently large outlet will cause arches or domes to collapse. The other factors that affect arching are the mechanical properties of the bulk material and the conditions that exist at the material/wall interface. An expression for the size of the critical outlet that separates arching from uninterrupted flow as a function of the geometry of the bin or hopper and the mechanical parameters of the bulk material can be called the *arching criterion*.

In terms of plastic models, the strength of bulk materials is characterized by the yield condition (Figure 7.1). The yield condition that characterizes flowing material is the effective yield condition. On the other hand, whenever the material ceases to move, and stresses change, further deformation requires the stresses to overcome the instantaneous yield condition. It is apparent that, if arching does occur, the stress state that exists next to the exposed surface of an arch or dome must differ from that during a storage or discharge phase. In fact, next to the exposed free surface the stress state can be, at most, biaxial (Figure 7.1), whereas at the same location during a flow or storage phase the state of stress is triaxial. Thus, arching is associated with redistribution of stresses, and occurs when the biaxial state of stress is located below the instantaneous yield condition, which is a function of the consolidating stresses. In our further discussion we will assume instantaneous yield condition (2.33), with cohesion c and angle of internal friction

ϕ being, in general, functions of the consolidating stress. Accordingly, the biaxial strength equals the uniaxial compressive strength S_c, and the latter can be regarded as a measure of the strength of an arch or dome.

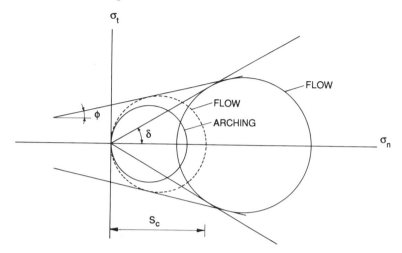

Figure 7.1 *State of stress at arching*

A rigorous analysis of the redistribution of stresses that takes place when flow is interrupted by arching is not possible within the available analytical methods for the rigid-perfectly plastic model. One must resort, therefore, to approximate analyses that render the problem tractable. In this chapter, we will discuss two approaches: the structural mechanics approach and the continuum mechanics approach. Both simplify the analysis by separately considering the strength of the bulk material that may develop once arching occurs, and the state of stress that exists next to an arch or dome. Further, our attention will be focused on arching in hoppers, since it occurs predominantly in storage structures with converging walls.

The structural mechanics approach is due to Jenike and Leser (1963). Modified versions have been suggested by Walker (1966), Mróz and Szymański (1971a), and Arnold and McLean (1976a, 1976b). The continuum mechanics approach can be found in works of Mróz and Drescher (1969) and Enstad (1975, 1981).

7.2. STRUCTURAL MECHANICS APPROACH

In the structural mechanics approach, an arch or dome is regarded as a structural member loaded exclusively by its own weight. Thus, the interaction between the material above an arch and the material within the arch modeling member is disregarded. This is equivalent to subdividing the material into a stack of arches or domes, each carrying its own weight (Figure 7.2). Next, the state of stress within the structural member is determined from assumptions regarding its shape and conditions that exist at the contact of the member and the walls of a bin or hopper. In general, the geometry of the structural member and the conditions at abutments are selected so as to make the stresses acting in the member statically determinate. Thus, the material properties, other than its unit weight, do not enter the derivation of stresses within the structural member.

Once the stresses acting in the structural member are determined, they are then compared with the strength of the material building an arch or dome. The strength of the material is found experimentally as a function of stresses that developed during the handling phase preceding arching. If this strength is greater than the stresses in the arch, then arching may occur. If the opposite holds, the arch or dome will collapse. Since neither the stresses nor the strength are necessarily constant along the structural member, the location of a point in the member at which such a comparison is performed must be selected. The most critical location corresponds to the point where the strength is the greatest and the stress acting in the member reaches a minimum. Since both the stresses in the structural member and the strength of the material can be related to the dimension of an arch or dome, the dimension of a critical outlet that prevents arching can eventually be found.

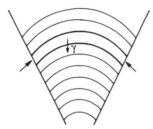

Figure 7.2   *Stack of arches in a plane hopper*

The differences between the results obtained by Jenike and Leser (1963), Walker (1966), and Mróz and Szymański (1971a), are due to the different shape of the structural member considered, and different solutions for the consolidating stresses assumed by these authors. To explain these differences in detail we first will outline the approach suggested by Jenike and Leser, beginning with the distribution of consolidating stresses.

The distribution of consolidating stresses assumed by Jenike and Leser is that corresponding to the passive vertex radial stress field (see Section 4.2). Although this solution is strictly valid only for an infinitely tall hopper, it closely approximates the distribution in a hopper with finite height in the vicinity of its vertex. Next, it is postulated that consolidation is governed exclusively by the major principal stress σ_1, which for the vertex radial stress field reaches a maximum along the walls of the hopper. Thus, the abutment of the structural member is selected as a point at which the comparison between the stress and strength is made. The major principal stress at this point can be expressed as

$$\sigma_1 = \gamma r f(\delta, \theta_w, \varphi_w) \tag{7.1}$$

and is a linear function of the radius r measured along the wall. Alternatively, using the relation between the radius r and the half-width of a hopper b

$$b = r \sin \theta_w \tag{7.2}$$

we can write expression (7.1) as

$$\sigma_1 = \gamma b g(\delta, \theta_w, \varphi_w) \tag{7.3}$$

The relation between the consolidating stress σ_1 and the uniaxial compressive strength S_c of the bulk material is determined experimentally (see Section 2.6).

Jenike and Leser derive rather than postulate the shape of the structural member by considering its equilibrium. Consider first a plane hopper of unit length in the direction normal to the plane of Figure 7.3. The mass of bulk material occupying the hopper is subdivided into a stack of elemental arches with their upper and lower surfaces matching the adjacent arches. In the polar coordinate system r, θ the shape of bounding arch surfaces is thus given by a function

$$r = p f(\theta) \tag{7.4}$$

where p is a parameter, and the function $f(\theta)$ is assumed to be smooth and symmetrical with respect to the vertical axis. For a given magnitude of the parameter p, equation (7.4) defines a curve, which makes an angle Ω with the ray r (Figure 7.3)

$$\tan \Omega = \frac{r}{dr/d\theta} \tag{7.5}$$

Differentiating (7.4) with θ =const, we obtain

$$dr = dp f(\theta) \tag{7.6}$$

and combining (7.4) and (7.6) we have

$$\frac{dr}{r} = \frac{dp}{p} \tag{7.7}$$

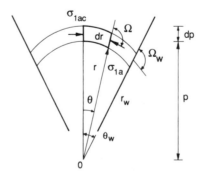

Figure 7.3 *Arch in a plane hopper*

Expression (7.7) relates the elemental thickness dr to the thickness dp at the crown of the arch. Each arch is in a biaxial state of stress, with the major compressive stress σ_{1a} acting along the arch, and the minor principal stress σ_{2a} acting perpendicularly to the plane of the arch. To derive an expression for the shape of the arch, we make use of the global equilibrium of a segment of an arch spanning angle θ. Global equilibrium requires that the weight of the segment is balanced by the vertical component of the stress σ_{1a} acting at the end of the segment. Thus

$$\gamma \int_0^\theta r\,dr\,dt = \sigma_{1a}dr \sin\Omega[-\cos(\theta+\Omega)] \tag{7.8}$$

and, using (7.7), we have

$$\sigma_{1a} = \frac{\gamma \int_0^\theta r^2 dt}{-r \sin\Omega \cos(\theta+\Omega)} \tag{7.9}$$

Further, the global equilibrium of the segment in the horizontal direction gives

$$\sigma_{1a}dr \sin\Omega \sin(\theta+\Omega) = \sigma_{1ac}dp \tag{7.10}$$

or

$$\sigma_{1a} = \frac{\sigma_{1ac}p}{r \sin\Omega \sin(\theta+\Omega)} \tag{7.11}$$

where σ_{1ac} is the principal stress σ_{1a} acting at the crown. Combining (7.9) and (7.11) we obtain

$$\sigma_{1ac}\frac{p}{\gamma}\cot(\theta+\Omega) + \int_0^\theta r^2 dt = 0 \tag{7.12}$$

For a given parameter p, the first part of the first term in (7.12) is a constant, A. Thus, equation (7.12) can be written as

$$A\cot(\theta+\Omega) + \int_0^\theta r^2 dt = 0 \tag{7.13}$$

which, differentiated with respect to θ, yields

$$\frac{d\Omega}{d\theta} = \frac{r^2}{A}\sin^2(\theta+\Omega) - 1 \tag{7.14}$$

Equations (7.5) and (7.14) can be used to determine $r(\theta, A)$ and $\Omega(\theta, A)$, which define the shape of the arch as a function of the constant A. The magnitude of the principal stress σ_{1a} can then be found from (7.11).

In the case of a conical hopper, the derivation is more complex, though it basically follows the analysis above. The shape of the dome can be found from (7.5) and the following equation

$$\frac{d\Omega}{d\theta} = -1 - \frac{\dfrac{r}{B} + \dfrac{\sin 2(\theta+\Omega)}{2\sin\theta}}{\cos(\theta+2\Omega)} \tag{7.15}$$

whereas the stress σ_{1a} appears to be constant along the dome, and is given by

$$\sigma_{1a} = \gamma B \qquad (7.16)$$

where B is a constant.

At the abutment of an arch or dome, (7.11) and (7.16) yield

$$\sigma_{1a} = \gamma b \frac{A}{r_w^2 \sin\theta_w \sin\Omega_w \sin(\theta_w + \Omega_w)}$$
$$\sigma_{1a} = \gamma b \frac{B}{r_w \sin\theta_w} \qquad (7.17)$$

Since Ω_w is a function of the angle θ_w, equations (7.17) can finally be written as

$$\sigma_{1a} = \gamma b f_1(\theta_w, A/r_w^2)$$
$$\sigma_{1a} = \gamma b f_2(\theta_w, B/r_w) \qquad (7.18)$$

and they define the major principal stresses acting at the abutments of an arch or dome in a plane and conical hopper, respectively. The smallest magnitude of these stresses is obtained by minimization of functions f_1 and f_2 with respect to parameters A/r_w^2 and B/r_w. Figure 7.4 shows functions f_1 and f_2 obtained numerically by Jenike and Leser (1963). Note that both functions depend exclusively on the half-included angle θ_w of the hopper. In other words, in the approach suggested by Jenike and Leser, the boundary conditions that exist at the walls of a hopper do not affect the stresses in an arch or dome.

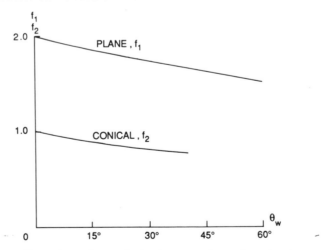

Figure 7.4   *Functions f_1 and f_2 in equations (7.18); (Jenike and Leser, 1963)*

Consider now how the solutions above can be used to derive the arching criterion. A mathematical expression for the arching criterion could only be derived if the uniaxial compressive strength S_c were expressed as a function of the consolidating stress σ_1. Then, by equating the uniaxial compressive strength S_c and the stress σ_{1a} acting in an arch or dome, both being a function of the span $2b$, a mathematical expression for the dimension of the critical outlet could be found. If, however, the dependence of the uniaxial compressive strength on the consolidating stress is taken directly from experiments, the only possiblity is to graphically compare S_c and σ_{1a}, e.g., by plotting their distributions along the height of the hopper. This is schematically shown in Figure 7.5. The intersection point of both distributions defines the dimension of the critical outlet. For outlets smaller than the critical one, the strength is greater than the stress in an arch or dome and arching may occur.

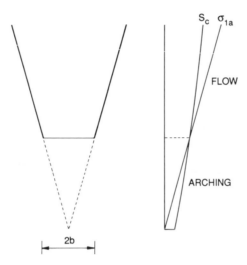

Figure 7.5   *Critical outlet dimension*

Jenike and Leser suggested a different graphical comparison. Their suggestion is based on the observation that the expressions for the consolidating stress σ_1, equation (7.3), and for stresses σ_{1a} in an arch or dome, equations (7.18), are linear functions of the span $2b$. Thus, their ratio is a constant for a given angle θ_w of the hopper, and given effective angle of friction δ and wall friction angle φ_w. This ratio is called the *flow-factor*, and is defined as

$$ff = \frac{\sigma_1}{\sigma_{1a}} \tag{7.19}$$

The flow-factor ff can actually be regarded as an approximate measure of the stress redistribution that takes place when flow is interrupted by arching. In a diagram where stress σ_{1a} is plotted against the stress σ_1, the inverse of the flow-factor is the slope of a straight line passing through the origin (Figure 7.6). The condition for arching is then

$$ff \geq \frac{\sigma_1}{S_c} \tag{7.20}$$

and can be evaluated graphically by plotting in the same diagram the experimentally determined function relating the uniaxial compressive strength S_c to the consolidating stress σ_1. The intersection point of both plots defines the critical stress

σ_{1a} that separates flow from arching; to the left of the intersection point $\sigma_{1a} < S_c$, and to the right, $\sigma_{1a} > S_c$. Using equations (7.18) and the diagrams presented in Figure 7.4, the dimension of the critical outlet can be found.

The introduction of the flow-factor makes it unnecessary to perform a separate evaluation of the consolidating stress σ_1, and the stresses σ_{1a} acting in an arch or dome. The shape of the arch that leads to the smallest magnitude of σ_{1a} is also of no importance. Accordingly, Jenike and Leser (1963), and Jenike (1964a), presented only graphs for the flow-factor in plane and conical hoppers; these graphs were obtained numerically. Figures 7.7 and 7.8 show examples of the contours of constant flow-factors for plane and conical hoppers, and for two effective angles of internal friction $\delta = 40°$ and $\delta = 50°$. The bounding dashed lines in Figures 7.7b and 7.8b limit the range of parameters θ_w and φ_w for which the solution for a radial stress field exists. According to Jenike (1964a), flow-factors for mass-flow in plane hoppers are located below the dotted lines in Figures 7.7a and 7.8a.

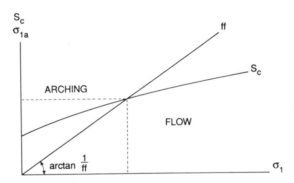

Figure 7.6 *Arching-no-arching condition*

Let us consider now the solutions presented by Walker (1966) and Mróz and Szymański (1971a). These authors simplify the analysis to arrive at analytical expressions for the flow-factor. Although the consolidating stresses σ_1 are again taken as those corresponding to the passive state in an infinitely tall hopper, they are evaluated from approximate solutions obtained by means of the direct method of slices. Walker selected plane slices, whereas Mróz and Szymański assumed cylindrical or spherical slices centered at the vertex. Furthermore, the stress that acts in an arch or dome is either evaluated from a simplified equilibrium consideration, or it is directly obtained from the postulated shape of the structural member. We will present the essential elements of this simplified approach here.

According to the derivations presented in Section 4.3.2, in an infinitely tall hopper the vertical stresses σ_y, or the radial stresses σ_r, are given by equations (4.86) and (4.87), respectively, i.e.,

$$\sigma_y = -\frac{\gamma y}{mN + 1}$$
$$\sigma_r = -\frac{\gamma M r}{mN + 1} \tag{7.21}$$

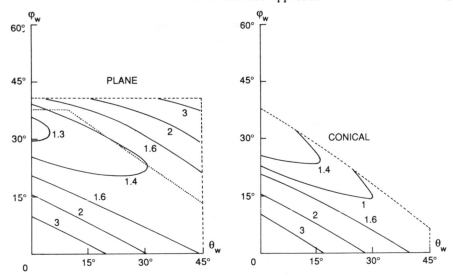

Figure 7.7   *Flow-factors for plane and conical hoppers; δ = 40° (Jenike, 1964a)*

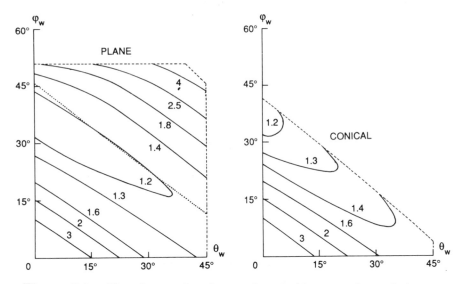

Figure 7.8   *Flow-factors for plane and conical hoppers; δ = 50° (Jenike, 1964a)*

where the constants m, M, and N are defined in Section 4.3.2. To relate the principal stresses σ_1 that act at the contact surface of a plane or cylindrical (spherical) slice and the wall of a hopper, to the vertical or radial stresses σ_y or σ_r, we make use of the geometrical representation of the stress state by Mohr's circle (Figure

4.20). It can thus be shown that

$$\sigma_1 = \frac{1 + \sin \delta}{1 - \sin \delta \cos(\omega + \varphi_w + 2\theta_w)}\sigma_y$$

$$\sigma_1 = \frac{1 + \sin \delta}{1 - \sin \delta \cos(\omega + \varphi_w)}\sigma_r \tag{7.22}$$

and ω is given by (3.33). Substituting (7.21) into (7.22), we obtain the following formulae for the consolidating stresses σ_1

$$\sigma_1 = -\frac{(1 + \sin \delta)\gamma y}{[1 - \sin \delta \cos(\omega + \varphi_w + 2\theta_w)](mN + 1)}$$

$$\sigma_1 = -\frac{(1 + \sin \delta)\gamma M r}{[1 - \sin \delta \cos(\omega + \varphi_w)](mN + 1)} \tag{7.23}$$

In a form analogous to (7.3), equations (7.23) can be written as

$$\sigma_1 = -\frac{\gamma b(1 + \sin \delta)}{\tan \theta_w[1 - \sin \delta \cos(\omega + \varphi_w + 2\theta_w)](mN + 1)}$$

$$\sigma_1 = -\frac{\gamma b(1 + \sin \delta)M}{\sin \theta_w[1 - \sin \delta \cos(\omega + \varphi_w)](mN + 1)} \tag{7.24}$$

Besides approximate solutions for the consolidating stresses σ_1, Walker, and Mróz and Szymański, introduced significant simplifications in the derivation of stresses acting in an arch or dome. The derivation suggested by Walker hinges on postulating the orientation of the maximum shear stresses that act at the abutment of the structural member modeling an arch or dome; this orientation is taken as vertical and horizontal. It follows, then, that the principal stress σ_{1a} is inclined at the angle $\psi = 135°$ with respect to the horizontal (Figure 7.9a). This is admissible, however, only if the friction that exists along the walls provides sufficient support. Thus, referring to Figure 7.9b

$$\begin{array}{llll} \psi = 135° & \text{if} & \theta_w \geq 45° - \varphi_w \\ \psi = 90° + \theta_w + \varphi_w & \text{if} & \theta_w < 45° - \varphi_w \end{array} \tag{7.25}$$

Assuming that the elemental height of the structural member is constant, from the global equilibrium in the vertical direction of the structural member we arrive at the following expressions for the stress σ_{1a}

$$\begin{array}{llll} \sigma_{1a} = \gamma b \dfrac{2}{m} & \text{if} & \theta_w \geq 45° - \varphi_w \\[2mm] \sigma_{1a} = \gamma b \dfrac{2}{m \sin 2(\theta_w + \varphi_w)} & \text{if} & \theta_w < 45° - \varphi_w \end{array} \tag{7.26}$$

where $m = 1$ for a plane hopper, and $m = 2$ for a conical hopper. It is apparent that the above expressions are much simpler than those derived by Jenike and Leser (1963), and they incorporate the frictional conditions at the walls of a hopper.

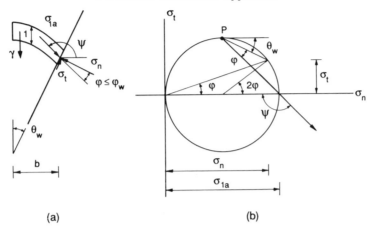

Figure 7.9 *(a) Orientation of principal stresses at the abutment of an arch and (b) Mohr's circle*

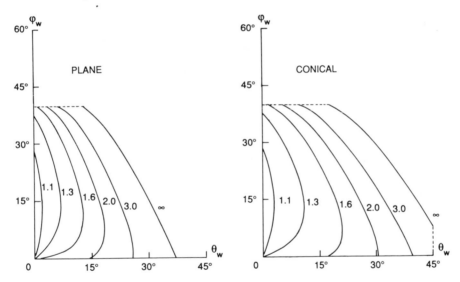

Figure 7.10 *Flow-factors for plane and conical hoppers; $\delta = 40°$ (equations [7.27])*

Although Walker arrives at a parabolic shape of the structural member, equations (7.26) hold for any shape of the member as long as its elemental height is kept constant.

Using definition (7.19) and equations (7.24)$_1$ and (7.26), we obtain the following expressions for the flow-factor

$$ff = -\frac{m(1 + \sin \delta)}{2 \tan \theta_w [1 - \sin \delta \cos(\omega + \varphi_w + 2\theta_w)](mN + 1)} \tag{7.27a}$$

if $\theta_{-v} \geq 45° - \varphi_w$, and

$$ff = -\frac{m \sin 2(\theta_w + \varphi_w)(1 + \sin \delta)}{2 \tan \theta_w [1 - \sin \delta \cos(\omega + \varphi_w + 2\theta_w)](mN + 1)} \tag{7.27b}$$

if $\theta_w < 45° - \varphi_w$.

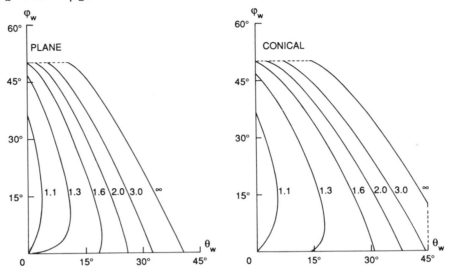

Figure 7.11 *Flow-factors for plane and conical hoppers; $\delta = 50°$ (equations [7.27])*

Figures 7.10 and 7.11 show contours of constant flow-factor values for plane and conical hoppers, respectively, for $\delta = 40°$ and $\delta = 50°$. The constant K appearing in the expression for N was determined from equation (4.109), i.e., the hypothesis of yielding at the walls was selected.

In the approach suggested by Mróz and Szymański (1971a), the expressions for the stress σ_{1a} are obtained by postulating the shape of the structural members beforehand. In the case of a plane hopper, Mróz and Szymański selected two simple members: a plane folded plate (Figure 7.12a), and a cylindrical arch of constant elemental thickness (Figure 7.12b). The unknown slope of the folded plate α is determined from the minimization of the principal stress σ_{1a} acting along the sides of the plate; this principal stress is found from the global equilibrium in the vertical direction, which gives

$$\sigma_{1a} = \gamma b \frac{2}{\sin 2\alpha} \tag{7.28}$$

and the minimum is reached at $\alpha = 45°$. From the frictional conditions along the walls (Figure 7.9b), the angle α cannot be greater than $\theta_w + \varphi_w$. Thus, the stress σ_{1a} is given by

$$\sigma_{1a} = 2\gamma b \qquad \text{if} \qquad \theta_w \geq 45° - \varphi_w$$

$$\sigma_{1a} = \gamma b \frac{2}{\sin 2(\theta_w + \varphi_w)} \qquad \text{if} \qquad \theta_w < 45° - \varphi_w \tag{7.29}$$

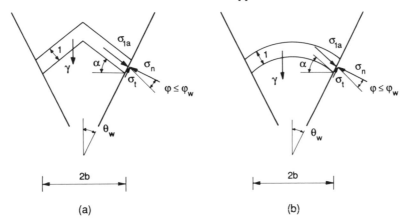

Figure 7.12   *An arch as (a) folded plate and (b) cylindrical shell*

and these equations are identical to those obtained by Walker (1966). Analogously, postulating a conical shell in the case of a conical hopper, we arrive at expressions that are identical to (7.26) with $m = 2$.

Considering the second type of member, i.e., a cylindrical arch, from the global equilibrium in the vertical direction we have

$$\sigma_{1a} = \gamma b \frac{\alpha}{\sin^2 \alpha} \tag{7.30}$$

and the minimum is reached at $\alpha \approx 67°$. Again using the frictional conditions at the wall of a hopper, we can finally write

$$\sigma_{1a} = 1.38 \gamma b \qquad \text{if} \qquad \theta_w \geq 67° - \varphi_w$$

$$\sigma_{1a} = \gamma b \frac{\theta_w + \varphi_w}{\sin^2(\theta_w + \varphi_w)} \qquad \text{if} \qquad \theta_w < 67° - \varphi_w \tag{7.31}$$

A similar derivation for a spherical shell spanning a conical hopper leads to

$$\sigma_{1a} = 0.772 \gamma b \qquad \text{if} \qquad \theta_w \geq 60° - \varphi_w$$

$$\sigma_{1a} = \gamma b \frac{1 - \cos(\theta_w + \varphi_w)}{\sin^3(\theta_w + \varphi_w)} \qquad \text{if} \qquad \theta_w < 60° - \varphi_w \tag{7.32}$$

It is clearly seen that the cylindrical or spherical structural member yields values for the stress σ_{1a} that are lower than those for the case of a folded plate or conical shell. Combining (7.31), (7.32), and (7.24)$_2$, we can obtain expressions for the flow-factor. Their explicit form is given below only for a conical hopper

$$ff = -\frac{1.29(1 + \sin \delta)M}{\sin \theta_w [1 - \sin \delta \cos(\omega + \varphi_w)](2N + 1)} \tag{7.33a}$$

if $\theta_w \geq 60° - \varphi_w$, and

$$ff = -\frac{(1 + \sin \delta) \sin^3(\theta_w + \varphi_w)M}{\sin \theta_w [1 - \sin \delta \cos(\omega + \varphi_w)](2N + 1)[1 - \cos(\theta_w + \varphi_w)]} \tag{7.33b}$$

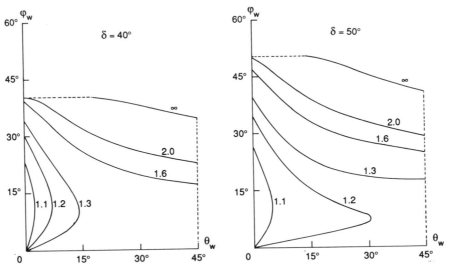

Figure 7.13 *Flow-factors for a conical hopper; $\delta = 40°$ and $\delta = 50°$ (equations [7.33])*

if $\theta_w < 60° - \varphi_w$.

An example of the flow-factor chart is shown in Figure 7.13, where the constant K appearing in the expression for N corresponds to the hypothesis of yielding at the walls (see Section 4.3.4).

Arnold and McLean (1976a, 1976b) followed the derivation above by assuming simplified distribution of consolidating stresses given by (4.86) or (4.88). In their derivation of the flow-factors, however, they utilized an approximation of expressions for the stresses in an arch or dome obtained by Jenike and Leser (1963), i.e., an analytic approximation to functions f_1 and f_2 given in Figure 7.4. The corresponding values of the flow-factors closely approximate those given in Figures 7.7 and 7.8.

In all cases the dimension of the outlet can be found using Figure 7.6 and an appropriate expression relating b to σ_{1a}. For instance, if the flow-factor is calculated from (7.27), the corresponding expression for b is (7.26).

7.3 CONTINUUM MECHANICS APPROACH

The fundamental assumption underlying the analysis of arching discussed in Section 7.2 is the lack of coupling between the stresses that exist in the bulk material next to the free surface of an arch or dome, and the mechanical properties of the hanging mass; these stresses are determined from the statics of discrete structural members. In the continuum mechanics approach, no discrete elements are introduced, and the properties of the material are directly incorporated into the analysis of stress. The condition that may lead to arching is identified with equilibrium of the whole mass of material in absence of stresses supporting the mass from below.

The location of an unsupported surface determines the critical dimension of the outlet.

Two methods for evaluating an equilibrated state of stress have been suggested in the literature. The first, due to Enstad (1975, 1977, 1981), utilizes the direct method of slices. The second makes use of the kinematical method of limit analysis (Mróz and Drescher, 1969). In the following we will present both methods separately, beginning with the direct method of slices.

7.3.1 Direct Method of Slices

To present the application of the method for determining the arching criterion in plane and conical hoppers we will make use of cylindrical or spherical slices centered at the hopper vertex. This is a slight modification of the solution given by Enstad (1975, 1977, 1981), who considered slices that are centered differently (see Section 4.3.2). It preserves, however, all the essential features of his approach.

The starting point is a solution for consolidating stresses in a plane or conical hopper corresponding to a handling phase prior to arching. Let us assume that arching occurs upon the opening of an outlet that has been intermittently closed during discharge, and the latter can be regarded as a quasi-static process of flow. For cylindrical or spherical slices, the distribution of radial stresses σ_r in a hopper of finite outer radius R_2 is given by equation (4.70) with $\sigma_{r2} = 0$, which is rewritten below

$$\sigma_r = \frac{\gamma M r}{mN + 1} \left\{ \left[\frac{R_2}{r} \right]^{mN+1} - 1 \right\} \tag{7.34}$$

where the constants m, M, and N are defined in Section 4.3.2. The corresponding wall stresses σ_n and σ_t can be computed by means of equations (4.27) and (4.36). Enstad suggested that the uniaxial compressive strength S_c that develops in the bulk material after stoppage of flow can be linearly related to the principal stress σ_1 corresponding to discharge. Thus,

$$S_c = \frac{2c \cos \phi}{1 - \sin \phi} = A\sigma_1 + B \tag{7.35}$$

where A and B are constants. Assuming, in addition, that the angle of internal friction ϕ is constant, we observe that equation (7.35) is equivalent to postulating a linear variation of the cohesion, c. Using $(7.22)_2$ and (7.34), we can write expression (7.35) in explicit form as

$$S_c = \frac{A\gamma L_1 M r}{mN + 1} \left\{ \left[\frac{R_2}{r} \right]^{mN+1} - 1 \right\} + B \tag{7.36}$$

where

$$L_1 = \frac{1 + \sin \delta}{1 - \sin \delta \cos(\omega + \varphi_w)} \tag{7.37}$$

Equation (7.36) describes the variation of the uniaxial compressive stress S_c along the wall of the hopper.

To evaluate the stresses σ_r that act in the mass of bulk material above an arch or dome, the equilibrium equation for a slice is used (see [4.66])

$$\frac{d\sigma_r}{dr} + \frac{m}{r}(\sigma_r - \sigma_n - \sigma_t \cot \theta_w) + \gamma M = 0 \qquad (7.38)$$

The relationships between the stresess σ_r, σ_n, and σ_t can be derived from the boundary conditions holding at the walls, and from the hypothesis regarding the location of points along the slice where the instantaneous yield condition is satisfied. The simplest relationships are obtained if we assume that friction is fully mobilized along the walls, and yielding takes place at the center of the slice. Then, the principal stresses at the center are $\sigma_2 = \sigma_r$ and $\sigma_1 = \sigma_n$. Using the instantaneous Mohr-Coulomb yield condition (2.33) and expression (2.36), we have

$$\sigma_n = \frac{1 + \sin \phi}{1 - \sin \phi}\sigma_r + S_c \qquad (7.39)$$

and, substituting equation (7.36) for S_c, we arrive at

$$\sigma_n = \frac{A\gamma L_1 M r}{mN + 1}\left\{\left[\frac{R_2}{r}\right]^{mN+1} - 1\right\} + B + C_0\sigma_r \qquad (7.40)$$

where

$$C_0 = \frac{1 + \sin \phi}{1 - \sin \phi} \qquad (7.41)$$

The boundary condition along the walls gives

$$\sigma_t = \sigma_n \tan \varphi_w \qquad (7.42)$$

providing $\varphi_w \leq \phi$ (see Section 4.3.3). Substituting (7.40) and (7.42) into (7.38), and integrating with the boundary condition

$$r = R_2 \qquad \sigma_r = 0 \qquad (7.43)$$

we arrive at the expression for the radial stress

$$\sigma_r = C_6\left[\frac{R_2}{r}\right]^{mE} + C_3\left[\frac{R_2}{r}\right]^{mN} - C_5 r + C_4 \qquad (7.44)$$

where

$$
\begin{aligned}
E &= 1 - C_0 C_1 \\
C_1 &= 1 + \tan \varphi_w \cot \theta_w \\
C_2 &= \frac{\gamma M}{1 + mE} + \frac{m\gamma A C_1 L_1 M}{1 + mN}\left[\frac{1}{1 + mE} - \frac{1}{1 + mN}\right] \\
C_3 &= \frac{\gamma A C_1 L_1 M R_2}{(1 + mN)(E - N)} \\
C_4 &= \frac{C_1 B}{E} \\
C_5 &= \frac{\gamma M}{1 + mE} + \frac{m\gamma A C_1 L_1 M}{(1 + mE)(1 + mN)} \\
C_6 &= C_2 R_2 - C_4
\end{aligned}
\qquad (7.45)
$$

and $E \neq 0$, $mE \neq -1$, $mN \neq -1$. Solution (7.44) gives a distribution of stresses that change sign at some radius R_*; for $r < R_*$ the radial stresses are tensile. The radius R_* thus defines the highest location of an arch or dome, because the mass of bulk material above this location is in equilibrium without the presence of supporting stresses. This critical radius can be determined from (7.44) by setting $\sigma_r = 0$. Due to the implicit form of (7.44) with respect to r, a numerical solution is required. The dimension of the critical outlet $2b$, is given by

$$2b = 2R_* \sin \theta_w \qquad (7.46)$$

The solid lines in Figure 7.14a show the dependence of the dimensionless size of the critical outlet $\gamma b/B$ on the half-included angle θ_w of a conical hopper where the passive state was assumed, and $\delta = 40°$, $\phi = 30°$, $A = 0.3$ and $\gamma R_2/B = 6$. The dashed line in Figure 7.14a corresponds to the size of the outlet equal to the span of the upper surface of the hopper.

The solution will be greatly simplified if an infinitely tall hopper is considered. The distribution of the consolidating radial stresses is given now by equation (4.87), i.e.,

$$\sigma_r = -\frac{\gamma M r}{mN + 1} \qquad (7.47)$$

the variation of the uniaxial compressive strength S_c is

$$S_c = -\frac{A\gamma L_1 M r}{mN + 1} + B \qquad (7.48)$$

and (7.40) reduces to

$$\sigma_n = -\frac{A\gamma L_1 M r}{mN + 1} + B + C_0\sigma_r \qquad (7.49)$$

On substituting (7.42) and (7.49) into (7.38), and performing integration, we finally arrive at

$$\sigma_r = C_4 - C_5 r \qquad (7.50)$$

where C_4 and C_5 are given by (7.45). The dimension of the critical outlet corresponding to $\sigma_r = 0$ is now

$$2b = 2\frac{C_4}{C_5} \sin \theta_w \qquad (7.51)$$

The dimensionless size of the critical outlet as a function of the angles θ_w and φ_w is shown in Figure 7.14b as solid lines; these curves were obtained for the same material parameters as those used in the example for a hopper with a finite radius R_2.

It should be noted here that the results will be affected if slices other than cylindrical or spherical ones are selected. This is demonstrated in Figure 7.14b by dashed lines which correspond to the solution for plane slices. For small angles θ_w the difference in the solutions is small; it becomes significant, however, for greater angles θ_w.

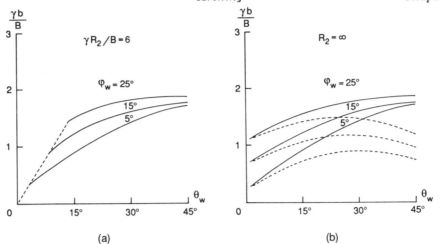

Figure 7.14 *Dimension of the critical outlet as a function of (a) angle θ_w and (b) angle φ_w; conical hopper, $\delta = 40°$, $\phi = 30°$, $A = 0.3$, yielding at the center, $\gamma R_2/B = 6$ and $R_2 = \infty$*

7.3.2 Kinematical Method of Limit Analysis

The only difference between the method discussed in Section 7.3.1 and the kinematical method of limit analysis is the way the condition for arching is effectively derived. Both methods consider equilibrium of the whole mass of bulk material hanging above an arch or dome. The direct method of slices operates with average stresses acting over the finite dimension of a slice that are subsequently set to zero at the possible location of an arch. The kinematical method of limit analysis, on the other hand, provides information only about the total limit load at collapse. When dealing with arching, the limit load is the reaction that acts from below an arch or dome, and that opposes flow induced by gravity. If for a given failure mechanism and outlet dimension this reaction is zero, then the mass is in equilibrium without support from below. Since the kinematical method furnishes a lower bound to this reaction, the critical dimension of the outlet determined by setting this reaction to zero cannot be less than the dimension corresponding to the true reaction. Thus, the kinematical method overestimates the true critical dimension of the outlet that may lead to arching.

In the work of Mróz and Drescher (1969), only the general concept of the application of this method to arching was presented, and an example was given for the critical outlet dimension in a tall bin. A more detailed consideration will be given below.

To systematically apply the kinematical method of limit analysis to the derivation of the arching criterion for a bin or hopper, one should begin with evaluating the variation of strength in the hanging mass of bulk material, also using this method. As pointed out in Section 3.5.1, however, this method is not suitable for the determination of local stresses within the mass. It seems more appropriate, therefore, to use other methods, such as the limit state or differential slice method, to arrive at stresses that consolidate the material. Thus, we will assume that the variation of strength, or, more precisely, of the parameters ϕ and c describing the instantaneous yield conditions, is known. Furthermore, only flow in plane hoppers, where the simple translational-motion incipient failure mechanisms discussed in Section 4.5 apply, will be considered below.

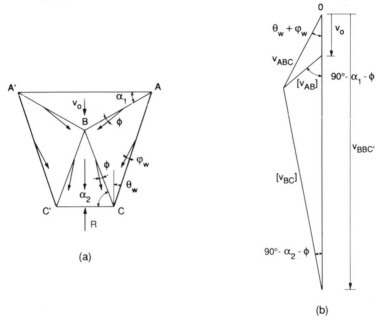

Figure 7.15 *(a) Failure mechanism in a short hopper and (b) hodograph*

Let us first consider a relatively short hopper with the upper and lower surfaces of the bulk material being flat and horizontal, although any curved shape can also be assumed (Figure 7.15a). The variation of the strength parameters and of the unit weight over the height of the hopper is disregarded, ϕ=const, c=const, and γ=const. Also, a purely frictional resistance along the hopper walls is postulated. As a failure mechanism, we select the four-triangle mechanism already discussed in Section 4.5, with the hodograph shown in Figure 7.15b. To arrive at an expression for the load supporting the material from below, we can either equate the rates of energies dissipated in and supplied for failure, or use the equivalent force equilibrium method. Choosing the first option, calculating the velocity jumps across discontinuities and making use of equation (3.102), we can express the rate of energy dissipation per unit length of the hopper as

$$
\dot{d}_n = v_0 c H_2 \cos\phi \tan\theta_w \left[\frac{\sin(\theta_w + \varphi_w)}{\cos\alpha_1 \cos(\alpha_1 + \phi + \varphi_w + \theta_w)} \right.
$$
$$
\left. + \frac{\sin(\theta_w + \varphi_w)\cos(\alpha_1 + \theta_w)\cos(\alpha_1 + \phi)}{\cos\alpha_1 \cos(\alpha_2 - \theta_w)\cos(\alpha_2 + \phi)\cos(\alpha_1 + \phi + \varphi_w + \theta_w)} \right] \tag{7.52}
$$

where the terms in brackets result from dissipation along discontinuities AB and BC, respectively, and the dissipation along the wall is zero. Since the assumed failure mechanism is identical to that from Figure 4.36, the expression for the total rate of energy supplied for failure is identical to (4.165) with $F_{EA} = 0$, and the angle δ replaced by ϕ, i.e.,

$$
\begin{aligned}
\dot{w} = v_o \frac{\gamma H_2^2 \tan^2 \theta_w}{2 \cos \alpha_1 \cos(\alpha_2 - \theta_w)} & \left[\sin \alpha_1 \cos(\alpha_2 - \theta_w) \right. \\
& + \frac{\sin(\alpha_1 + \alpha_2) \cos(\alpha_1 + \theta_w) \cos(\alpha_1 + \phi) \cos(\varphi_w + \theta_w)}{\cos \alpha_1 \cos(\alpha_1 + \phi + \varphi_w + \theta_w)} \\
& \left. + \frac{\sin \alpha_2 \cos \alpha_2 \cos(\alpha_1 + \phi) \cos^2(\alpha_1 + \theta_w) \cos(\alpha_2 + \phi - \varphi_w - \theta_w)}{\cos \alpha_1 \cos(\alpha_2 - \theta_w) \cos(\alpha_2 + \phi) \cos(\alpha_1 + \phi + \varphi_w + \theta_w)} \right] \\
& - v_o R_{CD} \frac{\cos(\alpha_1 + \phi) \cos(\alpha_2 + \phi - \varphi_w - \theta_w)}{\cos(\alpha_2 + \phi) \cos(\alpha_1 + \phi + \varphi_w + \theta_w)}
\end{aligned}
\tag{7.53}
$$

On setting $\dot{w} = \dot{d}_n$, and $R_{CD} = 0$, we obtain

$$
\begin{aligned}
c \cos\phi & \sin(\theta_w + \varphi_w)[\cos(\alpha_2 - \theta_w) + \cos(\alpha_1 + \theta_w) \cos(\alpha_1 + \phi)] \\
= \frac{1}{2} & \gamma H_2 \tan \theta_w \left[\sin \alpha_1 \cos(\alpha_2 - \theta_w) \cos(\alpha_1 + \phi + \varphi_w + \theta_w) \right. \\
& + \frac{\sin(\alpha_1 + \alpha_2) \cos(\alpha_1 + \theta_w) \cos(\alpha_1 + \phi) \cos(\theta_w + \varphi_w)}{\cos \alpha_1} \\
& \left. + \frac{\sin \alpha_2 \cos \alpha_2 \cos(\alpha_1 + \phi) \cos^2(\alpha_1 + \theta_w) \cos(\alpha_2 + \phi - \varphi_w - \theta_w)}{\cos \alpha_1 \cos(\alpha_2 - \theta_w) \cos(\alpha_2 + \phi)} \right]
\end{aligned}
\tag{7.54}
$$

Equation (7.54) interrelates angles α_1 and α_2, defining the failure mechanism in the absence of a supporting load. To derive an expression for the dimension of the outlet $2b$, one of the α-angles, e.g., α_2, is expressed as a function of b

$$
\alpha_2 = \arctan \left[\frac{H_2}{b}(1 - \tan \theta_w \tan \alpha_1) - \cot \theta_w \right]
\tag{7.55}
$$

and substituted into (7.54); the resulting expression is implicit. The least upper bound for the dimension of the outlet is obtained by minimizing b in (7.54) with respect to the angle α_1. Note that the range of admissible angles α_1 and α_2 is again given by inequalities (4.162).

The solution above can be generalized to include the variation of strength over the height of a hopper. For instance, we may assume that the angle of internal friction ϕ=const, but the cohesion c varies with height. The four-triangle mechanism shown in Figure 7.15a remains kinematically admissible, since the variation of the cohesion affects only the expression for the energy dissipation. Rather than postulating the variation of c with height, we will follow the analysis presented in Section 7.3.1, where the uniaxial compressive strength S_c was related to the consolidating principal stress σ_1 at the wall by equation (7.35). The consolidating principal stress

σ_1 can be found from the direct method of slices operating with a plane slice, i.e., from equations (4.59) and (7.22a). Using equation (7.35), we can finally write

$$c = \frac{A\gamma L_2 y(1 - \sin\phi)}{2(N+1)\cos\phi} \left\{ \left[\frac{H_2}{y}\right]^{N+1} - 1 \right\} + B\frac{1 - \sin\phi}{2\cos\phi} \tag{7.56}$$

where

$$L_2 = \frac{1 + \sin\delta}{1 - \sin\delta\cos(\omega + \varphi_w + 2\theta_w)} \tag{7.57}$$

To derive an expression for the rate of dissipated work along the discontinuity lines AB and BC, we integrate equation (3.102) along these lines, with c given by (7.56). The result is

$$\dot{d}_{nAB} = v_0 \frac{\sin(\theta_w + \varphi_w)\cos\phi}{\cos(\alpha_1 + \phi + \varphi_w + \theta_w)} \left\{ F_1[H_2^{N-1}(H_2 - F_4\sin\alpha_1)^{1-N} - 1] \right.$$
$$\left. - F_0 H_2 F_4 + F_0\sin\alpha_1 \frac{F_4^2}{2} + BF_4\frac{1 - \sin\phi}{2\cos\phi} \right\} \tag{7.58}$$

$$\dot{d}_{nBC} = v_0 \frac{\sin(\theta_w + \varphi_w)\cos(\alpha_1 + \phi)\cos\phi}{\cos(\alpha_1 + \phi + \varphi_w + \theta_w)\cos(\alpha_2 + \phi)} \left\{ F_2[(F_3 - F_5\sin\alpha_2)^{1-N} - F_3^{1-N}] \right.$$
$$\left. - F_0 F_3 F_5 + F_0\sin\alpha_2 \frac{F_5^2}{2} + BF_5\frac{1 - \sin\phi}{2\cos\phi} \right\} \tag{7.59}$$

where

$$F_0 = \frac{A\gamma L_2(1 - \sin\phi)}{(N+1)2\cos\phi} \qquad F_1 = \frac{F_0 H_2^2}{\sin\alpha_1(N-1)}$$

$$F_2 = \frac{F_0 H_2^{1+N}}{\sin\alpha_2(N-1)} \qquad F_3 = H_2(1 - \tan\theta_w\tan\alpha_1) \tag{7.60}$$

$$F_4 = \frac{H_2\tan\theta_w}{\cos\alpha_1} \qquad F_5 = \frac{H_2\tan\theta_w\cos(\theta_w + \alpha_1)}{\cos\alpha_1\cos(\theta_w - \theta_w)}$$

The rate of external energy is given by (7.53). Following the procedure outlined previously, we obtain the dimension of the critical outlet from the minimization of b with respect to α_1.

The last example we will consider is an infinitely tall hopper, with the failure mechanism shown in Figure 7.16a. This implies that the angle of internal friction ϕ is assumed to be constant throughout the mass of the bulk material. The variation of the cohesion again results from equation (7.35), where this time σ_1 is calculated from equations (4.86) and (7.22)$_1$, which gives

$$c = \frac{A\gamma L_2 y(1 - \sin\phi)}{2(N+1)\cos\phi} + \frac{B(1 - \sin\phi)}{2\cos\phi} \tag{7.61}$$

From Figure 7.16a, the distance H_n to each element $A'ACC'$ of the failure mechanism can be expressed as

$$H_n = H_0 M_1^n \qquad (n = 0, 1, 2, \dots, \infty)$$
$$M_1 = \frac{1 + \tan\theta_w\tan\alpha_2}{1 - \tan\theta_w\tan\alpha_1} \tag{7.62}$$

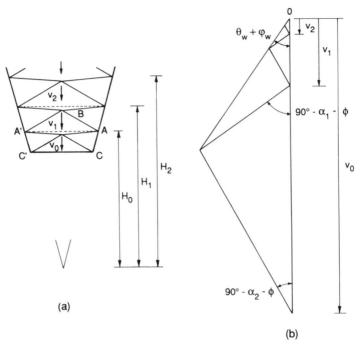

Figure 7.16 (a) Failure mechanism in an infinitely tall hopper and (b) hodograph

Also, from the hodograph (Figure 7.16b), the velocity v_n is given by

$$v_n = v_0 M_2^{-n} \qquad (n = 0, 1, 2, \ldots, \infty)$$

$$M_2 = \frac{\cos(\alpha_1 + \phi)\cos(\alpha_2 + \phi - \varphi_w - \theta_w)}{\cos(\alpha_2 + \phi)\cos(\alpha_1 + \phi + \varphi_w + \theta_w)} \tag{7.63}$$

The total rate of work of body forces is an infinite sum of the rate of work within each element. Using (7.53) we can write

$$\dot{w} = \frac{1}{2}\gamma H_0^2 v_0 G_0(1 + q + q^2 + \ldots) \tag{7.64}$$

where

$$q = \frac{M_1^2}{M_2}$$

$$\begin{aligned}
G_0 = &\frac{\tan^2\theta_w \sin\alpha_1 \cos(\alpha_2 - \theta_w)}{\cos\alpha_1 \cos(\alpha_2 - \theta_w)} \\
&+ \frac{\sin(\alpha_1 + \alpha_2)\cos(\alpha_1 + \theta_w)\cos(\alpha_1 + \phi)\cos(\varphi_w + \theta_w)}{\cos\alpha_1 \cos(\alpha_1 + \phi + \varphi_w + \theta_w)} \\
&+ \frac{\sin\alpha_2 \cos\alpha_2 \cos(\alpha_1 + \phi)\cos^2(\alpha_1 + \theta_w)\cos(\alpha_2 + \phi - \varphi_w - \theta_w)}{\cos\alpha_1 \cos(\alpha_2 - \theta_w)\cos(\alpha_2 + \phi)\cos(\alpha_1 + \phi + \varphi_w + \theta_w)}
\end{aligned} \tag{7.65}$$

On the other hand, the total dissipation is the sum of dissipations along the discontinuity lines within each element. Integration of (3.102) over lines AB and BC gives

$$\dot{d}_{nAB(n)} = \frac{1}{2}\gamma H_n^2 v_n G_1 G_2 G_3 + \frac{1}{2} H_n v_n B G_2 G_4$$

$$\dot{d}_{nBC(n)} = \frac{1}{2}\gamma H_n^2 v_n G_1 G_5 G_6 + \frac{1}{2} H_n v_n B G_5 G_7$$

(7.66)

where

$$G_1 = \frac{AL_2(1 - \sin\phi)}{2(N+1)\cos\phi}$$

$$G_2 = \frac{\sin(\varphi_w + \theta_w)\cos\phi}{\cos(\alpha_1 + \phi + \varphi_w + \theta_w)}$$

$$G_3 = \frac{\tan\theta_w(\tan\theta_w \tan\alpha_1 - 2)}{\cos\alpha_1}$$

$$G_4 = \frac{\tan\theta_w(1 - \sin\phi)}{\cos\alpha_1 \cos\phi}$$

$$G_5 = \frac{\sin(\varphi_w + \theta_w)\cos(\alpha_1 + \phi)\cos\phi}{\cos(\alpha_2 + \phi)\cos(\alpha_1 + \phi + \varphi_w + \theta_w)}$$

$$G_6 = \frac{\sin\alpha_2 \tan^2\theta_w \cos^2(\alpha_1 + \theta_w)}{\cos^2\alpha_1 \cos^2(\alpha_2 - \theta_w)}$$
$$\quad - \frac{2(1 - \tan\theta_w \tan\alpha_1)\tan\theta_w \cos(\alpha_1 + \theta_w)}{\cos\alpha_1 \cos(\alpha_2 - \theta_w)}$$

$$G_7 = \frac{\tan\theta_w \cos(\alpha_1 + \theta_w)(1 - \sin\phi)}{\cos\alpha_1 \cos(\alpha_2 - \theta_w)\cos\phi}$$

(7.67)

and the total dissipation can be written as

$$\dot{d} = \frac{1}{2}\gamma H_0^2 v_0 G_1(G_2 G_3 + G_5 G_7)(1 + q + q^2 + \dots)$$

$$+ \frac{1}{2} H_0 v_0 B(G_2 G_4 + G_5 G_7)(1 + p + p^2 + \dots)$$

(7.68)

where

$$p = \frac{M_1}{M_2}$$

(7.69)

For the range of α-angles given by inequalities (4.162), we have

$$q < 1 \qquad p < 1$$

(7.70)

and

$$(1 + q + q^2 + \dots) = \frac{1}{1-q} \qquad (1 + p + p^2 + \dots) = \frac{1}{1-p}$$

(7.71)

Using the result above, and equating the total energy supplied and dissipated in failure, we finally obtain

$$\frac{\gamma H_0}{B} = \frac{(p - q^2)(G_2 G_4 + G_5 G_7)}{(p - q)(G_0 - G_1 G_2 G_3 - G_0 G_5 G_6)}$$

(7.72)

Equation (7.72) is an implicit expression for b, which is related to the distance H_0 by (7.55) with $H_2 = H_0$. The smallest outlet $2b$ can be found from equation (7.72) by minimization with respect to α_1 and α_2.

7.4 CLOSING REMARKS

The two approaches described above for analyzing arching are approximate, although the degrees of approximation are different. The structural mechanics approach disregards the influence of the weight of the material above the structural member. One may expect, therefore, that the resulting stresses that act in an arch or dome are lower than the true ones, and consequently the dimensions of the critical outlet are overestimated. Analogously, the kinematical method of limit analysis gives the dimensions of outlets larger than the true ones; it provides a safe estimate of the critical outlet. This time, however, the conclusion is based on a rigorous proof. In regard to the approach utilizing the direct method of slices, there is no argument, other than an experimental one, that would lead to an estimate of the resulting size of the outlet with respect to the true critical outlet, although the results of calculations give smaller outlets than those predicted by the structural mechanics approach. This is demonstrated in Figure 7.17, where the dimensions of critical outlets resulting from the solutions presented above are compared for a plane infinitely tall hopper; $\theta_w = 15°$, $\delta = 40°$, $\phi = 30°$, $\varphi_w = 15°$, and $A = 0.3$, $B = 3$ kN/m^2, $\gamma = 18$ kN/m^3. It is seen that the smallest outlet results from the direct method of slices, whereas limit analysis yields an outlet that is significantly greater than any other solution.

Each method allows for further modifications to the solutions presented. For instance, different structural members, not necessarily plane or axisymmetric, can be postulated; a bi-folded plate could be considered for analyzing arching in hoppers that are square or rectangular in cross-section. Within the direct method of slices, various types of slices and various hypotheses regarding yielding can be analyzed (cf. Enstad, 1981). In the kinematical method of limit analysis, continuous and axisymmetric velocity fields can also be investigated.

Furthermore, the boundary conditions that exist along the hopper walls could be modified. In all the solutions presented, except that of Jenike and Leser (1963), the boundary conditions were identified with friction defined by the angle $\varphi_w \leq \phi$, which characterizes the dry frictional resistance of the interface when slippage occurs. It is possible, however, that, when arching occurs, some adhesion develops at the interface, and the allowable inclination of the stress vector may differ from the angle φ_w (see Section 2.6). This has been recognized by Enstad (1981), and leads to difficulties in the application of the direct method of slices. On the other hand, this effect can be incorporated easily into the kinematical method of limit analysis, where an additional term due to dissipation along the walls would contribute to the total energy balance.

It should also be noted that the concept of a flow-factor can be applied only within the structural mechanics approach, and for distributions of consolidating stresses that are linear functions of the distance r or y. In relatively short hoppers,

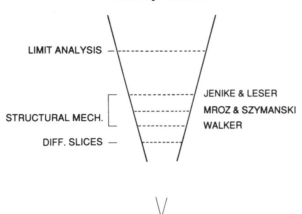

Figure 7.17 *Dimensions of the critical outlet in an infinitely tall plane hopper resulting from different methods of analysis; $\theta_w = 15°$, $\delta = 40°$, $\phi = 30°$, $\varphi_w = 15°$, $A = 0.3$, $B = 3\ kN/m^2$, $\gamma = 18\ kN/m^3$*

the distribution of consolidating stresses differs significantly from the vertex radial stress distribution. In this case, a graphical comparison between the strength S_c and the stress in arch σ_{1a}, shown in Figure 7.5, could be used.

An important assumption that underlies all the solutions presented is the quasi-static character of the handling phase that precedes arching. As a result, the distribution of consolidating stresses is unaffected by the location of the outlet (see Chapter 4). This is not the case, however, if an inertial, steady or unsteady, process of discharge is considered (see Chapters 5 and 6). An iterative procedure would have to be used then, in which the stress distribution for each location of the critical outlet would be determined. Since quasi-static analysis yields consolidating stresses that are greater than those in inertial flow, it leads to an overestimate of the size of the critical outlet.

Finally, all solutions aim at the determination of the size of an outlet for a given geometry of a hopper. A different approach has been presented by Richmond and Gardner (1962), Gardner (1963), and Richmond and Morrison (1979): they sought a hopper shape that would not allow tensile stresses to develop within the bulk material. The solutions presented in these works utilize an approximate limit state method, and are restricted to constant cohesion of the material. The resulting profiles of hoppers are concave, asymptotically approaching the symmetry line.

8 CHANNELING

8.1 INTRODUCTION

The formation of empty channels, extending from the outlet of a bin or hopper to the upper surface of the bulk material, is observed during discharge in plug- or funnel-flow storage structures. The flow in these facilities is restricted to a central region, as opposed to flow in mass-flow bins and hoppers where all the particles undergo motion (see Figure 1.3). The shape of empty channels depends on the geometry of the bin or hopper and on the geometry of the outlet. In plane or rectangular bins and hoppers with slot openings, the channel extends over the whole length of the outlet and its sides are nearly vertical. In cylindrical or square bins, with circular or square outlets, the shape of the channel can be approximated by a vertical cylinder. The material adjacent to the empty channel forms a stable slope that is bounded by the walls of the container. A stable slope can form only if the strength of the bulk material exceeds the stresses induced by its own weight. Thus, the analysis of the formation of empty channels is equivalent to the analysis of the stability of plane or cylindrical vertical slopes loaded by their own weight. Since the stability of a slope depends on its geometry, and, in particular, on its inner radius and height, it is possible to derive a criterion relating the critical geometry of a stable slope to the strength of the bulk material. This criterion can be called the *channeling criterion*, and may serve for selecting the size of the outlet or height of the stored bulk material that prevents channeling.

The idea of analyzing channeling as a problem of the initial stability of surrounding channel slopes belongs to Jenike and Yen (1962). These authors considered a limit state solution in a cylindrical slope horizontally unrestricted. They also assumed that the vertical stress in the slope is independent of the vertical coordinate, and the strength of the bulk material is described by Mohr-Coulomb instantaneous yield condition (2.33) with constant ϕ and c. Then, local equilibrium equations (3.58) could be transformed into a set of hyperbolic partial differential equations for the mean normal stress σ, and the orientation ψ of the major principal stress σ_1 (see Section 3.3.2). Alternatively, both equations could be combined into a non-linear partial differential equation for the inclination ψ as a function of the radial r-coordinate. The numerical solution of this equation revealed that the trajectories of principal stress σ_1, and thus the mesh of the stress characteristics inclined at the angle $\pm\epsilon = (\pi/4 - \phi/2)$ with respect to ψ, depend for a given ϕ on the ratio between the inner diameter $2R_1$, unit weight γ, and cohesion c. A critical ratio $2R_1\gamma/c$ exists that separates the characteristics field that extends horizontally without limit (Figure 8.1a) from the characteristics field with a vertical envelope (Figure 8.1b).

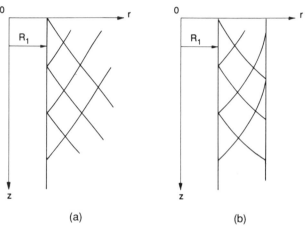

(a)   (b)

Figure 8.1 *(a) Unbounded and (b) bounded characteristics fields*

Jenike and Yen identified the stress characteristics with the velocity characteristics, and employed a kinematic argument that collapse of a slope requires a bounded characteristics field. Then, the critical ratio $2R_1\gamma/c$ may serve as a criterion for channeling. For an inner radius R_1 less than that given by the critical ratio $2R_1\gamma/c$, the slope is stable (unbounded field), otherwise a stable slope cannot form and channeling does not occur (bounded field). The above solution may apply to very tall bins, where neither the vertical stress nor the strength parameters ϕ and c depend on the vertical coordinate (see Section 4.2), and to bins with walls at a great distance apart that do not influence the stability of the slope.

In the following sections, we will present approximate solutions of the stability of vertical, plane and axisymmetric slopes bounded by the walls of a bin or hopper with a moderate height. These solutions have been suggested by Drescher (1983), Drescher and Vgenopoulou (1985), and Drescher (1986), and are based on the kinematical method of limit analysis.

8.2 KINEMATICAL METHOD OF LIMIT ANALYSIS APPROACH

The analysis of the initial stability of slopes surrounding empty channels by means of the kinematical method of limit analysis bears similarity to the analysis of arching presented in Section 7.3.2. In both cases, the method furnishes an upper bound to the dimension of an arch or channel at collapse, regardless of whether the flow rule is associative or non-associative (see Section 3.5.2). For example, the height of a slope determined from a kinematically admissible solution guarantees the slope will fail, since the true height for a stable slope cannot be greater. Alternatively, the inner radius of a failing slope can be selected as a parameter for designing outlets that do not cause channeling.

To apply the kinematical method of limit analysis to stability of slopes, the yield condition modeling the strength of a bulk material upon stoppage of flow has to be selected first. As in the case of arching, the instantaneous yield condition of a bulk material depends on stresses that existed in the bin or hopper prior to or during discharge, and that consolidated the initially loose assembly of particles. In the following analysis we will assume that the strength of the material in a slope is characterized by one instantaneous yield condition. Thus, the variation of strength with the location of the material element is disregarded. Also, a constant unit weight is assumed throughout the slope. These assumptions are made to simplify the analysis, although it is possible to consider the variation of strength and unit weight.

The instantaneous yield condition selected here is linear Mohr-Coulomb condition (2.33) with two material parameters: cohesion c, and angle of internal friction ϕ. However, since the stability of a surrounding channel slope may depend on the material tensile strength, the Mohr-Coulomb yield condition will be modified by a tension cut-off (Figure 2.17). Thus, an additional material parameter, uniaxial tensile strength S_t, defines the strength of the material (see [2.40]).

To account for the material/wall interface in the stability analysis of slopes bounded by bin or hopper walls, some resistance to failure along the interface should be incorporated. As mentioned in Section 7.4, wall friction angle φ_w may not characterize the resistance at the interface at the onset of failure. One may expect, indeed, that, besides frictional resistance, some resistance to tension may develop due to adhesion between the bulk material and the wall during filling or storage operations. Thus, for stability analysis, the interface can be modeled as an infinitely thin layer of a perfectly plastic material with a yield condition similar to that for the bulk material, and with a different angle of internal friction $\phi_w = \varphi_w$, cohesion c_w, and tensile strength S_{tw}.

Two types of failure mechanisms will be considered separately. The first type, called *partial*, refers to a mechanism in which a prismatic portion of a slope undergoes translational motion. Along the sides of a prism either a shear or shear/separation type of velocity discontinuity is postulated (see Section 3.5.4). This type of failure may apply equally to slopes surrounding empty channels that are rectangular or circular in cross-section. The second, *axisymmetric* failure mechanism, with or without velocity discontinuities present, is applicable only to cylindrical channels.

8.2.1 Partial Collapse

As the first example of a kinematic solution utilizing a partial collapse mechanism in a vertical slope, we will consider a plane bin with a slot opening of width $2w$ extending over the whole length $2L \gg 2B$ (Figure 8.2a). If we disregard resistance to failure at the end walls of the bin (plane failure), two simple rigid-block motion failure mechanisms can be postulated. The first one is sliding of triangular prism $ABCDEF$ over a plane velocity discontinuity surface $BEFD$. The velocity of the prism v_0 is inclined to surface $BEFD$ at angle of internal friction ϕ. In the second mechanism, the prism $ABCDEF$ rotates with angular velocity ω. Rigid rotation of a block implies a log-spiral velocity discontinuity, with the velocity jump increasing exponentially. The above failure mechanisms, well-known in stability analysis of vertical soil cuts, assume the shear type of velocity discontinuity surfaces (c.f. Chen, 1975).

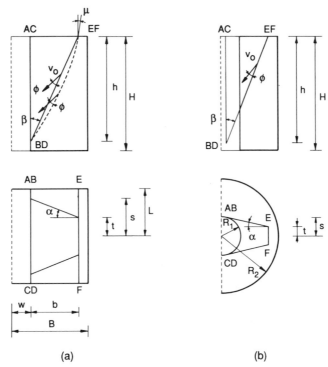

(a) (b)

Figure 8.2 *Shear type partial collapse mechanisms, (a) rectangular bin and (b) cylindrical bin*

For the mechanism of sliding, the rate of energy dissipated in failure along velocity discontinuity surface $BEFD$ is (see equation [3.102])

$$\dot{d}_n = 2cv_0hL\frac{\cos\phi}{\cos\beta} \tag{8.1}$$

and the rate of energy provided by the unit weight is

$$\dot{w} = v_0h^2L\gamma\tan\beta\cos(\beta+\phi) \tag{8.2}$$

On setting $\dot{d}_n = \dot{w}$, we obtain the following expression

$$\frac{c}{\gamma} = \frac{h\sin\beta\cos(\beta+\phi)}{2\cos\phi} \tag{8.3}$$

which can be written in a dimensionless form as

$$\frac{c}{\gamma H} = \frac{h}{H} \frac{\sin \beta \cos(\beta + \phi)}{2 \cos \phi} \tag{8.4}$$

where H is the height of the bin.

For the rotational mechanism we obtain

$$\frac{c}{\gamma H} = \frac{h}{H} \frac{K_1 - K_2 - K_3}{K_4} \frac{\cos(\theta_3 - \beta)}{\sin(\theta_3 - \theta_1) \cos \beta} \tag{8.5}$$

where

$$K_1 = \frac{e^{-3\theta_1 \tan \phi}}{3(9 \tan^2 \phi + 1)} \left[e^{3\theta_3 \tan \phi} (3 \tan \phi \cos \theta_3 + \sin \theta_3) \right.$$

$$\left. - e^{3\theta_1 \tan \phi} (3 \tan \phi \cos \theta_1 + \sin \theta_1) \right]$$

$$K_2 = \frac{\sin^3 \theta_1}{6} \left[\frac{1}{\sin^2 \theta_1} - \frac{1}{\sin^2 \theta_2} \right] \tag{8.6}$$

$$K_3 = \frac{e^{3(\theta_3 - \theta_1) \tan \phi}}{3} \cos^3 \theta_3 (\tan \theta_3 - \tan \theta_2)$$

$$K_4 = \frac{1}{2 \tan \phi} \left[e^{2(\theta_3 - \theta_1) \tan \phi} - 1 \right]$$

the angles θ_1, θ_2, and θ_3 are defined as

$$\theta_1 = \phi + \mu \qquad \theta_2 = \theta_1 + \varepsilon \qquad \theta_3 = \theta_1 + \alpha \tag{8.7}$$

with μ defined in Figure 8.2a

$$\varepsilon = \arctan \frac{\sin \theta_1 \sin \alpha \sin \beta}{\cos(\alpha + \theta_1 - \beta) - \cos \theta_1 \sin \alpha \sin \beta} \tag{8.8}$$

and α resulting from

$$e^{\alpha \tan \phi} \left[\cos \alpha - \tan(\mu + \phi - \beta) \sin \alpha \right] = 1 \tag{8.9}$$

If the length $2L$ of a bin is comparable with the width $2B$, plane failure cannot be assumed. A modified sliding mechanism can be postulated instead, where the prism is trapezoidal, and shear failure takes place along all bounding prism walls (Figure 8.2a). Because all the walls are now velocity discontinuity surfaces inclined to the velocity of prism v_0 at angle ϕ, the intersection of the side walls with the upper surface of the slope makes an angle α given by

$$\alpha = \arcsin \frac{\sin \phi}{\sin(\beta + \phi)} \tag{8.10}$$

The resulting expression for the ratio $c/\gamma H$ becomes

$$\frac{c}{\gamma H} = \frac{h}{H} \frac{L_1}{L_2 + L_3} \frac{\cos(\beta + \phi)}{\cos \phi} \tag{8.11}$$

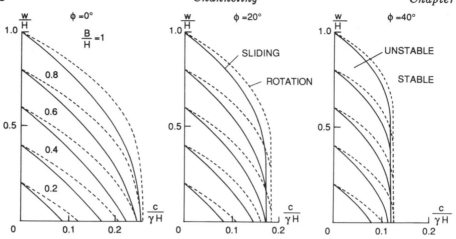

Figure 8.3 *Critical ratios $c/\gamma H$ for plane bins; shear failure*

where

$$L_1 = \frac{1}{3}(t + 2s)\tan\beta \qquad L_2 = \frac{s - t}{\sin\alpha}$$

$$L_3 = \frac{s + t}{\cos\beta} \qquad\qquad s = h\tan\alpha\tan\beta + t \tag{8.12}$$

Equations (8.4), (8.5), and (8.11) interrelate the geometry of the prism (h and β in [8.4]) and the material parameters c, ϕ, and γ at collapse. For a ratio $c/\gamma H$ less or equal to that resulting from these equations the slope will fail, since the rate of energy provided for failure surpasses or equals the rate of energy resisting failure. On the other hand, for a ratio $c/\gamma H$ greater than the critical one, the slope may or may not fail. In fact, the kinematic approach yields only a bound to the true collapse load, which, identified with γ, for instance, can be smaller than results from the critical ratio $c/\gamma H$. Since γ appears in the denominator, the best estimate of the collapse load is obtained by maximizing ratio $c/\gamma H$ with respect to the geometric parameters. The geometric parameters cannot be arbitrary, however, since the prism must be enclosed within the material in a bin. For instance, for the sliding mechanism, the range of parameters is

$$0 < \frac{h}{H} \le 1$$

$$0 < \beta \le \arctan\left\{\left[\frac{B}{H} - \frac{w}{H}\right]\frac{H}{h}\right\} \tag{8.13}$$

The results of maximization of ratios $c/\gamma H$ can be presented in a graphical form as lines separating ratios $c/\gamma H$ for unstable slopes, and, thus, no channeling, from ratios that correspond to slopes that may not fail, and channeling may occur; these lines graphically represent the channeling criterion. This is shown in dimensionless diagrams in Figures 8.3 and 8.4, from which the size of an outlet that prevents channeling can be found directly. It is seen from Figure 8.3 that the rotational mechanism for a plane bin yields greater, less conservative ratios $c/\gamma H$.

The mechanism of sliding of a trapezoidal prism discussed above also can be applied to a cylindrical bin in which a centrally located cylindrical channel forms (Figure 8.2b). Here, the exposed surface of the prism is cylindrical rather than flat. Denoting the radius of the channel by R_1, the expression for ratio $c/\gamma H$ at collapse is

$$\frac{c}{\gamma H} = \frac{h}{H} \frac{L_1 + M_1}{L_2 + L_3 - M_2} \frac{\cos(\beta + \phi)}{\cos \phi} \tag{8.14}$$

where L_1, L_2, L_3, and s are given by (8.12), and

$$M_1 = \frac{\cot \beta}{3h^2} \left[s\left(3R_1^2 - s^2\right) - 3R_1^3 \frac{\lambda}{2} \cos \frac{\lambda}{2} \right] - \frac{R_1^2}{h}(\lambda - \sin \lambda)$$

$$M_2 = \frac{\sqrt{1 + \cot^2 \beta}}{h} \left\{ R_1^2 \arccos \left[\frac{1}{R_1} \sqrt{R_1^2 - s^2} \right] - s\sqrt{R_1^2 - s^2} \right\} \tag{8.15}$$

$$\lambda = 2 \arcsin \frac{s}{R_1}$$

Examples of computational results obtained by maximizing equation (8.14) with respect to geometrical parameters of a prism are shown in Figure 8.5.

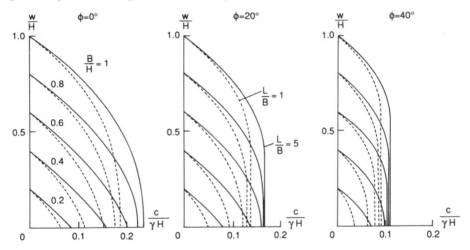

Figure 8.4 *Critical ratios $c/\gamma H$ for rectangular bins; shear failure*

All the partial failure mechanisms considered above are based on the shearing mode of failure along all walls of a prism, and thus failure by tensile separation is excluded. It is possible, however, to modify the mechanisms if we postulate shear/separation along one of the walls of the prism. An example of such a mechanism for a cylindrical channel in a cylindrical bin is shown in Figure 8.6a. The prism is bounded by three flat walls $ABFE$, $DCGH$, and $EFGH$, and cylindrical surface $BCGF$. Along side walls $ABFE$ and $DCGH$, and along bottom wall $EFGH$, the shear mode of failure operates, whereas along cylindrical surface $BCGF$ failure involves shear and tensile separation. For the shear mode, the velocity v_0 with which the prism fails is inclined to the walls at angle of internal friction ϕ; for the shear/separation mode the angle ν between velocity v_0 and surface $BCGH$ is greater than ϕ, and is given by

$$\nu = \arcsin[\sin(\beta + \phi)\cos\theta] \tag{8.16}$$

with θ being the circumferential coordinate. Note that the rate of energy dissipation for the shear/separation discontinuity surface is given by equation (3.103) or (3.104). By equating the total rate of energy dissipation and the rate of work of weight, we obtain the following expression

$$\frac{c}{\gamma H} = \frac{1}{H}\frac{N_1 + N_2 - N_3}{N_4 + N_5 + N_6 + N_7 - N_8}\frac{\cos(\beta + \phi)}{\cos\phi} \tag{8.17}$$

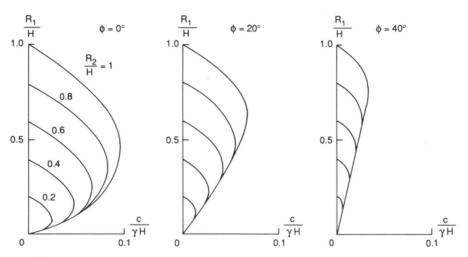

Figure 8.5 *Critical ratios $c/\gamma H$ for cylindrical bins; shear failure*

where

$$N_1 = \frac{1}{3}(h_1 - h_2)^2 \tan\beta(t + 2s) - \frac{1}{2}(h_1 - h_2)(2\lambda - \sin 2\lambda)R_1^2$$
$$+ \frac{1}{3}\cot\beta(3sR_1^2 - s^3 - sR_1^3\lambda\cos\lambda)$$

$$N_2 = h_2\left[(h_1 - h_2)(t + s)\tan\beta - \frac{1}{2}(2\lambda - \sin 2\lambda)R_1^2 + \frac{1}{2}(2\omega - \sin 2\omega)R_3^2\right]$$

$$N_3 = \frac{1}{3}\cot\beta(3tR_3^2 - t^3 - 3R_3^3\omega\cos\omega)$$

$$N_4 = \frac{(h_1 - h_2)^2\tan\beta}{\cos\alpha} + \frac{(h_1 - h_2)(s + t)}{\cos\beta} - \frac{R_1}{\sin\beta}(R_1\lambda - s\cos\lambda)$$

$$N_5 = \frac{2h_2 R_3}{\cos\phi}\left\{\left[\frac{q}{\cos\phi} - \frac{\cos\phi}{1 - \sin\phi}\right]\sin\nu_0\sin\omega - \omega\left[q\tan\phi - \frac{\cos\phi}{1 - \sin\phi}\right]\right\}$$

$$N_6 = \frac{R_3}{\sin\beta}(R_3\omega - t\cos\omega)$$

$$N_7 = \frac{2h_2(s-t)}{\sin \alpha}$$

$$N_8 = \frac{2R_3^2}{\tan \beta \cos \phi} \left\{ \frac{\sin \nu_0}{4} \left[\frac{q}{\cos \phi} - \frac{\cos \phi}{1 - \sin \phi} \right] (2\omega + \sin 2\omega) \right.$$

$$+ \frac{\cos \phi \sin \omega}{1 - \sin \phi}(1 + \cos \omega \sin \nu_0) - \frac{q \sin \omega}{\cos \phi}(\sin \phi + \cos \omega \sin \nu_0)$$

$$\left. + \omega \cos \omega \left[q \tan \phi - \frac{\cos \phi}{1 - \sin \phi} \right] \right\}$$

(8.18)

and

$$\nu_0 = \beta + \phi \qquad \lambda = \arcsin \frac{s}{R_1}$$

$$\omega = \arcsin \frac{t}{R_3} \qquad t = s - (h_1 - h_2)\tan \alpha \tan \beta$$

(8.19)

Due to the complexity of the above expressions, and four independent variables defining the geometry of a prism, i.e., h_1, h_2, s, and β, the greatest ratio $c/\gamma H$ can be found only numerically.

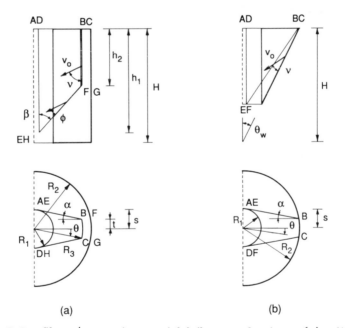

(a)   (b)

Figure 8.6   *Shear/separation partial failure mechanisms, (a) cylindri-*
cal bin and (b) conical hopper

If we set the radius of cylindrical surface $BCGF$ equal to the radius of the bin, $R_3 = R_2$, failure would involve separation from the wall of the bin. In this case, the material parameters defining resistance of the interface, i.e., c_w, ϕ_w, and S_{tw}, or c_w, ϕ_w, and q_w, will enter the solution. Equation (8.17) and expressions (8.18) still hold, with N_5 and N_8 given by

$$N_5 = \frac{c_w}{c} \frac{2h_2 R_2}{\cos \phi} \left\{ \left[\frac{q_w}{\cos \phi_w} - \frac{\cos \phi_w}{1 - \sin \phi_w} \right] \sin \nu_0 \sin \omega \right.$$

$$\left. - \omega \left[q_w \tan \phi_w - \frac{\cos \phi_w}{1 - \sin \phi_w} \right] \right\}$$

$$N_8 = \frac{c_w}{c} \frac{2R_2^2}{\tan \beta \cos \phi} \left\{ \frac{\sin \nu_0}{4} \left[\frac{q_w}{\cos \phi_w} - \frac{\cos \phi_w}{1 - \sin \phi_w} \right] (2\omega + \sin 2\omega) \right. \tag{8.20}$$

$$+ \frac{\cos \phi_w \sin \omega}{1 - \sin \phi_w} (1 + \cos \omega \sin \nu_0) - \frac{q_w \sin \omega}{\cos \phi_w} (\sin \phi_w + \cos \omega \sin \nu_0)$$

$$\left. + \omega \cos \omega \left[q_w \tan \phi_w - \frac{\cos \phi_w}{1 - \sin \phi_w} \right] \right\}$$

and the number of independent variables reduces to three: h_1, h_2, and s.

Figure 8.7 shows the results for a cylindrical bin with aspect ratio $R_2/H = 0.2$. The mechanisms leading to the greatest ratio $c/\gamma H$ are indicated as follows: dashed lines correspond to collapse of a prism that is enclosed within the material, whereas solid lines correspond to collapse of a prism with cylindrical surface $BCGF$ coinciding with the wall of the bin. Clearly, for very small ratios R_1/H, collapse takes place entirely within the material, and, for greater ratios R_1/H, failure involves separation from the wall. Also, the greatest region of instability, i.e., the smallest risk of channeling, occurs for a wall that does not provide any resistance to separation, $c_w/c = 0$. Note that for the associative flow rule, frictional resistance does not contribute to energy dissipation (see Section 3.5.5).

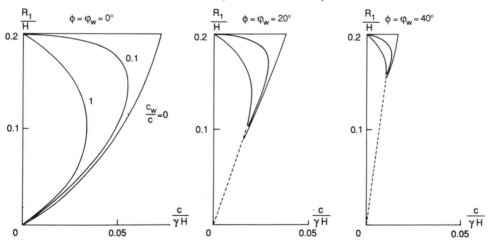

Figure 8.7 *Critical ratios $c/\gamma H$ for cylindrical bins; shear/separation failure, $R_2/H = 0.2$, $q = q_w = 2$*

It is possible to account for the sloping walls of a hopper by a further modification of the translational failure mechanism. Consider a conical hopper inscribed in a cylinder of height H and radius R_2, with an outlet of radius R_1, and with half-included angle θ_w (Figure 8.6b). As with cylindrical bins, the partial failure mechanism (confined to the bulk material) may be selected, with the relationship between the material parameters and the geometry of the prism at collapse given by equations (8.14) or (8.17). The dominant collapse mechanism, however, is probably failure along the hopper wall. In what follows, the latter mechanism is discussed.

It is assumed that the failing prism is bounded by two flat walls ABE and CDF, and conical surface $BCFE$. For a rigid-block motion of the prism, the shear mode of failure, requiring a constant inclination of velocity vector v_0 at angle ϕ, is not admissible along conical surface $BCFE$. The shear/separation mode is postulated, instead, with angle $\nu \geq \phi$ given by

$$\nu = \arcsin[\cos\beta\cos\theta\sin(\beta + \nu_0) - \sin\beta\cos(\beta + \nu_0)] \qquad (8.21)$$

where ν_0 is the angle ν at $\theta = 0$. The resulting expression for $c/\gamma H$ contains terms which are difficult to integrate analytically

$$\frac{c}{\gamma H} = \frac{1}{H}\frac{P_1 - P_2 - P_3 + P_4}{P_5 - P_6 - P_7}\cos(\beta + \nu_0) \qquad (8.22)$$

where

$$P_1 = s\cos\alpha\left[\frac{R_2}{H}F_2 - 2R_1 h\cos(\lambda + \alpha)\right]$$

$$P_2 = \sin\alpha\cos\alpha\left\{\frac{R_2^2[H^3 - (H-h)^3]}{3H^2} + R_1^2 h\cos 2(\lambda + \alpha) - \frac{R_1 R_2}{H}\cos(\lambda + \alpha)F_2\right\}$$

$$P_3 = \frac{R_1^2 h}{2}(2\lambda - \sin 2\lambda)$$

$$P_4 = R_2^2\int_{H-h}^{H} f(z)\,dz - \frac{R_2^2}{2}\int_{H-h}^{H}\sin 2f(z)\,dz$$

$$P_5 = h\left\{\frac{c_w}{c}F_1[s + R_1\sin\alpha\cos(\lambda + \alpha)] - 2R_1\cos\phi\cos(\lambda + \alpha)\right\}$$

$$P_6 = \frac{R_2}{2H}\left[\frac{c_w}{c}F_1\sin\alpha - 2\cos\phi\right]F_2$$

$$P_7 = \frac{c_w}{c}F_3\int_{H-h}^{H} zf(z)\,dz$$

$$F_1 = 2\sin(\beta + \nu_0)\left[\frac{q_w}{\cos\phi_w} - \frac{\cos\phi_w}{1 - \sin\phi_w}\right]$$

$$F_2 = H\sqrt{H^2 - F_4^2} - (H-h)^2\cos(\lambda + \alpha) + F_4^2\ln\left[\frac{1 + \cos(\lambda + \alpha)}{H + \sqrt{H^2 - F_4^2}}(H - h)\right]$$

$$F_3 = \frac{2\tan\beta}{\cos\beta}\left\{\frac{q_w\sin\beta\cos(\beta + \nu_0) + \sin\phi_w}{\cos\phi_w} - \frac{\cos\phi_w[1 + \sin\beta\cos(\beta + \nu_0)]}{1 - \sin\phi_w}\right\}$$

$$F_4 = \frac{R_1}{R_2}H\sin(\lambda + \alpha) \qquad (8.23)$$

and

$$f(z) = \arcsin\left\{ \frac{sH + HR_1 \sin\alpha \cos(\lambda + \alpha)}{zH \tan\beta} - \frac{\sin\alpha\sqrt{R_2^2 z^2 - R_1^2 H^2 \sin^2(\lambda + \alpha)}}{zH \tan\beta} \right\}$$
(8.24)

The angle λ is given in expressions (8.19), and the angle α is

$$\alpha = \arcsin\frac{\sin\phi}{\sin(\beta + \nu_0)}$$
(8.25)

The solution above contains one independent geometric variable s, and an unknown angle ν_0. Both can be determined from a maximization procedure for the greatest ratio $c/\gamma H$. The results for a hopper with $R_2/H = 0.6$ ($\theta_w = 30.96°$) are depicted in Figure 8.8.

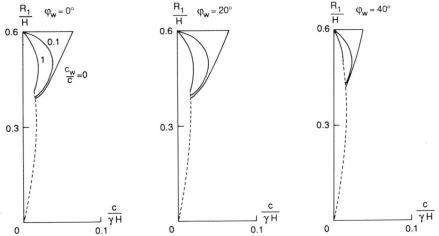

Figure 8.8 *Critical ratios $c/\gamma H$ for conical hoppers; shear/separation failure, $R_2/H = 0.6$, $q = q_w = 1$, $\phi = 40°$*

8.2.2 Axisymmetric Collapse

Although the following considerations are devoted primarily to kinematically admissible axisymmetric velocity fields in application to channeling, they equally apply to other problems where axisymmetric velocity fields may develop (see Sections 4.5 and 7.3.2).

An axisymmetric mode of failure of a slope surrounding a cylindrical channel requires the velocities of material points of the slope to be independent of the θ-coordinate of a cylindrical system r, θ, z (Figure 8.9)

$$v_r = v_r(r, z) \qquad v_z = v_z(r, z) \qquad v_\theta = 0$$
(8.26)

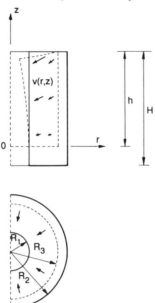

Figure 8.9 *Axisymmetric failure mechanism in a cylindrical bin*

For a slope failing toward the channel, we have

$$v_r < 0 \qquad v_z < 0 \tag{8.27}$$

Circumferential strain-rates $\dot\varepsilon_\theta = -v_r/r > 0$ imply deformation in the circumferential direction. Thus, translational motion type axisymmetric collapse mechanisms are not permissible.

A kinematically admissible axisymmetric velocity field for a rigid-perfectly plastic material obeying the associative flow rule must guarantee the corresponding strain-rates to be normal to the yield surface, where the geometrical representation of the stress and strain-rate state as vectors is used. The question now arises of how to find a velocity field that satisfies the normality requirement.

Let us consider first a material without internal friction, $\phi = 0$, whose yielding is described by Tresca yield condition (2.35). In this case, the normality condition implies that plastic deformation takes place without any change in volume, i.e., the material behaves as an incompressible one. Incompressibility condition (2.48), written in terms of velocities, is

$$\dot\varepsilon_r + \dot\varepsilon_z + \dot\varepsilon_\theta = \frac{\partial v_r}{\partial r} + \frac{\partial v_z}{\partial z} + \frac{v_r}{r} = 0 \tag{8.28}$$

Suppose now that the distribution of one of the velocity components, v_r or v_z, is given. The other component then can be determined easily by integration of equation (8.28). Examples of such a procedure in application to the stability of frictionless slopes surrounding boreholes are given by Britto and Kusakabe (1982, 1983). A similar procedure was used by Drescher (1983), to derive the channeling criterion for cylindrical bins. We will present this solution now in more detail.

It is assumed that the velocity field is bounded by a cylindrical region $R_1 < r < R_3$ and $z > 0$, with $v_r = v_z = 0$ at boundaries $r = R_3$ and $z = 0$ (Figure 8.9). The boundary conditions are fulfilled if the radial velocity is postulated as

$$v_r = -A(r - R_3)^2 z \qquad (8.29)$$

and the vertical velocity resulting from integration of (8.28) is

$$v_z = -A\frac{z^2}{2}\left[2(r - R_3) + \frac{(r - R_3)^2}{r}\right] \qquad (8.30)$$

for $r \leq R_3$ and $z \geq 0$, where A is an arbitrary positive constant. A realistic mechanism of failure, confined within the material, is obtained if the inner radius of the empty channel $R_1 \geq R_* = R_3/\sqrt{3}$. The total rate of energy dissipation, obtained by integration of the specific rate of energy over the failing region, is

$$\dot{d} = 2\pi c \int_{R_1}^{R_3} \int_0^h (\dot{\varepsilon}_1 - \dot{\varepsilon}_2 - \dot{\varepsilon}_3) r\,dr\,dz \qquad (8.31)$$

where the principal strain-rates given by

$$\dot{\varepsilon}_{1,2} = \frac{1}{2}(\dot{\varepsilon}_r + \dot{\varepsilon}_z) \pm \frac{1}{2}[(\dot{\varepsilon}_r - \dot{\varepsilon}_z)^2 + 4\dot{\varepsilon}_{rz}^2]^{1/2} \qquad (8.32)$$

with

$$\dot{\varepsilon}_r = -\frac{\partial v_r}{\partial r} \qquad\qquad \dot{\varepsilon}_z = -\frac{\partial v_z}{\partial z}$$

$$\dot{\varepsilon}_{rz} = -\frac{1}{2}\left[\frac{\partial v_r}{\partial z} + \frac{\partial v_z}{\partial r}\right] \qquad \dot{\varepsilon}_3 = \dot{\varepsilon}_\theta = -\frac{v_r}{r} \qquad (8.33)$$

are

$$\dot{\varepsilon}_{1,2} = \frac{A}{2}(R_3 - r)z\left[5 - \frac{R_3}{r}\right]$$

$$\pm \frac{A}{2}\left\{(r - R_3)^4 \frac{z^2}{r^2} + \left((r - R_3)^2 + \left[3 - \frac{R_3^2}{r^2}\right]\frac{z^2}{2}\right)^2\right\}^{1/2} \qquad (8.34)$$

$$\dot{\varepsilon}_3 = \frac{A(r - R_3)^2 z}{r}$$

Because analytic integration of expressions (8.34) is complicated, numerical integration is recommended.

The rate of energy supplied by the unit weight is

$$\dot{w} = -A\pi\gamma \int_{R_1}^{R_3} \int_0^h z^2 \left[2(r - R_3) + \frac{(r - R_3)^2}{r}\right] r\,dr\,dz \qquad (8.35)$$

By setting $\dot{d} = \dot{w}$, we obtain the following expression for ratio $c/\gamma H$

$$\frac{c}{\gamma H} = \frac{h^3 R_1 (R_1 - R_3)^2}{6 H f(R_1, R_3, h)} \qquad (8.36)$$

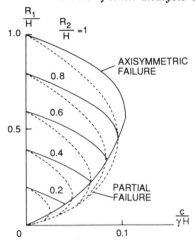

Figure 8.10 *Critical ratios $c/\gamma H$ for a cylindrical bin; $\phi = 0$*

where function $f(R_1, R_3, h)$ is the result of numerical integration of (8.34) and (8.35). By maximizing equation (8.36) with respect to geometric parameters h and R_3, we obtain the computational results for a bin with aspect ratio $R_2/H = 1$ that are graphically presented in Figure 8.10. For comparison, the results corresponding to a partial failure mechanism and the prism sliding within the bulk material are shown as dashed lines.

In the case of a material with internal friction described by Mohr-Coulomb yield condition (2.33), incompressibility condition (2.48) does not hold, and the material dilates when deforming plastically. For the velocity field given by inequalities (8.27), and $\dot\varepsilon_3 = \dot\varepsilon_\theta > 0$, the possible location of the strain-rate vector on the Mohr-Coulomb pyramid is limited to face OBC, including edges OB and OC (Figure 2.22). Our further analysis will be restricted to the edge OB, where principal strain-rates $\dot\varepsilon_1$ and $\dot\varepsilon_2$ satisfy the following inequalities

$$\dot\varepsilon_1 > 0 \qquad \dot\varepsilon_2 < 0 \tag{8.37}$$

From flow rule (2.24), and yield condition (2.33), the principal strain-rates are given by

$$\begin{aligned}
\dot\varepsilon_1 &= \dot\lambda_1(1 - \sin\phi) \\
\dot\varepsilon_2 &= -(\dot\lambda_1 + \dot\lambda_2)(1 + \sin\phi) \\
\dot\varepsilon_3 &= \dot\lambda_2(1 - \sin\phi)
\end{aligned} \tag{8.38}$$

Elimination of multipliers $\dot\lambda_1$ and $\dot\lambda_2$ from (8.38) yields

$$\dot\varepsilon_1 + \dot\varepsilon_2 + \dot\varepsilon_3 - (\dot\varepsilon_2 - \dot\varepsilon_1 - \dot\varepsilon_3)\sin\phi = 0 \tag{8.39}$$

Equation (8.39) interrelates the principal strain-rates, and, eventually, the velocities v_r and v_z, for a kinematically admissible axisymmetric collapse mechanism corresponding to edge OB. Inspection of equation (8.39) indicates that the procedure used for finding the velocity field for a frictionless material fails. In fact, equation (8.39), written in terms of the velocity components, becomes a non-linear partial differential equation with four partial derivatives. Then a procedure suggested by Drescher (1986) can be used.

This procedure makes use of the expression for inclination ξ of major principal strain-rate $\dot{\varepsilon}_1$ with respect to the r-coordinate

$$\tan 2\xi = \frac{2\dot{\varepsilon}_{rz}}{\dot{\varepsilon}_r - \dot{\varepsilon}_z} \tag{8.40}$$

which, in terms of the velocity components, can be written as

$$\tan 2\xi \frac{\partial v_r}{\partial r} - \frac{\partial v_z}{\partial r} - \frac{\partial v_r}{\partial z} - \tan 2\xi \frac{\partial v_z}{\partial z} = 0 \tag{8.41}$$

The principal strain-rates $\dot{\varepsilon}_1$ and $\dot{\varepsilon}_2$ now can be expressed as

$$\dot{\varepsilon}_{1,2} = \frac{\dot{\varepsilon}_r + \dot{\varepsilon}_z}{2} \pm \frac{\dot{\varepsilon}_r - \dot{\varepsilon}_z}{2\cos 2\xi} \tag{8.42}$$

and, using (8.33), we can write equation (8.39) as

$$\left[1 + \frac{\sin \phi}{\cos 2\xi}\right] \frac{\partial v_r}{\partial r} + \left[1 - \frac{\sin \phi}{\cos 2\xi}\right] \frac{\partial v_z}{\partial z} + (1 + \sin \phi) \frac{v_r}{r} = 0 \tag{8.43}$$

If angle $\xi = \xi(r, z)$ is given, equations (8.41) and (8.43) form a set of linear partial differential equations. As shown by Cox, Eason and Hopkins (1961), this set is always hyperbolic and can be solved by the method of characteristics. The velocity characteristics are non-orthogonal, with their orientation given by

$$\frac{dz}{dr} = \tan(\xi + \varepsilon) \qquad \alpha\text{-line}$$
$$\frac{dz}{dr} = \tan(\xi - \varepsilon) \qquad \beta\text{-line} \tag{8.44}$$

where

$$\varepsilon = \frac{\pi}{4} - \frac{\phi}{2} \tag{8.45}$$

and the relations along the characteristics are

$$dv_r + \tan(\xi + \varepsilon)dv_z = -\frac{1 + \sin \phi}{\sin 2(\xi + \varepsilon)} \frac{v_r}{r} dz \qquad \alpha\text{-line}$$
$$dv_r + \tan(\xi - \varepsilon)dv_z = -\frac{1 + \sin \phi}{\sin 2(\xi - \varepsilon)} \frac{v_r}{r} dz \qquad \beta\text{-line} \tag{8.46}$$

For $r = \infty$, equations (8.46) reduce to those for the plane-strain state in the r, z axial plane (see [3.85]). Velocity discontinuities are admissible, and they coincide with the characteristics. The jump in velocity across a velocity discontinuity is inclined at an angle ϕ, and propagates along, e.g., an α-line, according to

$$\ln \frac{[v_\alpha]}{[v_{\alpha 0}]} = \tan \phi(\xi - \xi_0) + \frac{1 + \sin \phi}{\cos \phi} \int_{r_0}^{r} \frac{\sin(\xi - \varepsilon)}{\cos(\xi + \varepsilon)} \frac{d\rho}{2\rho} \tag{8.47}$$

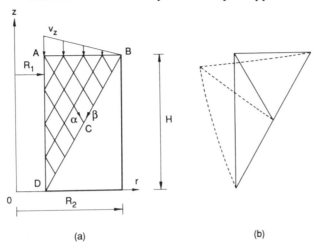

Figure 8.11 *(a) Characteristics mesh in a cylindrical bin and (b) deformed mesh; $\xi = \pi/2$, $\phi = 30°$*

where $[v_\alpha]$ is the projection of the jump in velocity $[v]$ onto the α-line, and $[v_{\alpha 0}]$ is the jump $[v_\alpha]$ at $r = r_0$, $\xi = \xi_0$.

To apply the method of characteristics for determination of a kinematically admissible axisymmetric velocity field, the function $\xi = \xi(r, z)$ must be known, and the velocity boundary conditions for a well-posed boundary-value problem must be selected. Relations (8.46), holding along the characteristics, then can be used to determine the velocities at nodal points of the characteristics mesh. The solution to equations (8.46) can be obtained numerically by means of finite difference approximation. Once the velocities at nodal points are found, the local principal strain-rates can be calculated from equations (8.32) and (8.33) using an appropriate approximation scheme. Due to the linearity of velocity equations (8.41) and (8.43), there is no restriction on the velocity boundary conditions. However, the solution will be admissible providing inequalities (8.37) hold. The total rate of energy dissipated within the deforming region can be determined by volume integration of the specific dissipation given by equation (3.99). If the velocity field contains a velocity discontinuity surface, the dissipation along it results from surface integration of equation (3.102). We will now give the application of this procedure for determining the channeling criterion for a cylindrical bin.

The simplest form of relation $\xi = \xi(r, z)$ is selected, namely, $\xi = \pi/2$ throughout the slope. Thus, the principal strain-rate trajectories are horizontal and vertical and the characteristics mesh consists of straight lines (Figure 8.11a). Since only failure within the material is considered in this example, the characteristics mesh is limited to region ABD, with lines parallel to BD being the β-lines. For a well-posed boundary-value problem within ABD, it suffices to assume that boundary BD separates the deforming region from the material at rest, and either v_r or v_z is specified along AB. First, a distribution of v_z, which is linear and increasing toward the z-axis, is considered, with v_z at point B being zero. Thus, along boundary BD we have $v_r = v_z = 0$. Within regions ABC and ACD, the mixed and the

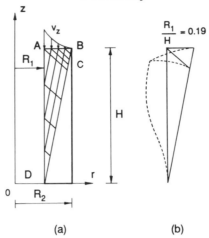

Figure 8.12 *(a) Characteristics mesh in a cylindrical bin and (b) deformed mesh; $\xi < \pi/2$, $\phi = 30°$*

characteristic boundary-value problems are formulated, respectively.

Figure 8.11b shows the deformed mesh of characteristics corresponding to a small time step and velocity field obtained by finite difference approximation of equations (8.46), for ratio $R_1/H = 1$, and for $\phi = 30°$. Due to the increasing magnitude of v_r towards the channel, the deformed shape of section AB becomes concave. As anticipated, the solution satisfies inequalities (8.37), i.e., it is kinematically admissible, and may be used to derive the channeling criterion for bins with aspect ratio $R_2/H > R_1/H + (h/H)\tan 30°$. For very small ratios R_1/H, however, numerical calculations have revealed that, regardless of the magnitude of the velocity v_z^A, first inequality (8.37) is violated, and both principal strain-rates $\dot{\varepsilon}_1$ and $\dot{\varepsilon}_2$ become negative in the vicinity of point A; the solution is kinematically inadmissible for edge OB of the yield pyramid. A similar result is found if velocity v_z at point B is set greater than zero, and boundary BCD becomes a velocity discontinuity.

A kinematically admissible solution for any ratio R_1/H, and for any bin aspect ratio R_2/H, exists if we assume $\xi = $ const. $< \pi/2$ (Figure 8.12), and velocities v_z along AB increase parabolically toward the z-axis, with $v_z^B = 0$. With these assumptions, the results of numerical maximization of ratio $c/\gamma H$, for a bin with $R_2/H = 0.4$, and for $\phi = 20°$, and $\phi = 40°$, are presented in Figure 8.13. The dashed lines in Figure 8.13 correspond to a partial failure mechanism, and they were obtained using equation (8.14). Clearly, the axisymmetric failure mechanism, however simple, gives a better, less conservative estimate of the channeling criterion.

8.3 CLOSING REMARKS

The kinematical method of limit analysis gives a safe estimate of the geometry of an unstable slope, and therefore of the dimension of an outlet that prevents channeling,

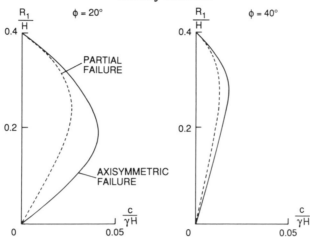

Figure 8.13 *Critical ratios $c/\gamma H$ in a cylindrical bin; partial and axisymmetric failure mechanisms, $R_2/H = 0.4$*

for any kinematically admissible mechanism of failure. The problem thus reduces to finding a mechanism that yields the least conservative estimate. It is generally accepted that the best estimate is obtained for a mechanism closer to reality. The mechanisms considered in Sections 8.2.1 and 8.2.2 are merely examples, and may give an estimate that is too conservative.

Although the partial collapse mechanisms oversimplify the actual mode of failure, they can be applied easily to non-symmetrical bins and hoppers or bins and hoppers with non-centrally located outlets. It may appear, however, that when a portion of the slope collapses, the remaining material will form a new stable slope. One may merely hypothesize that local collapse triggers the adjacent particles to follow, and failure spreads over the entire cross-section of the bin or hopper. Obviously, there is nothing that prevents simultaneous collapse of more than one prism around the channel. The axisymmetric failure mechanisms seem more realistic for cylindrical channels. However, the mathematical analysis of the latter mechanisms requires a more sophisticated method. Other than edge OB states of deformation could be considered also (cf. Cox, Eason and Hopkins, 1961).

In the examples given in Sections 8.2.1 and 8.2.2, one instantaneous yield condition and a constant unit weight of the bulk material were assumed. Generally, any variation of these parameters can be included in the analysis, with appropriately modified mechanisms. For instance, a variation of the cohesion and of the unit weight will not affect the mechanisms discussed, but only the calculation of the rate of energy dissipation (see Section 7.3.2). The resulting expressions will certainly be more complicated, but a safe estimate of channeling is ensured if the maximum values of the parameters are used in the computation.

The derived channeling criteria assume the dimensions of the channel to be identical to the dimensions of the outlet. This assumption can be modified by introducing a ratio between the dimension of the channel and the dimension of the outlet.

Among the material parameters that affect channeling, cohesion c plays the primary role; for $c = 0$, channeling cannot occur. With increasing angle of internal friction ϕ, there is a greater risk of channeling. Also, the risk increases if the bulk material adheres to the walls of the bin or hopper, $c_w > 0$.

It is interesting to compare the results presented in Sections 8.2.1 and 8.2.2 with the solution given by Jenike and Yen (1962). These authors derived a criterion for a stable slope as

$$\frac{R_1 \gamma}{c} \leq \frac{1}{2} f(\phi) \tag{8.48}$$

where $f(\phi)$ is given in graphical form in their work. Expression (8.48) depends neither on the height of bin H, nor on its outer radius R_2. To make a comparison possible, the shearing type of partial collapse mechanism for cylindrical bins was selected, and very small ratios R_1/H and R_2/H were assumed. The results are plotted in Figure 8.14. It is seen that the present results are located much above those of Jenike and Yen, particularly for low angles of internal friction where solution (8.48) predicts no channeling. A conclusive comparison of both methods, however, would require considering mechanisms other than simple, shearing, partial failure mechanisms.

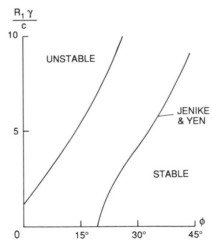

Figure 8.14 *Critical ratios $\gamma R_1/c$ for an infinitely tall cylindrical bin*

Finally, we will discuss the mutual relation between the channeling criterion and the arching criterion. In Chapter 7 and in this chapter, these criteria were analyzed separately. However, both criteria aim at predicting the geometry of a bin or hopper that guarantees uninterrupted gravitational discharge of a bulk material. In particular, the dimension of the outlet is sought. It is interesting, therefore, to consider whether for a given outlet there is a greater potential for arching or channeling to occur. It seems reasonable to assume that, for a given bulk material with a cohesion greater than zero, an arbitrarily small outlet does exist that prevents material from flowing freely by formation of an arch or dome. With an increase of the dimension of the outlet, the arch will collapse, and either mass-flow or funnel-flow will develop. In the latter case, channeling may or may not occur. The answer to this question can be found by graphically comparing the regions of unstable arches and channels in a plot similar to those used for representing the channeling criterion in Sections 8.2.1 and 8.2.2. If the curve bounding the region of unstable channels is located markedly above the curve bounding the region of unstable arches, then an increase of the dimension of the outlet should result in channeling. If, however, both curves are close, or coincide, then channeling should not occur. Note that the region of unstable channels cannot encompass the region of unstable arches; channeling cannot precede arching if the size of the outlet is gradually increased.

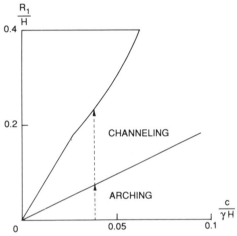

Figure 8.15   *Critical ratios $c/\gamma H$ for arching and channeling in a cylindrical bin; $R_2/H = 0.4$, $\phi = 20°$, $c_w = 0$*

To illustrate the remarks above, two simple arching and channeling criteria derived in Chapters 7 and 8 for a cylindrical bin were selected. For arching, the dimension of the critical outlet was calculated from equation (7.26) with angle $\theta_w = 0$, i.e., by considering arching in the central cylinder with a radius equal to the radius of the outlet. Also, a constant uniaxial compressive strength S_c over the height of the bin, and $\phi = 20°$, was assumed. A partial failure mechanism with the prism extending up to the wall of a bin with aspect ratio $R_2/H = 0.4$, and $c_w = 0$, were chosen for analyzing channeling (equation [8.17]). The comparison presented in Figure 8.15 indicates that, upon increasing the radius of the outlet from zero, arching should occur first, and then be followed by channeling, until a sufficiently large outlet is selected and the material flows freely.

REFERENCES

Arnold, P.C. and McLean, A.G. (1976). An analytical solution for the stress function at the wall of a converging channel. *Powder Technol.*, 13, 255-260.

Arnold, P.C. and McLean, A.G. (1976). Improved analytical flowfactors for mass-flow hoppers. *Powder Technol.*, 15, 279-281.

Arnold, P.C., McLean, A.G. and Roberts, A.W. (1981). The design of storage bins for bulk solids handling. *Bulk Solids Handl.*, 1, 13-23.

Atkinson, J.H. and Bransby, P.L. (1978). *The Mechanics of Soils*. McGraw-Hill, Maidenhead.

Benink, E.J. (1989). *Flow and Stress Analysis of Cohesionless Bulk Materials in Silos Related to Codes*. Ph.D. Thesis, University of Twente.

Berezantsev, V.G. (1948). Limit equilibrium of a medium with internal friction and cohesion in axisymmetric stress state. *Prikl. Mat. Mekh.*, 12, 99-100 (in Russian).

Beverloo, W.A., Leniger, H.A. and van de Velde, J. (1961). The flow of granular solids through orifices. *Chem. Engng Sci.*, 15, 260-269.

Bishop, A.W. and Henkel, D.J. (1962). *The Measurements of Soil Properties in the Triaxial Test*, E. Arnold, London.

Blair-Fish, P.M. and Bransby, P.L. (1973). Flow patterns and wall stresses in a mass-flow bunker. *J. Engng Ind., Trans. ASME*, 95, 17-26.

Bransby, P.L. and Blair-Fish, P.M. (1975). Initial deformations during mass flow from a bunker: observations and idealizations. *Powder Technol.*, 11, 273-288.

Brennen, C. and Pearce, J.C. (1978). Granular material flow in two-dimensional hoppers. *J. Appl. Mech., Trans. ASME*, 45, 43-50.

Britto, A.M. and Kusakabe, O. (1982). Stability of unsupported excavations in soft clay. *Géotechnique*, 32, 261-270.

Britto, A.M. and Kusakabe, O. (1983). Stability of axisymmetric excavations in clays. *J. Geotech. Engng, Trans. ASCE*, 109, 666-681.

Brown, R.L. and Richards, J.C. (1959). Exploratory study of the flow of granules through apertures. *Inst. Chem. Engrs, Trans.*, 37, 108-116.

Brown, R.L. and Richards, J.C. (1970). *Principles of Powder Mechanics*, Pergamon Press, Oxford.

Carr, J.F. and Walker, D.M. (1967/68). An annular shear cell for granular materials. *Powder Technol.*, 1, 369-373.

Chen, W.F. (1975). *Limit Analysis and Soil Plasticity*, Elsevier, Amsterdam.

Collins, I.F. (1969). The upper-bound theorem for rigid/plastic solids generalized to include Coulomb friction. *J. Mech. Phys. Solids*, 17, 323-338.

Coulomb, C.A. (1773). Sur une application des règles de maximis et minimis à quelques problèmes de statique relatifs à l'architecture. *Mem. Math. Phys. Acad. Roy. Sci. Paris*, 7, 343-382.

Cowin, S.C. (1979). The pressure ratio in the theory of bin pressures. *J. Appl. Mech., Trans. ASME*, 46, 524-528.

Cowin, S.C. and Comfort, W.J. (1982). Gravity-induced density discontinuity waves in sand columns. *J. Appl. Mech., Trans. ASME*, 49, 497-500.

Cox, A.D., Eason, G. and Hopkins, H.G. (1961). Axially symmetric plastic deformations in soils. *Phil. Trans. Roy. Soc. London*, A1036, 1-45.

Davidson, J.F. and Nedderman, R.M. (1973). The hour-glass theory of hopper flow. *Trans. Inst. Chem. Engrs*, 51, 29-35.

Desai, C.S. and Siriwardane, H.J. (1984). *Constitutive Laws for Engineering Materials with Emphasis on Geologic Materials*. Prentice-Hall, Englewood Cliffs.

Dorodnitsyn, A.A. (1959). A contribution to the solution of mixed problems of transonic aerodynamics. in *Advances in Aeronautical Sciences*, 2, 832-844, Pergamon Press, New York.

Dorodnitsyn, A.A. (1962). General method of integral relations and its application to boundary layer theory. in *Advances in Aeronautical Sciences*, 3, 207-219, Macmillan, New York.

Drescher, A. (1983). Limit plasticity approach to piping in bins. *J. Appl. Mech., Trans. ASME*, 50, 549-553.

Drescher, A. (1986). Kinematics of axisymmetric vertical slopes at collapse. *Int. J. Num. Anal. Meth. Geomech.*, 10, 431-441.

Drescher, A., Cousens, T.W. and Bransby, P.L. (1978). Kinematics of the mass flow of granular material through a plane hopper. *Géotechnique*, 28, 27-42.

Drescher, A. and Vardoulakis, I. (1982). Geometric softening in triaxial tests on granular material. *Géotechnique*, 32, 291-303.

Drescher, A. and Vgenopoulou, I. (1985). A theoretical analysis of channeling in bins and hoppers. *Powder Technol.*, 42, 181-191.

Drescher, A. and Zhang, Y. (1986). An approximate analysis of the bearing capacity of prismatic rock pillars. *Int. J. Rock Mech. Sci. Geomech. Abstr.*, 23, 355-362.

Drucker, D.C. (1953). Limit analysis of two- and three-dimensional soil mechanics problems. *J. Mech. Phys. Solids*, 1, 217-226.

Drucker, D.C., Gibson, R.E. and Henkel, D.J. (1957) Soil mechanics and work-hardening theories of plasticity. *Trans. ASCE*, 122, 338-346.

Drucker, D.C. and Prager, W. (1952). Soil mechanics and plastic analysis or limit design. *Q. Appl. Math.*, 10, 157-165.

Enstad, G. (1975). On the theory of arching in mass-flow hoppers. *Chem. Engng Sci.*, 30, 1273-1283.

Enstad, G. (1977). A note on the stresses and dome formation in axially symmetric mass flow hoppers. *Chem. Engng Sci.*, 32, 339-342.

Enstad, G., (1981). *A Novel Theory on the Arching and Doming in Mass Flow Hoppers.* The Chr. Michelsen Institute, Bergen.

Gardner, G.C. (1963). The "best" hopper profile for cohesive material. *Chem. Engng Sci.*, 18, 35-39.

Haar, A. and von Kármán, T. (1909). Zur Theorie der Spannungszustande in plastichen und sandartigen Medien. *Nachr. Ges. Wiss. Gott., Math. Phys. K1.*, 204-218.

Hill, R., (1950). *The Mathematical Theory of Plasticity*, Clarendon Press, Oxford.

Horne, R.M. and Nedderman, R.M. (1976). Analysis of the stress distribution in two-dimensional bins by the method of characteristics. *Powder Technol.*, 14, 93-102.

Horne, R.M. and Nedderman, R.M. (1978). Stress distribution in hoppers. *Powder Technol.*, 19, 243-254.

Horne, R.M. and Nedderman, R.M. (1978). An analysis of switch stresses in two-dimensional bunkers. *Powder Technol.*, 19, 235-241.

Janssen, H.A. (1895). Versuche über Getreidedruck in Silozellen. *Zeit. Ver. Deutsch. Ing.*, 39, 1045-1049.

Jenike, A.W. (1961). *Gravity Flow of Bulk Solids.* Utah Univ. Eng. Exp. Stn, Bull. 108.

Jenike, A.W. (1964). *Storage and Flow of Solids.* Utah Univ. Eng. Exp. Stn, Bull. 123.

Jenike, A.W. (1964). Steady gravity flow of frictional-cohesive solids in converging channels. *J. Appl. Mech., Trans. ASME*, 31, 5-11.

Jenike, A.W. (1987). A theory of flow of particulate solids in converging and diverging channels based on a conical yield function. *Powder Technol.*, 50, 229-236.

Jenike, A.W., Elsey, P.J. and Woolley, R.H. (1960). Flow properties of bulk solids. *Proc. ASTM*, 60, 1168-1181.

Jenike, A.W., Johanson, J.R. and Carson, J.W. (1973). Bin loads-part 2: Concepts. *J. Engng Ind., Trans. ASME*, 95, 1-5.

Jenike, A.W., Johanson, J.R. and Carson, J.W. (1973). Bin loads-part 3: Mass-flow bins. *J. Engng Ind., Trans. ASME*, 95, 6-12.

Jenike, A.W., Johanson, J.R. and Carson, J.W. (1973). Bin loads-part 4: Funnel-flow bins. *J. Engng Ind., Trans ASME*, 95, 13-16.

Jenike, A.W. and Leser, T. (1963). A flow-no-flow criterion in the gravity flow of powders in converging channels. *Proc. 4th Int. Congr. Rheol.*, Brown Univ. Providence, 125-141.

Jenike, A.W. and Shield, R.T. (1959). On the plastic flow of Coulomb solids beyond original failure. *J. Appl. Mech., Trans. ASME*, 26, 599-602.

Jenike, A.W. and Yen, B.C. (1962). Slope stability in axial symmetry. *Proc. 5th Symp. Rock. Mech.*, Univ. Minnesota, 689-710.

Jenkins, J.T. and Cowin, S.C. (1979). Theories for flowing granular materials. In *Mechanics Applied to the Transport of Bulk Materials*, ASME, AMD-31, 79-90.

Johanson, J.R. (1964). Stress and velocity fields in the gravity flow of bulk solids. *J. Appl. Mech., Trans. ASME*, 31, 499-506.

Johanson, J.R. (1966). The use of flow-corrective inserts in bins. *J. Engng Ind., Trans. ASME*, 88, 224-230.

Johanson, J.R. (1967/68). The placement of inserts to correct flow in bins. *Powder Technol.*, 1, 328-333.

Johnson, W. and Mellor, P.B. (1983). *Engineering Plasticity*, E. Horwood, Chichester.

Ketchum, M.S. (1929). *The Design of Walls, Bins and Grain Elevators*, McGraw-Hill, New York.

Kwaszczyńska, K., Mróz, Z. and Drescher, A. (1969). Analysis of compression of short cylinders of Coulomb material. *Int. J. Mech. Sci.*, 11, 145-158.

Lévy. M. (1871). Extrait du mémoire sur les équations générales des mouvements intérieurs des corps solides ductile au delà des limites où l'élasticité pourrait les ramener à leur premier état. *J. Mec. Purres Appl.*, 16, 369-372.

Lippman, H. (1960). Elementary methods for the analysis of certain forging processes. *Int. J. Mech. Sci.*, 1, 109-120.

Meric, R.A. and Tabarrok, B. (1982). On the gravity flow of granular materials. *Int. J. Mech. Sci.*, 24, 469-478.

Michalowski, R.L. (1983). Approximate theory of loads in plane asymmetrical converging hoppers. *Powder Technol.*, 36, 5-11.

Michalowski, R.L. (1984). Flow of granular material through a plane hopper. *Powder Technol.*, 39, 29-40.

Michalowski, R.L. (1987). Flow of granular media through a plane parallel/converging bunker. *Chem. Engng Sci.*, 42, 2587-2596.

Molerus, O. (1978). Effect of interparticle cohesive forces on the flow behaviour of powders. *Powder Technol.*, 20, 161-175.

Moriyama, R. and Jimbo, G. (1986). Effects of the filling method on wall friction coefficient. *J. Bulk Solids Stor. Silos*, 2, 1-6.

Mróz, Z. and Drescher, A. (1969). Limit plasticity approach to some cases of flow of bulk solids. *J. Engng Ind., Trans. ASME*, 91, 357-364.

Mróz, Z. and Kwaszczyńska, K. (1971). Some boundary-value problems for density-hardening granular media. *Rozpr. Inz.*, 19, 15-42 (in Polish).

Mróz, Z. and Szymański, C. (1971). Simplified theory of granular material flow in converging channels. *Arch. Inz. Lad.*, 17, 551-578 (in Polish).

Mróz, Z. and Szymański, C. (1971). Gravity flow of a granular material in a converging channel. *Arch. Mech.*, 23, 897-917.

Nanninga, N. (1956). Does the usual method of calculation for establishing pressures on walls and bottom of silos give safe results? *De Ingenieur*, 44, 190-194 (in Dutch).

Neal, B.G. *The Plastic Methods of Structural Analysis*. J. Wiley & Sons, New York, 1956.

Nedderman, R.M. (1981). Hopper studies at Cambridge University, England: a review of ten years progress. *Bulk Solids Handl.*, 1, 25-30.

Nedderman, R.M., Tüzün, U., Savage, S.B. and Houlsby, G.T. (1982). The flow of granular materials-I: Discharge rates from hoppers. *Chem. Engng Sci.*, 37, 1597-1609.

Nguyen, T.V., Brennen, C. and Sabersky, R.H. (1979). Gravity flow of granular materials in conical hoppers. *J. Appl. Mech., Trans. ASME*, 46, 529-535.

Pariseau, W.C. (1969/70). Discontinuous velocity fields in gravity flows of granular materials through slots. *Powder Technol.*, 3, 218-226.

Paul, B. (1968). Generalized pyramidal fracture and yield criteria. *Int. J. Solid Struct.*, 4, 175-196.

Perry, M.G., Rothwell, E. and Woodfin, W.T. (1976). Model studies of mass-flow bunkers. II. Velocity distributions in the discharge of solids from mass-flow bunkers. *Powder Technol.*, 14, 81-92.

Pitman, E.B. (1986). Stress and velocity fields in two- and three-dimensional hoppers. *Powder Technol.*, 47, 219-231.

Polderman, H.G., Scott, A.M. and Boom, J. (1985). Solids stresses in bunkers with inserts. *Int. Chem. Engng Symp. Ser.*, No. 91, 227-240.

Prager, W. and Hodge, P.G. (1968). *Theory of Perfectly Plastic Solids*, Dover Publ., New York.

Rankine, W. (1857). On the stability of loose earth. *Phil. Trans. Roy. Soc. London*, 147, 9-28.

Richmond, O. and Gardner, G.C. (1962). Limiting spans for arching of bulk materials in vertical channels. *Chem. Engng Sci.*, 17, 1071-1078.

Richmond, O. and Morrison, H.L. (1979). Positive pressure hoppers of maximum convergence. In *Mechanics Applied to the Transport of Bulk Materials*, ASME, AMD-31, 103-111.

Roberts, A.W., Ooms, M. and Scott, O.J. (1984). Surface friction and wear in the storage, gravity flow and handling of bulk solids. *Inst. Mech. Engng (Austral.)*, C355, 123-134.

Rooda, J.L. (1975). A numerical method for the calculation of the powder flow properties obtained with the Jenike Flow Factor Tester. *Powder Technol.*, 12, 97-102.

Roscoe, K.H. and Poorooshasb, H.B. (1963). A theoretical and experimental study of strains in triaxial compression tests on normally consolidated clays. *Géotechnique*, 13, 12-38.

Roscoe, K.H., Schofield, A.N. and Thurairajah, A. (1963). Yielding of clays in states wetter than critical. *Géotechnique*, 13, 211-240.

Roscoe, K.H., Schofield, A.N. and Wroth, C.P. (1958). On the yiedling of soils. *Géotechnique*, 8, 22-52.

Rowe, P.W. (1962). The stress dilatancy relation for static equilibrium of an assembly of particles in contact. *Phil. Trans. Proc. Roy. Soc. London.* A269, 500-567.

Salençon, J. (1977). *Applications of the Theory of Plasticity in Soil Mechanics*, J. Wiley & Sons, New York.

Savage, S.B. (1965). The mass flow of granular materials derived from coupled velocity-stress fields. *British J. Appl. Phys.*, 16, 1885-1888.

Savage, S.B. (1967). Gravity flow of a cohesionless bulk solid in a converging conical channel. *Int. J. Mech. Sci.*, 9, 651-659.

Savage, S.B. and Sayed, M. (1979). Gravity flow of cohesionless granular materials in wedge-shaped hoppers. In *Mechanics Applied to the Transport of Bulk Materials*, ASME, AMD-31, 1-24.

Savage, S.B. and Sayed, M. (1981). Gravity flow of coarse cohesionless granular materials in conical hoppers. *J. Appl. Math. Phys. (ZAMP)*, 32, 125-143.

Savage, S.B. and Yong, R.N. (1970). Stresses developed by cohesionless granular materials in bins. *Int. J. Mech. Sci.*, 12, 675-693.

Savage, S.B., Yong, R.N. and McInnes, D. (1969). Stress discontinuities in cohesionless particulate materials. *Int. J. Mech. Sci.*, 11, 595-602.

Schofield, A.N. and Wroth, C.P. (1968). *Critical State Soil Mechanics*. McGraw-Hill, London.

Schubert, H. (1975). Tensile strength of agglomerates. *Powder Technol.* 11, 107-119.

Shield, R.T. (1953). Mixed boundary value problems in soil mechanics. *Q. Appl. Math.*, 11, 61-75.

Shroeder, W. and Webster, D.A. (1949). Press-forging thin sections, effect of friction, area and thickness on pressures required. *J.. Appl. Mech., Trans. ASME*, 16, 289-294.

Sokolovskii, V.V. (1939). The plane problem of the theory of earth pressure. *Dokl. Akad. Nauk SSSR*, 22 (in Russian).

Sokolovskii, V.V. (1960). *Statics of Soil Media*, Butterworths, London.

Sokolovskii, V.V. (1965). *Statics of Granular Media*, Pergamon Press, New York.

Spink, C.D. and Nedderman, R.M. (1978). Gravity discharge rate of fine particles from hoppers. *Powder Technol.*, 21, 245-261.

Stainforth, P.T., Ashley, R.C. and Morley, J.N.B. (1970/71). Computer analysis of powder flow characteristics. *Powder Technol.*, 4, 250-256.

Takahashi, H. and Yanai, H. (1973). Flow profile and void fraction of granular solids in a moving bed. *Powder Technol.*, 7, 205-214.

Terzaghi, K. (1943). *Theoretical Soil Mechanics*, J. Wiley & Sons, New York.

Tüzün, U., Houlsby, G.T., Nedderman, R.M. and Savage, S.B. (1982). The flow of granular materials-II; Velocity distributions in slow flow. *Chem. Engng Sci.*,

37, 1691-1709.

Van Zuilichem, D.J., van Egmond, N.D. and de Swart, J.G. (1974). Density behaviour of flowing granular material. *Powder Technol.*, 10, 161-169.

Vardoulakis, I., Graf, B. and Gudehus, G. (1981). Trap-door problem with dry sand: A statical approach based upon model test kinematics. *Int. J. Num. Anal. Meth. Geomech.*, 5, 57-78.

Walker, D.M. (1966). An approximate theory for pressures and arching in hoppers. *Chem. Engng Sci.*, 21, 975-997.

Walters, J.K. (1973). A theoretical analysis of stresses in silos with vertical walls. *Chem. Engng Sci.*, 28, 13-21.

Walters, J.K. (1973). A theoretical analysis of stresses in axially-symmetric hoppers and bunkers. *Chem. Engng Sci.*, 28, 779-789.

Williams, J.C. (1977). The rate of discharge of coarse granular materials from conical mass flow hoppers. *Chem. Engng Sci.*, 32, 247-255.

Wilms, H. and Schwedes, J. (1985). Analysis of the active stress field in hoppers. *Powder Technol.*, 42, 15-25.

Wol-Gajewska, B. (1978). *Application of Plasticity Equations to the Analysis of Unsteady Discharge of Granular Materials from Containers.* Inst. Fund. Tech. Res. Polish Acad. Sci. 28, (in Polish).

APPENDIX A
CHARACTERISTICS

The type of two simultaneous first-order partial differential equations

$$A_1\frac{\partial u}{\partial x} + B_1\frac{\partial u}{\partial y} + C_1\frac{\partial v}{\partial x} + D_1\frac{\partial v}{\partial y} = F_1$$

$$A_2\frac{\partial u}{\partial x} + B_2\frac{\partial u}{\partial y} + C_2\frac{\partial v}{\partial x} + D_2\frac{\partial v}{\partial y} = F_2$$

(A.1)

where A_1, B_1, etc., are functions of x, y, u, v, can be determined by equating to zero the characteristic determinant of equations (A.1) supplemented by expressions for the differentials

$$du = \frac{\partial u}{\partial x}dx + \frac{\partial u}{\partial y}dy$$

$$dv = \frac{\partial v}{\partial x}dx + \frac{\partial v}{\partial y}dy$$

(A.2)

The characteristic determinant of (A.1) and (A.2) is

$$\begin{vmatrix} A_1 & B_1 & C_1 & D_1 \\ A_2 & B_2 & C_2 & D_2 \\ dx & dy & 0 & 0 \\ 0 & 0 & dx & dy \end{vmatrix}$$

(A.3)

and, when equated to zero, yields the following quadratic equation in dy/dx

$$(A_1C_2 - A_2C_1)\left[\frac{dy}{dx}\right]^2 + (B_1C_2 + A_2D_1 - A_1D_2 - C_1B_2)\frac{dy}{dx}$$

$$+ (B_1D_2 - B_2D_1) = 0$$

(A.4)

The roots of (A.4) depend on the sign of the discriminant

$$\Delta = (B_1C_2 + A_2D_1 - A_1D_2 - C_1B_2)^2 - 4(A_1C_2 - A_2C_1)(B_1D_2 - B_2D_1)$$ (A.5)

If $\Delta < 0$, the roots are imaginary, and equations (A.1) are said to be *elliptic*. If $\Delta = 0$, the roots are equal, and equations (A.1) are *parabolic*. If $\Delta > 0$, two roots are real, and equations (A.1) are *hyperbolic*.

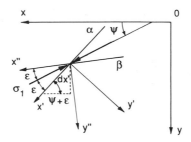

Figure A.1   *Orientation of stress characteristics*

For set (3.18) and (A.2), the characteristic determinant is

$$\begin{vmatrix} 1 + \sin\phi\cos 2\psi & \sin\phi\sin 2\psi & -2\sigma\sin\phi\sin 2\psi & 2\sigma\sin\phi\cos 2\psi \\ \sin\phi\sin 2\psi & 1 - \sin\phi\cos 2\psi & 2\sigma\sin\phi\cos 2\psi & 2\sigma\sin\phi\sin 2\psi \\ dx & dy & 0 & 0 \\ 0 & 0 & dx & dy \end{vmatrix} \qquad (A.6)$$

and, when equated to zero, gives

$$(\cos 2\psi + \sin\phi)\left[\frac{dy}{dx}\right]^2 - 2\sin 2\psi\frac{dy}{dx} + \sin\phi - \cos 2\psi = 0 \qquad (A.7)$$

whose discriminant

$$\Delta = 4\cos^2\phi \qquad (A.8)$$

is greater than zero for all real values of ϕ. Thus, equations (3.18) are hyperbolic, and the roots of (A.7) are

$$\frac{dy}{dx} = \frac{\sin 2\psi + \cos\phi}{\cos 2\psi + \sin\phi} = \tan\left[\psi + \frac{\pi}{4} - \frac{\phi}{2}\right]$$

$$\frac{dy}{dx} = \frac{\sin 2\psi - \cos\phi}{\cos 2\psi + \sin\phi} = \tan\left[\psi - \frac{\pi}{4} - \frac{\phi}{2}\right] \qquad (A.9)$$

Equations (A.9) define two families of lines, α- and β-lines, that are inclined to the direction of principal stress σ_1 at angle

$$\varepsilon = \pm\left[\frac{\pi}{4} - \frac{\phi}{2}\right] \qquad (A.10)$$

where the upper sign corresponds to the α-line, and the lower sign to the β-line (Figure A.1). Along these lines, equations (3.18) become ordinary differential equations, and the α-and β-lines are called the *characteristics*. In fact, choosing a local x', y'-coordinate system with the x'-axis aligned along the α-line (Figure A.1), using (A.10), we can write equations (3.18) as

$$(1 + \sin^2\phi)\frac{\partial\sigma}{\partial x'} - \sin\phi\cos\phi\frac{\partial\sigma}{\partial y'} + 2\sigma\sin\phi\cos\phi\frac{\partial\psi}{\partial x'} + 2\sigma\sin^2\phi\frac{\partial\psi}{\partial y'} = \gamma\sin(\psi + \varepsilon)$$

$$-\sin\phi\cos\phi\frac{\partial\sigma}{\partial x'} + \cos^2\phi\frac{\partial\sigma}{\partial y'} + 2\sigma\sin^2\phi\frac{\partial\psi}{\partial x'} - 2\sigma\sin\phi\cos\phi\frac{\partial\psi}{\partial y'} = \gamma\cos(\psi + \varepsilon)$$

$$(A.11)$$

Multiplying $(A.11)_1$ by $\cos\phi$, and $(A.11)_2$ by $\sin\phi$, adding both equations and rearranging, we obtain

$$\frac{d\sigma}{dx'} + 2\sigma\tan\phi\frac{d\psi}{dx'} = \gamma[\sin(\psi+\varepsilon) + \cos(\psi+\varepsilon)\tan\phi] \qquad (A.12)$$

and using

$$\sin(\psi+\varepsilon) = \frac{dy}{dx'} \qquad \cos(\psi+\varepsilon) = \frac{dx}{dx'} \qquad (A.13)$$

(Figure A.1), we can write equation (A.12) as

$$d\sigma + 2\sigma\tan\phi\, d\psi = \gamma(dy + \tan\phi\, dx) \qquad (A.14)$$

A similar procedure for the x''-axis aligned along the β-line (Figure A.1), yields

$$d\sigma - 2\sigma\tan\phi\, d\psi = \gamma(dy - \tan\phi\, dx) \qquad (A.15)$$

APPENDIX B
LIMIT ANALYSIS THEOREMS

The derivation of the limit analysis theorems makes use of the principle of virtual work in rate form. This principle states that the rate of work of external forces equals the rate of work of internal forces. The rate of work of external forces $\dot{w}$ is the sum of the dot products of tractions T_i and velocities v_i along the boundary S_t, reactions R_i and velocities v_i along the moving boundary S_r, and body forces γ_i and velocities v_i within the volume of the body V (Figure B.1a)

$$\dot{w} = \int_{S_t} T_i v_i dS_t - \int_{S_r} R_i v_i dS_r + \int_V \gamma_i v_i dV \tag{B.1}$$

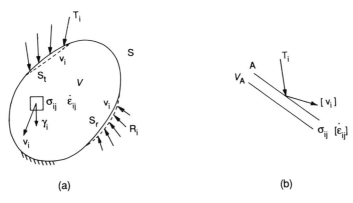

(a)   (b)

Figure B.1 *Notation in the principle of virtual work, (a) volume V and (b) velocity discontinuity V_A*

The rate of work of internal forces $\dot{d}$ is the dot product of stresses σ_{ij} and strain-rates $\dot{\varepsilon}_{ij}$ within the volume V

$$\dot{d} = \int_V \sigma_{ij} \dot{\varepsilon}_{ij} dV \tag{B.2}$$

The following identity then can be written

$$\int_V \sigma_{ij} \dot{\varepsilon}_{ij} dV = \int_{S_t} T_i v_i dS_t - \int_{S_r} R_i v_i dS_r + \int_V \gamma_i v_i dV \tag{B.3}$$

If the deformation field contains a velocity discontinuity surface A regarded as the limit of a thin layer (Figure B.1b), the rate of work of internal forces is supplemented by the dot product of the stresses, σ_{ij}, and strain-rates within the layer, $[\dot{\varepsilon}_{ij}]$,

$$\int_{V_A} \sigma_{ij}[\dot{\varepsilon}_{ij}]dV_A \equiv \int_A T_i[v_i]dA \tag{B.4}$$

Note that the existence of a stress discontinuity does not add any term to the virtual work equation, for both the stress vector and velocity are continuous across such a surface.

Identity (B.3) holds if the stresses σ_{ij} satisfy equilibrium equations (3.3), and the tractions T_i and reactions R_i satisfy boundary conditions (3.5). The strain-rates $\dot{\varepsilon}_{ij}$ must result from the velocities v_i according to equation (3.10). Further, changes in the boundary S and the volume V of the body are negligibly small, and the equilibrium equations refer to the undeformed state of the body. Equation (B.3) holds for any stress field and any velocity field satisfying the above restrictions, i.e., these fields need not be related by a constitutive law. Therefore, it equally applies to the true stress and velocity field for a rigid-perfectly plastic model, and to any virtual stress and velocity field.

Limit Theorems based on a Statically Admissible Solution

Consider a true static and kinematic solution for a rigid-perfectly plastic material that leads to the true limit load, tractions T_i on part S_L of the surface S. Let the tractions T_i on part S_t of the surface S, and body forces γ_i over the volume V be given, and $R_i v_i = 0$. Since the solution is true, the stress field σ_{ij} satisfies equilibrium equations (3.3), and the velocity field v_i is related to the strain-rate field $\dot{\varepsilon}_{ij}$ by equation (3.10). Applying the principle of virtual work (B.3) to the true stress and strain-rate (velocity) field, we have

$$\int_V \sigma_{ij}\dot{\varepsilon}_{ij}dV + \int_{V_A} \sigma_{ij}[\dot{\varepsilon}_{ij}]dV_A = \int_{S_t} T_i v_i dS_t + \int_{S_L} T_i v_i dS_L + \int_V \gamma_i v_i dV \tag{B.5}$$

Now assume a statically admissible solution σ^s_{ij} with the corresponding limiting tractions T^s_i on the surface S_L; $T^s_i = T_i$ on the surface S_t, and $\gamma^s_i = \gamma_i$ over the volume V. Combining the solution σ^s_{ij}, T^s_i, and the true solution v_i, $\dot{\varepsilon}_{ij}$, in the principle of virtual work, we obtain

$$\int_V \sigma^s_{ij}\dot{\varepsilon}_{ij}dV + \int_{V_A} \sigma^s_{ij}[\dot{\varepsilon}_{ij}]dV_A = \int_{S_t} T_i v_i dS_t + \int_{S_L} T^s_i v_i dS_L + \int_V \gamma_i v_i dV \tag{B.6}$$

By subtracting equation (B.6) from (B.5) we arrive at

$$\int_V (\sigma_{ij} - \sigma^s_{ij})\dot{\varepsilon}_{ij}dV + \int_{V_A} (\sigma_{ij} - \sigma^s_{ij})[\dot{\varepsilon}_{ij}]dV_A = \int_{S_L} (T_i - T^s_i)v_i dS_L \tag{B.7}$$

Let us examine the sign of the first left-hand side term in equation (B.7). Referring to the geometrical representation of the stress and strain-rate state as vectors (Figure B.2a), we observe that the vector representing the true stress state ends at

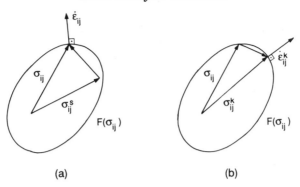

Figure B.2   *Representations of (a) statically admissible and (b) kinematically admissible solutions in the stress space*

the yield surface. In view of the third requirement for a statically admissible field, the vector representing the admissible stress state ends either inside the surface or at the surface. For a convex yield surface the vector representing the difference $\sigma_{ij} - \sigma_{ij}^s$ lies entirely within the surface. Due to normality of the strain-rate vector to the yield surface implied by the associative flow rule, the dot product of the stress difference vector and the strain-rate vector cannot be negative, and neither can the integral. A similar conclusion applies to the second left-hand side term. Accordingly, the right-hand side term in equation (B.7) is also non-negative, and

$$\int_{S_L} T_i v_i \, dS_L \geq \int_{S_L} T_i^s v_i \, dS_L \tag{B.8}$$

Inequality (B.8) means that the rate of work of true limiting tractions cannot be less than the rate of work of tractions resulting from a statically admissible field. A similar relation can be derived for the limit load identified with body forces γ_i.

Consider now three cases where inequality (B.8) leads to an estimate of the surface limit load. The first case takes place when the velocities along the boundary S_L are uniform, and (B.8) becomes

$$v_i \int_{S_L} T_i \, dS_L \geq v_i \int_{S_L} T_i^s \, dS_L \tag{B.9}$$

or

$$v_i P_i \geq v_i P_i^s \tag{B.10}$$

where P_i is the resultant of surface tractions T_i. If P_i is colinear with P_i^s, we finally have

$$P_i \geq P_i^s \tag{B.11}$$

Now assume that the velocities along S_L correspond to rigid rotation with angular velocity ω_k. Then, relation (B.8) can be written as

$$\int_{S_L} \varepsilon_{ijk} T_i x_j \omega_k \, dS_L \geq \int_{S_L} \varepsilon_{ijk} T_i^s x_j \omega_k \, dS_L \tag{B.12}$$

Since $\varepsilon_{ijk} T_i x_j = m_k$, and $\omega_k =$ const., we obtain

$$M_k \geq M_k^s \tag{B.13}$$

where M_k is the moment of tractions T_k.

In the last case, let the intensity of limiting tractions T_i over S_L be specified by a multiplier μ, then

$$\mu \geq \mu^s \tag{B.14}$$

In the case of the limit load identified with body forces γ_i of intensity κ, we obtain

$$\kappa \geq \kappa^s \tag{B.15}$$

Thus, only the resultant force, the resultant moment, the intensity of tractions, and the intensity of body forces can be obtained from a statical solution. The corresponding lower bound theorem for loads inducing collapse is given in Section 3.5.2. Physically, the inequalities above mean that a body under limit loads determined from a statically admissible solution will not collapse unless the solution is a true one, and equalities hold.

A similar proof applies to the limit load resisting collapse at the moving boundary S_r. This time, however, the resulting inequality is reversed, for the rate of work of reactions on velocities is negative

$$\int_{S_r} R_i v_i \, dS_r \leq \int_{S_r} R_i^s v_i \, dS_r \tag{B.16}$$

and the upper bound theorem for loads resisting collapse follows (see Section 3.5.2).

Limit Theorems based on a Kinematically Admissible Solution

Consider a kinematically admissible solution v_i^k, $\dot{\varepsilon}_{ij}^k$ with corresponding limiting tractions T_i^k on the surface S_L; $T_i^k = T_i$ on the surface S_t, $\gamma_i^k = \gamma_i$ over the volume V, and $R_i v_i = 0$. Since plastic strain-rates require stresses that satisfy the yield condition, for any $\dot{\varepsilon}_{ij}^k$ a stress σ_{ij}^k exists such that its geometrical representation is a vector with its end at the yield surface (Figure B.2b).

Let us equate the rate of energy dissipated within a body by stresses σ_{ij}^k with the rate of work of external forces T_i^k, T_i, and γ_i

$$d = \int_V \sigma_{ij}^k \dot{\varepsilon}_{ij}^k \, dV + \int_{V_A} \sigma_{ij}^k [\dot{\varepsilon}_{ij}^k] \, dV_A = \int_{S_t} T_i v_i^k \, dS_t + \int_{S_L} T_i^k v_i^k \, dS_L + \int_V \gamma_i v_i^k \, dV \tag{B.17}$$

Note that equation (B.17) does not express the principle of virtual work, for the stresses σ_{ij}^k need not satisfy the local equilibrium equations.

On the other hand, the principle of virtual work for the true stresses σ_{ij}, true limiting tractions T_i, and a kinematically admissible field v_i^k, $\dot{\varepsilon}_{ij}^k$, gives

$$\int_V \sigma_{ij} \dot{\varepsilon}_{ij}^k \, dV + \int_{V_A} \sigma_{ij} [\dot{\varepsilon}_{ij}^k] \, dV_A = \int_{S_t} T_i v_i^k \, dS_t + \int_{S_L} T_i v_i^k \, dS_L + \int_V \gamma_i v_i^k \, dV \tag{B.18}$$

By subtracting equation (B.18) from (B.17) we have

$$\int_V (\sigma_{ij}^k - \sigma_{ij})\dot{\varepsilon}_{ij}^k dV + \int_{V_A} (\sigma_{ij}^k - \sigma_{ij})[\dot{\varepsilon}_{ij}^k]dV_A = \int_{S_L} (T_i^k - T_i)v_i^k dS_L \qquad (B.19)$$

Referring to Figure B.2b, we conclude that the left-hand side terms in (B.19) are non-negative, and so is the right-hand term. This leads to

$$\int_{S_L} T_i^k v_i^k dS_L \geq \int_{S_L} T_i v_i^k dS_L \qquad (B.20)$$

Thus, the rate of work done by true limiting tractions on the velocities resulting from a kinematically admissible field cannot be greater than the rate of work done on the same velocities by the tractions resulting from a kinematically admissible field. This also applies to limiting body forces γ_i. The corresponding upper bound theorem for loads inducing collapse is given in Section 3.5.2. In contrast to the case of a statically admissible solution, a body under limit loads determined from a kinematically admissible solution must collapse.

The proof of the lower bound theorem for loads resisting collapse given in Section 3.5.2 is obtained analogously, with the resulting inequality

$$\int_{S_r} R_i^k v_i^k dS_r \leq \int_{S_r} R_i v_i^k dS_r \qquad (B.21)$$

Equality in expressions (B.20) and (B.21) holds if the kinematic solution is a true one. Note that again only the resultant force, the resultant moment, the intensity of tractions or the intensity of body forces can be determined from a kinematic solution.

GLOSSARY OF SYMBOLS

a_i	acceleration vector
$a_{x(y,r,...,\theta)}$	component of a_i
$A, B, \ldots, N$	constant
b, B	half-width or radius of a bin or hopper
c	instantaneous cohesion (cohesion)
c_e	effective cohesion
c_w	wall cohesion
c_ν	pseudo cohesion
$d\varepsilon_{ij}$	strain-increment tensor
$d\varepsilon_p$	volumetric strain-increment for the triaxial compression test
$d\varepsilon_q$	shear strain-increment for the triaxial compression test
$d\varepsilon_{x(y,r,...,\theta)}$	normal component of $d\varepsilon_{ij}$
$d\varepsilon_{xy(yz,...,r\theta)}$	shear component of $d\varepsilon_{ij}$
$d\varepsilon_{1(2,3)}$	principal strain-increment
$d\lambda, \dot{\lambda}$	multiplier in the flow rule
$\dot{d}$	total rate of work dissipated in deformation (energy dissipation)
D	distribution factor
$f(\ ), g(\ )$	function
ff	flow-factor
$F, F(\ )$	yield condition
F_i	force vector
$F_{x(y,z)}$	component of F_i
g_i	acceleration of gravity vector

G, $G(\ )$	plastic potential
h, H	height
i, j, k	indices $(x, y, z$, etc.$)$
k	ratio between the wall normal stress and the average stress acting on a slice (Janssen's coefficient)
K, K_1, K_2	proportionality factor relating the wall shear stress to the average stress acting on a slice
l, L	length
m	pure number; $m = 1$ for a plane bin or hopper, $m = 2$ for a cylindrical bin or conical hopper
p	isotropic stress for the triaxial compression test
P	limit load inducing collapse
q	shear stress for the triaxial compression test
q	constant relating S_c, S_t, and ϕ
q	volume flow rate
Q	mass flow rate
r, R	radius
r, θ	polar coordinate axes
r, θ, z (x, y, θ)	cylindrical coordinate axes
r, θ, ω	spherical coordinate axes
R	hydraulic radius
R	limit load resisting collapse
s, t, w	distance
S	surface
S_t	uniaxial tensile strength
S_c	uniaxial compressive strength
S_{tw}	wall adhesion
t	time
T_i	traction vector
$T_{x(y,z)}$	component of T_i
u_i	displacement-increment vector
v_i	velocity vector

$v_{n(t)}$	normal (tangential) component of v_i
$v_{x(y,r,...,\theta)}$	component of v_i
$v_{\alpha(\beta)}$	projection of the velocity vector onto the velocity characteristics
$[v_i]$	velocity jump vector
$[v_{n(t)}]$	normal (tangential) component of $[v_i]$
$[v_\alpha]$	jump in v_α
V	volume
$\dot{w}$	total rate of work of tractions and body forces
W	weight
x, y, z	Cartesian coordinate axes
α	pure number; $\alpha = 1$ for the active state of stress, $\alpha = -1$ for the passive state of stress
α, β	stress or velocity characteristics
$\alpha, \beta, ..., \omega$	angle
γ_i	unit weight vector
δ	effective angle of internal friction
$\Delta\dot{d}$	rate of work dissipated in deformation per unit volume
$\Delta\dot{d}_n$	rate of work dissipated in deformation per unit length of the velocity discontinuity
Δn	thickness
$\Delta\dot{w}$	rate of work of body forces per unit volume
ε	angle between σ_1 or $\dot{\varepsilon}_1$ and the stress or velocity characteristics
$\varepsilon_{1(2,3)}$	principal strain
$\dot{\varepsilon}_{ij}$	strain-rate tensor
$\dot{\varepsilon}_{x(y,r,...,\theta)}$	normal component of $\dot{\varepsilon}_{ij}$
$\dot{\varepsilon}_{xy(yz,...,r\theta)}$	shear component of $\dot{\varepsilon}_{ij}$
$\dot{\varepsilon}_{1(2,3)}$	principal strain-rate
η	angle between σ_1 and the r-axis
ψ	angle between σ_1 and the x- or r-axis
θ_w	hopper half-included angle
θ_i	insert half-included angle

$\kappa(\ )$	function in the radial stress field
ν	pseudo instantaneous angle of internal friction
ξ	angle between $\dot{\varepsilon}_1$ and the x- or r-axis
ρ	density
σ	stress variable in plane-strain
σ_{ij}	stress tensor
σ_n	normal stress on a plane (wall)
σ_r	average radial stress acting on a slice
σ_t	shear stress on a plane (wall)
$[\sigma_{n(t)}]$	jump in σ_n ($[\sigma_t]$)
$\sigma_{x(y,r,\dots,\theta)}$	normal component of σ_{ij}
$\sigma_{xy(yz,\dots,r\theta)}$	shear component of σ_{ij}
σ_y	average vertical stress acting on a slice
$\sigma_{1(2,3)}$	principal stress
σ_{1a}	principal stress along an arch or dome
ϕ	instantaneous angle of internal friction
$\varphi_w,\ \phi_w$	wall angle of friction
φ_i	insert angle of friction

AUTHOR INDEX

SUBJECT INDEX